37/6

THE STUDY OF
PLANT COMMUNITIES

An Introduction to Plant Ecology

BY

HENRY J. OOSTING

Professor of Botany
Duke University

1950
W. H. FREEMAN AND COMPANY
San Francisco, California

PRINTED IN THE UNITED STATES OF AMERICA

TYPOGRAPHY BY MACKENZIE & HARRIS, INC., SAN FRANCISCO

TO
MY STUDENTS
from whom
I have learned much more
than they realize

Preface

This book grew out of several successive reorganizations of an introductory course in plant ecology. Since it is intended as an introduction to plant ecology, effort has been made to make it as stimulating as possible while presenting basic information. From experience we know that this ideal is best achieved through study of plant communities with emphasis on field work. The plant community, therefore, is made the basis of this book.

The plan, in brief, proceeds from a consideration of the nature and variation of communities to methods of distinguishing and describing them. This is followed by a discussion of the factors which limit, maintain, and modify communities both locally and regionally. Thus the interrelationships between organisms and environment are emphasized and a foundation is laid for presentation of the concepts of succession and climax. Then the climax regions of North America become a logical consideration since they are illustrative of all that comes before. To answer the questions which must arise regarding the permanence of climax, a section is devoted to past climaxes and their study and reconstruction. Finally, the potentialities of the ecological point of view in practical considerations are emphasized by a survey of its possible and desirable applications in range management, agriculture, conservation, landscaping, forestry, and even human relations.

The intent has been to write a textbook with a wide usefulness. It was assumed that, in some instances, the text material might serve as the complete subject-matter of a course. To this end, the presentation aims at a fairly broad but solid foundation for ecological thinking and appreciation. At the same time there is no attempt at completeness, either in subject matter or bibliography, such as might be expected in a reference volume. Although controversial issues are not deliberately obscured, they are not em-

6

phasized. The assumption has been that a beginning student should acquire a working knowledge and appreciation of the field before he is introduced to matters that might confuse him.

A reasonable background of botanical and scientific experience is assumed so that, in general, college juniors and seniors might be expected to have the greatest appreciation of a course of this kind. A reasonable knowledge of plant physiology is expected, at least enough for comprehension of ordinary physiological processes. Although a student without some taxonomic training could hardly fully appreciate or enjoy an ecology course dealing with communities, he could use this book if he had some knowledge of plants. Both common and scientific names have been given regularly or at least the first time a species is mentioned. The plants which are named are almost without exception rather generally known species of long standing. It is not considered necessary, therefore, to include authorities with scientific names since they may invariably be found in standard manuals.

Suggestions for collateral reading may be found in the selected general references at the ends of chapters. Cited references are indicated in the text by number only and are listed in the bibliography at the end of the book. Citations are made where it seemed desirable to indicate the authority for or give credit for statements used in the text. Again, for those who may wish to go to original sources, references to survey and review papers are included. The bibliographies of these references are usually so extensive that the advanced student who uses them may quickly accumulate all the source material he needs.

Those who contributed directly or indirectly to the development of this book are too numerous to mention specifically, but I am deeply aware of my debt to former instructors, my colleagues, and my students. Many have given invaluable aid in the actual preparation of the book. A very special acknowledgment of assistance is due Miss Ruby Williams who, through a careful reading of the manuscript, did much to improve the mechanics of organization and to clarify and simplify the presentation.

The use of the book in mimeographed form provided a test of its value under a variety of conditions in different sections of the country. It was used in classes by Dr. W. D. Billings at the University of Nevada, Dr. M. F. Buell at Rutgers University, Dr. R. B. Livingston at the University of Missouri, and by Dr. J. F. Reed at the University of Wyoming, as well as at Duke University. The comments and suggestions derived from both students and instructors led to revisions and additions which are invaluable, particularly in their contribution to wider utility. It is truly with deep appreciation that the cooperation and assistance from all these sources is acknowledged.

Finally, although credit lines indicate the sources of illustrations, it is a real pleasure to acknowledge the courtesies and helpfulness of the numerous individuals and organizations involved. The excellent material they made available, sometimes with considerable trouble to themselves, often made it necessary to choose from several possibilities for a single illustration. It is regretted that not all the pictures could be used. The line-drawings were done by George A. Thompson and Robert Zahner whose assistance is gratefully acknowledged.

HENRY J. OOSTING

Durham, North Carolina
February, 1948.

Table of Contents

Part 1 · Introduction

CHAPTER I

THE SUBJECT MATTER OF ECOLOGY

"What is Ecology and What Good Is It?"[250] the title of an address made before the Ecological Society of America some years ago, is a compact, perhaps oversimplified, statement of the questions this textbook aims to answer. Its intention is to present an adequate introduction to the various phases of the subject, to show its position in relation to other sciences, and to indicate the possibilities and advantages of applying the methods and point of view of ecology in solving biological problems.

THE TERM AND BASIC CONCEPTS

The term, *ecology*, carries a more familiar ring than it did a relatively few years ago. Although it was used commonly in many fields of science, it did not, until recently, appear elsewhere. Now, it is occasionally seen in magazines and sometimes even in newspapers. This is partly the outgrowth of a gradual maturing of the science and partly the result of a growing appreciation of its meaning and potentialities.

Although the subject matter of ecology is as old as that of any other science and although much of it has long been a part of scientific knowledge, ecology as a field of science is relatively new. The name first appeared, in 1869, as "oecology,"[112] but the greatest advancement has come during the past fifty years, following the impetus supplied by the writing and thinking of a few men in the late 1890's. The term "ecology" is particularly appropriate. Its Greek root, *oikos*, means home and thus indicates a dwelling place; this, of course, implies that organisms are present and that certain conditions link the two. Ecology is, therefore, the study of organisms, their environment, and all the interrelationships between the two. It is commonly defined as the study of organisms in relation to their environment.

11

ALL LIFE BOUND TO ENVIRONMENT

An organism without environment is inconceivable,[122] for living things have certain requirements that must be satisfied by their surroundings if life is to continue. Their physiological processes, which, to sustain life, must all continue at rates above definite minima, are largely controlled by environmental conditions or substances. Most of the processes use water or require its presence; food manufacture is dependent upon carbon dioxide and light conditions; the universal process of respiration requires oxygen; and all processes are limited by, or vary with, temperature.

Since organisms must grow and reproduce to survive, they require energy, which they derive from food by respiration. Food, therefore, becomes a major consideration in explaining the activities of organisms. Green plants must be able to manufacture enough food to grow and reproduce and still leave a surplus for dependent organisms. Among the latter, there are usually several dependent upon each other for food in a relationship called a food-chain. For example, in aquatic environments the food-producing algae are eaten by miscroscopic animals that may in turn be eaten by larger animals upon which small fish feed. Small fish are often eaten by larger fish, and many of these are eaten by man. Any number of things may disrupt such a food-chain, but, under normal conditions, all the organisms are interrelated by their mutual requirement of food, whose ultimate production is dependent upon algal activity in the presence of light.

Regardless of the environment and the group of organisms adapted to survival in it, similar food-chains and dependencies can be found everywhere. Thus we see that the basic relationship binding all organisms to each other and to the environment is, invariably, one traceable to energy needs and uses; and, because the ultimate source of energy for both plants and animals is the sun, all organisms are mutually related to each other and to their environment.

If groups of organisms live together successfully, their demands and effects upon the energy cycle will not disrupt it. All the processes and activities taking place within the group will be in balance with the available supply of energy. A major concern of ecology, therefore, is to learn what that balance is and what controls it.

ENVIRONMENT A COMPLEX OF FACTORS

Environment includes everything that may affect an organism in any way. It is, therefore, a complex of *factors*, which may be : substances, such as soil and water; forces, such as wind and gravity; conditions, such as temperature and light; or other organisms. These factors may be studied or measured individually, but they must always be considered in terms of their interacting effects upon organisms and each other. The resulting complexity of environment and the array of subject matter encompassed suggest the necessity for drawing upon the knowledge of all fields of science for its understanding. Therein lie a complete justification of and explanation for ecology. Its special function is to consider such subject matter in terms of organisms. Any one field of science is relatively restricted to its own subject matter, whereas ecology brings together the knowledge of various sciences with the object of interpreting the responses of organisms to their environment.

Since all plants and animals, including man, are organisms, and since environment can at times include almost anything in the universe, the subject matter of ecology is almost unlimited. As a result, it is dependent upon the specialized fields of science for much of the knowledge it uses. It requires an understanding of the fundamentals of other sciences, an alertness to changes and new discoveries in various fields, and a constant consideration of the possibilities of using such information for interpreting or explaining the peculiarities, responses, and nature of organisms under the conditions in which they live.

SCOPE OF THE FIELD OF ECOLOGY

Since the subject is concerned with organisms, it must include both plants and animals. Such a broad biological basis presupposes a solid foundation in both botany and zoology, and, if man is to be considered, an additional need for understanding of sociological, psychological, and economic problems. Although the latter are not ordinarily considered biological subjects, they may become more so in the future. Sociologists are more and more concerned with "human ecology," and some phases of ecology have come to be known as "plant sociology."

It is, unfortunately, unusual to find students, teachers, or investigators today with sufficient training or experience to deal adequately with the entire field of biology. This explains why specialists usually concentrate on either plant ecology or animal ecology, and why textbooks emphasize either plants or animals, even though all organisms should be considered. In an introduction to the subject, however, it is probably advantageous to restrict the subject matter for effective discussion. We shall, therefore, be concerned primarily with the ecology of plants, although their relationships to animals will not be ignored. Furthermore, the major emphasis will be upon natural groupings or communities of plants and the reasons for finding them as we do.

BROAD TRAINING DESIRABLE

At first thought, the diversity of subject matter included in the scope of ecological application is discouraging. It ranges through all the sciences, but obviously one person can hardly become master of all scientific knowledge. Specialists, however, working on different phases of a problem, can contribute to its solution, provided they all have the same objectives and points of view. Most ecologists are specialists in some phase of the subject, but the ecological approach provides the necessary unity for holding their interests together. A truly complete ecological training is impossible; yet it is possible to acquire a broad enough training to appreciate the importance of subject matter in fields with which one may not be entirely familiar.

An appreciation of ecology necessitates certain fundamentals of training for a background. The specialist then expands his knowledge along lines of interest. A basic biological foundation is, of course, a necessity, with taxonomy and physiology as absolute prerequisites because of their constant use. Because ecological problems frequently range through any of the biological fields from morphology to pathology to genetics, the advantages of an extensive preparation should be evident.

The desirability of a basic understanding of physics and chemistry need hardly be emphasized since both have their obvious uses in the interpretation of environmental conditions as well as in applications to physical and physiological problems. Some knowledge of geology is very useful, and, for certain types of work, a broad training in this field is a necessity. Soils are a constant concern of the ecologist both as to their origin and development and as to the paralleling vegetational characteristics as modified by water, aeration, and nutrition. The frequent recurrence of problems related to climatology suggests its desirability, and the increasing use of quantitative methods requires an appreciation of, if not actual facility in, the use of statistical methods and experimental design. Also, ecological problems frequently overlap those of applied fields such as agriculture, forestry, and range management. In addition to the terrestrial ecology with which we shall primarily concern ourselves in this text, there are the special fields of limnology, dealing with fresh-water environments, and marine ecology and oceanography with all their particular problems.

These suggestions are indicative of the diversity of subject matter included in ecology. Specialization is a natural and desirable result so long as it contributes to the ultimate goal of understanding the interrelationships of organisms and environment and to clarifying the natural laws under which the complex operates.

HISTORICAL DEVELOPMENT OF PLANT ECOLOGY

The origins of modern plant ecology are, of necessity, diverse. Designation of the limits and ranges of species by Linnaeus and other early systematic botanists led to the development of floristic plant geography, which considers the origin and spread of species. The next step was in the direction of explaining distribution of species. Humboldt, a taxonomist who was a great traveler, was impressed by the correlations with climate that he observed. As a result, he developed his ideas so effectively at the beginning of the nineteenth century[126] that the influence of his thinking is still apparent in the interpretations of climatic plant geography. Schouw,[214] one of Humboldt's students, was the first to attempt the formulation of laws regarding the effectiveness of light, moisture, and temperature in species distribution. Somewhat later (1855), still another taxonomist, A. de Candolle, published studies along this line but with major emphasis upon temperature as a controlling factor. Attempts to correlate vegetational distribution with single factors continued for several years and culminated in Merriam's[173] study of temperature zones for all of North America.

The geographer's preoccupation with climatic causes for the distribution of species was paralleled by another significant trend of interest initiated by the writings of Grisebach in the nineteenth century. He recognized groups of plants, or communities, as units of study and described the vegetation of the earth on this basis.[111] This was the first step in the direction of modern studies of plant communities. Although further expanded by the publications of Drude,[94] the trend received its greatest impetus from the writings of Warming, particularly his *Oecology of Plants*,[266] originally published in Danish in 1895. This publication marks the beginning of modern ecology as it is concerned with communities and the interrelationships of organisms and environment. Although Warming must be credited with recognizing the complexity of these relationships, he tended to place too much stress on water as a controlling factor. In 1898, Schimper published his monumental *Plant Geography upon a Physiological Basis*, which was later (1903) translated from the German into English. Its author followed the general plan of presentation begun by Warming but contributed substantially from his broad experience and travels. He came nearer to the modern interpretation of causes of distribution of vegetation by emphasizing the complexity of environment and the interraction of factors.

These, briefly, are the foundations of modern community studies and the philosophy of modern ecology. From them stem studies of the structure and classification of communities as emphasized by continental European ecologists particularly, intensive studies of habitat in the search for causes, and analysis and interpretation of vegetational change as developed by American and English workers. The history of modern ecology is so brief that the last of these developments can hardly be treated historically. They are the fundamentals of ecology today and, therefore, will be considered as part of the text material of this book.

APPROACHES TO THE SUBJECT

Considering the diversity of subject matter in ecology and the variety of possible interests, it is not surprising that problems have been studied in many different ways. Certain investigations must be made in the laboratory and others in the field. Some ecologists have focused all their attention upon single factors; others have attempted to analyze the joint effect of several factors.

Autecology and Synecology.—Certain problems can best be solved by working with individual organisms or species in the laboratory or in the field. Others can be solved only when the groupings of organisms are investigated as they occur naturally. Similarly, the environment may be analyzed one factor at a time or considered in its entirety as a complex of several factors. Each approach has its merits under conditions that should become apparent later. The two are distinguished as *autecology*—from the Greek root *autos* meaning self— which deals with individual organisms or factors, and *synecology*—from the Greek prefix *syn* meaning together—applied to studies of groups of organisms or to complexes of factors.

Autecology is not always distinguishable from some kinds of physiology; in fact, there is probably no point in doing so. The very nature of autecology brings about overlapping with other fields. Furthermore, autecology is justifiable because of the contributions it can make to synecology. The latter is clearly a field in itself whose objectives make it distinct from all other fields of science. This is a partial reason for giving major consideration to synecology in this text and for bringing in autecology only when it contributes to the understanding of discussions of community problems.

Static and Dynamic Viewpoints.—Plant communities may be studied as they are, without regard to what may have preceded them or to what their natural future may be. This leads to consideration of the abundance and significance of the species making up the community and permits detailed descriptions and precise classification of communities according to one system or another. It is typical of the work of several early continental Europeans, who, as a result, developed systems of classifying and describing communities and their structure. In America and England, the view was early adopted that a community is a changing thing whose origin, development, and probable future can be reconstructed or predicted. These two approaches have come to represent what are known as the *static* and *dynamic* points of view in community studies. The static approach is undoubtedly a product

FIG 1.   Communities of contrasting life form as illustrated by vegetation on Roan Mountain in the southern Appalachians. (1) Deciduous forest of beech and maple. (2) Portion of a grassy bald in which grasses and sedges

of the restricted areas of study in Europe where civilization has long since destroyed or modified most natural communities. In the same way, the vast areas of virgin forest and grassland in America,

predominate. (3) Portion of a shrub community made up largely of rhododendron (open coniferous forest in background). (4) Moss community in
which young conifers are becoming established.—*Photos by D. M. Brown.*

with opportunities to observe natural variation on a large scale and
under a variety of circumstances, must have contributed to de-

velopment of the dynamic point of view. Undoubtedly each
method has its place and usefulness. In fact, each has profited from
the other, but, since the dynamic point of view has the broadest
usefulness in both pure and applied ecology, it will be emphasized
here.

BACKGROUND FOR COMMUNITY STUDY

Systems of description of vegetation that are based upon appearance or general nature of the plants have been used with some success, particularly by plant geographers. Such systems indicate size
and form of plants; whether they are evergreen or deciduous,
herbaceous or woody;[210] position of buds in the dormant season,[202]
and various other characters classified under the general headings
of growth forms or life forms. This makes possible the visualization
and superficial comparison of otherwise unfamiliar vegetation and
likewise may serve to bring out certain characteristics of communities that otherwise might not be apparent. Such systems are
either based upon previous detailed studies of the species, or they
may be a means of superficially characterizing vegetation of which
the taxonomy is still inadequately known. They can only supple-
ment studies based upon taxonomy since description of a community, to be adequate for all purposes, must be based upon species.
The field ecologist must, therefore, have a thorough working
knowledge of taxonomy and, preferably, some experience with
the flora of the region of his studies.

Just as the study of vegetation must remain more or less superficial without a solid taxonomic foundation, so will interpretations
and explanations be limited by the amount of autecological information available about the species and their environments. Physi-
ological-ecological investigations, in the field and under natural
conditions, constantly modify synecological conclusions that have
been made deductively, or they suggest new interpretations and
investigations. The quality of community studies, therefore, depends upon certain fundamentals, which include a knowledge of
the individual species and their requirements and responses.

Part 2 · The Plant Community

CHAPTER II

NATURE OF THE COMMUNITY

Recognition of a plant community or distinguishing one community from another is probably simpler than recording the characteristics by which the community is recognizable. To refer to a stand of pine, a grassy field, or a lowland forest is, in a sense, recognizing communities, and most of us have done this from childhood. Such communities are the basic vegetational units of the ecologist, and, therefore, their specific and general characters should be stated to insure agreement as to concepts.

DEFINITION

A good working definition is as follows: A community is an aggregation of living organisms having mutual relationships among themselves and to their environment. This applies to the specific example which one has in mind or which one is observing—that is, the concrete community or *stand*. At the same time, it does not exclude the possibility of visualizing an abstract community synthesized from several or many concrete examples or stands. Thus a particular stand of pine would be a concrete community and the community in the abstract would include all the stands of that species.

A stand need not be limited to trees. Any group of plants satisfying the definition of a community may be so termed—a mat of lichens on a rock, covering only a few square inches, an algal mat on a pond, or a forest of fairly homogeneous composition extending over a thousand acres or more.

MUTUAL RELATIONSHIPS AMONG ORGANISMS

These include all the direct or indirect effects that organisms have upon each other. Foremost among these is *competition*,

21

FIG. 2.   A stand of mixed conifers in Idaho.—*U. S. Forest Service.*

which results whenever several organisms require the same things in the same environment. The intensity of competition is determined by the amount by which the demands exceed the supply. Competition may occur between individuals of the same species. Because they are alike, their demands are identical, and, if the supply of water or nutrients or light is insufficient to satisfy the needs of all, then some will be eliminated. This is particularly noticeable in young, crowded forest stands but is equally true among roadside weeds or in a vegetable garden. All plants may survive for a time in a stunted condition; then some individuals are gradually eliminated. Whether in the forest or in the garden, thinning to reduce competition between species usually pays with more lumber or better vegetables.

Stratification.—Usually there are several species involved in competition within a stand. If plants of several species that start simultaneously make the same demands upon the habitat, they may survive in about equal numbers and occupy the same position in the community. Those whose requirements differ will affect each other less but will most certainly not be of equal importance in the community. A tall-growing species outgrows a potentially short one under the same conditions. If the latter then survives, it does so because its light requirements are not great. Thus the one tends to occupy a higher level than the other and to form an overstory. In this way *stratification* may develop in a stand in which the upper stratum of plants usually includes the controlling and characteristic species for the community. These are termed the *dominant* individuals. If they are removed for any reason, as by selective cutting or disease, dominance is usually assumed by other species, and the character of the community is changed completely. This is not true when lesser species in *subordinate* strata are removed, for, with the dominants intact, the same type of community can regenerate itself.

Stratification may likewise be seen among the shrubs and herbs beneath the trees, since some may be tall and some low. The lowest

Fig. 3. A stand of moss (*Hypnum crista-castrensis*) (note coin) in northern Wisconsin. Although this species is a dependent within the forest community, it forms a stand nevertheless.—*Photo by L. E. Anderson.*

FIG. 4. Very much overstocked stand of naturally seeded, eight-year-old, loblolly pine. Although many individuals will die in the next few years and thus produce natural thinning, the remaining trees will remain spindly and growth will not be satisfactory. Artificial thinning to reduce competition is apt to pay dividends in such stands.—*Photo by C. F. Korstian.*

FIG. 5. Young loblolly pine stand, which was overstocked (left) for best growth. The stand was thinned experimentally soon after it was photographed. Same stand (right) only two years after thinning, shows marked increase in size in the reduced number of trunks. The increase in rate of growth will be apparent for a number of years.—*Photo by C. F. Korstian.*

exposed stratum is made up of mosses, lichens, and sometimes algae, which may form a mat or ground cover on the forest floor, and a final stratum of fungi, bacteria, and algae in the upper layers of the soil can also be recognized. The species making up these lesser strata probably offer little direct competition to the trees above them. Most of these plants have appeared, and are able to survive, here because of conditions provided by the tree strata.

FIG. 6. Stratification in an oak-hickory forest community as seen in spring when the subordinate tree stratum is especially marked by flowering of dogwood and redbud.—*Photo by H. L. Blomquist.*

Indirectly, however, they may offer serious competition to the continued dominance of the trees because, if the trees are to maintain themselves in the community, they must be able to reproduce themselves. If the seedlings of tree species cannot meet the competition of lesser species, whether it be in the herb or shrub stratum, such trees must eventually disappear from the community. Thus permanent or true dominance involves the ability to compete successfully in all strata of the community. The effects of competition are most apparent in the lesser strata, and undoubtedly competition is greatest between the seedlings of species of all strata since all must start small and in the same restricted environment of the forest floor.

Some ecologists maintain that each of these strata is itself a community (synusia), which should be considered as a distinct unit of vegetation. Whether or not the strata are so recognized, they cannot be neglected in any study of communities. Often an understanding of the community as a whole is possible only after information is complete on the individual strata.

Dependence.—Within any community some species, although a part of the community, are at the same time dependent upon the whole for their survival. To a great extent, these are inconspicuous organisms, which, at first glance, might well be overlooked or ignored. Most of the bryophytes and thallophytes, as well as a few vascular plants, require the special conditions provided by larger seed plants; shade and moisture are usually of greatest importance to their survival. Such dependent organisms would soon disappear if the dominant vegetation were removed.

Epiphytes grow on the trunks, the branches, and even on the leaves of the larger plants. In subtropical and tropical forests they may be conspicuous because of both size and abundance. In forests of temperate zones they may be easily overlooked, for they are usually mosses, liverworts, or lichens. These may be restricted to certain communities, and sometimes individual species will grow only on specific trees. Fungi, including bacteria, make up an important part of many communities, especially forests. Here they may be parasitic and cause diseases that may at times become so serious as to destroy a stand or even to eliminate a community. Other saprophytic fungi, living in the soil or litter of the forest floor, although dependent upon the community, likewise contribute to its perpetuation through their activities in decomposition of organic matter. Still others, again often host-specific, live in an association with the roots of vascular plants in a relationship termed mycorhiza (see Fig. 91).

Finally, animals, largely as dependents but also as influents, are likewise a part of the biotic community. Large species such as deer, which move about freely, are not necessarily associated with a single community. However, many smaller, less widely ranging species are definitely restricted to single communities, and even some birds and flying insects may be constantly associated with certain types of vegetation. Many beetles, borers, moths, etc. are extremely destructive parasites, while other similar small animals live on the remains of dead plants. The animals are apt to be related to the community through food requirements and, if present in large numbers, may have extremely destructive effects.

Fig. 7. Indian pipe (*Monotropa uniflora*), a saprophyte (on left), and squaw root (*Conopholis americana*), a parasite dependent upon the shade, moisture, and nutrients available only on the floor of a mature forest.—*Indian pipe photo by H. L. Blomquist.*

MUTUAL RELATIONSHIPS TO ENVIRONMENT

Plants must be adapted to the environment in which they live if they are to survive for long. Some can withstand heat, some cold;

some require a large continuous supply of moisture, others require only a small amount which need be available only periodically. Thus the climate of a region definitely controls the kinds of plants that may grow there. The general vegetation type or growth

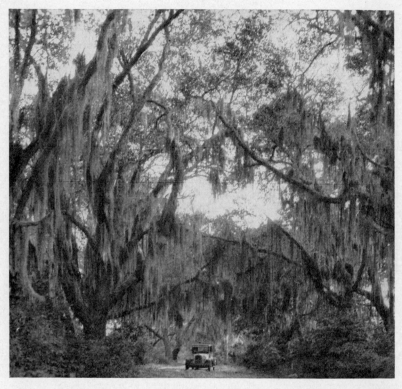

FIG. 8. Spanish "moss" (*Tillandsia usneoides*), an epiphytic flowering plant, growing on live oak, North Carolina coast.—*Photo by H. L. Blomquist.*

form, such as grassland, desert, or forest, is a product of the complex of climatic factors effective in a region and can be used as a generalized basis for evaluating the climate. For example, knowing something of the growth forms able to survive under the extreme conditions of moisture and temperature associated with a desert, a repetition of these growth forms anywhere else in the world automatically may be accepted as indicative of desert conditions. The scrubby broad-leaved evergreens (chaparral) that cover much of southern California are a product of the climatic conditions peculiar to the area. The same growth form is repeated in a few widely separated regions of the world where, although made up of quite different species, it is a product of a similar complex of climatic conditions. In the same way the vast expanses of deciduous or coniferous forests in the temperate regions of the world are each found where climatic characteristics fall within definite limits, similar throughout.

General Climate and Vegetation Type.—Within the general

FIG. 9. Transition zones between stands of two life forms. The forest at right (mostly buckeye) shows the usual gradual transition from a closed stand to scattered, widely spaced individuals over a wide band—such as is typical of most transitions from one community to another. The abrupt transition from beech forest to grassland (at left) is unusual. Roan Mt. on the southern Appalachians.—*Photo by D. M. Brown.*

vegetation type, certain variations may be expected. Species differences are not uncommon although the growth form may be uniform for all. Such differences are most pronounced when a type of growth form extends over a wide latitudinal range. In the arctic flora, which has an otherwise uniform physiognomy, the number of species declines steadily northward. Within the grassland areas of the Middle West, there is obvious uniformity of growth form from Canada to Texas, yet some species found in the south are not found in the north and other species may be found only in the north. Even those species that seem to range from one limit of a growth form to another may likewise have certain characteristics, probably physiological, which limit the extent of their area of favorable growth. Recently it has been shown that certain grasses that seem to range throughout the latitudinal extent of the prairie cannot be satisfactorily used to reseed northern areas when the seed has been obtained in the south. Foresters, too, recognize that it is advisable to replant with seedlings grown from locally produced seed.

The more extreme (less favorable) the climatic conditions, the less diversity can there be in the species and the fewer the species will be because not many will have the adaptations necessary for their survival. The numbers of species in a general vegetation type are by no means constant throughout, especially nearing the limits of the type. Here it might be expected that conditions would be something less than optimum and that some species would be less well adapted to the extremes than others. The same can be said for numbers of individuals of a species. As conditions favoring a species vary from their maximum, the number of individuals may be expected likewise to fluctuate, and, near the limits of the range of a growth form, the numbers of individuals of that growth form would also decline. In the same sense, but in the opposite direction, this marginal area would support a few species and individuals of the contiguous growth form; thus *transition zones* between communities are characteristic. Sometimes these transitions are wide, sometimes relatively narrow, but rarely does one community, large or small, have a sharp line of demarcation between itself and its neighbor.

Local Habitats and Species Differences.—Climatic areas are of considerable extent and usually include local diverse conditions of soil or topography. Often these variations are so great as to result in localized environments (habitats) quite unfavorable to the species and even to the growth form of the region as a whole. Often the conditions may be so much more favorable than those of the general climate that a growth form from a neighboring region can compete successfully. This is well illustrated by the trees and shrubs extending far into the prairie along the streams, where the favorable soil moisture is sufficient for them to compete successfully in a grassland climate.

A south-facing bluff forms a habitat that is almost always warmer and drier than the average for the region, while a north-facing bluff is cooler and wetter. Barren exposures of rock or high, rocky ridges represent one extreme in local habitats, while flood plains of streams, lakes, and lake margins represent the other. Such habi-

Fig. 10. Aerial view of the forest that extends along the meandering Souris River far into the grassland of Nebraska.—*U. S. Forest Service.*

tats are bound to support numerous species that are not characteristic of the general climate and may even differ in their growth forms. These local variations may be extremely restricted in area, scarcely affecting the general physiognomic picture, as would be true of the vegetation around a spring, or on a boulder in the woods; but they may also be so extensive as to be misleading. Cypress or cypress-gum swamps in some sections of the southern states are so large that they might be viewed solely as a product of climate, especially where little drained land is near supporting upland vegetation. Many of the pine forests of New England and the other northern states lie in a climatic region where spruce and fir should eventually predominate. They are so extensively distributed that some ecologists recognize them as the ultimate growth form for the region and as strictly controlled by climate, whereas, their occurrence within the climatic area is closely associated with light, sandy soils.

The kinds of plants, as to form and appearance, that can gr⸱ in a climatic region are, therefore, determined by the overall climate. The species within the general growth form may vary from place to place or from one limit of the climatic area to another as determined by local variations in some factors. Local habitats may have such marked differences in growing conditions that not only will species differ but even the growth form may not be that of the climate of the region.

GENERAL REFERENCES*

J. BRAUN-BLANQUET. *Plant Sociology : The Study of Plant Communities.*
A. F. W. SCHIMPER. *Plant Geography upon a Physiological Basis.*
E. WARMING. *Oecology of Plants.*
J. E. WEAVER and F. E. CLEMENTS. *Plant Ecology.*
  *See *References Cited* on page 362 and following for complete listings.

CHAPTER III

VEGETATIONAL ANALYSIS
QUANTITATIVE METHODS

FIXING THE CONCEPT OF A COMMUNITY

The fallacy of doing detailed physiological studies with an unnamed plant is obvious. If the physiologist does not know the species with which he is working, his conclusions will be limited to the particular group of plants he is using in his experiments. The studies of taxonomists, floristic geographers, and geneticists represent an accumulation of information and data upon which the physiologist can draw and which he can use to make generalizations and comparisons. All this information is connoted by the scientific name of the plant being studied.

The ecologist, although working with communities, deals with problems similar to those of the physiologist when he sets up theories, attempts to find causes, to draw conclusions, or to formulate laws. But the ecologist is faced with the necessity of determining the make-up of the community with which he works before he can proceed to an investigation of causes or to experimental considerations. At present, most of the larger, regional, climatic vegetation types are so well known that their concepts are probably as distinct to the ecologist as are those of most common species to the taxonomist. For lesser communities, however, this is not true. Furthermore, identification of such a community in terms of a specific concept requires more than a superficial examination. Perhaps an ecological classification of plant communities will never be achieved with the same degree of perfection found in taxonomic classification; perhaps such perfection is not necessary. It is necessary, however, that there be means of characterizing a community with sufficient accuracy to permit identification at any time, to compare it with other similar communities, and to have an adequate permanent record of its nature and occurrence. Undoubtedly, if such work is well done, it is justified on its own merits as a phase of ecological investigation.

If the major interest in a community is an experimental one and the preliminary analysis and description of the vegetation have not previously been made, the experimenter must first learn and record the characteristics of the community with which he intends to work. Again, after experimentation or treatment, whether it be of the community as a whole or of individual species, it often becomes necessary to evaluate the results in terms of the community as a whole. There must also be a means of comparing the original and the resulting communities at the beginning and at the end of each experiment or treatment. The relationship of the individual species to the community and the responses of the individual species can best be interpreted when the constitution of the entire community is positively established.

It is illogical to proceed with explanations when the subject itself is indefinite or unknown. Therefore, the first objective in ecological work is to learn the composition and structure of the community under consideration. Then, and only then, logically follow a search for causes, experimentation, and interpretations based upon a firm foundation.

QUANTITATIVE DATA A NECESSITY

In the early days of ecology, observation and description were considered adequate for recording the characteristics of a community, but few observers see the same thing in the same way, and few writers have the ability to translate exactly into words the things they have seen. Thus, as in other sciences, ecology has become more precise as it has developed and, with its concern for greater detail, has demanded accurate measurement and precise records of vegetation. This has led naturally to quantitative methods and terminology, which are becoming more uniform and, therefore, more useful. Their use permits positive statements concerning the numbers and sizes of individuals as well as the space they occupy within a stand. With such data in hand, it is possible to make comparisons of species or groups of species within a stand or between stands. Likewise, the data constitute a permanent record, which can be referred to again if the same stand or similar stands are studied later. Also, as a permanent record, they are subject to reconsideration by other investigators, who may reinterpret them in the light of additional experience or information.

SAMPLING

The need for quantitative records has made it necessary to give serious consideration to methods of sampling. Usually the members of an entire community cannot be counted or measured, and even if this were done, the information would be no more useful or significant than an adequate set of data acquired by proper sampling. Since this is true, it becomes of prime importance to determine what constitutes an adequate sample in terms of the community as a whole and how to obtain such a sample with a minimum of effort. At best, sampling for vegetational data is tedious and time-consuming; often it may be extremely hard work. Nevertheless, sampling conserves both time and labor as compared with an attempt to analyze a whole community, and its results are much more significant than those obtained by mere observation.

In this connection it should be emphasized that the early procedures of observation and reconnaissance are still of extreme importance in determining where, how, and what to sample. These activities are still a necessary part of community study although they cannot be substituted for detailed analysis. They serve to form a basis for theories or ideas that may in turn be substantiated by quantitative evidence obtained by sampling. Preliminary reconnaissance may likewise help to reduce the effort expended in sampling. No sampling should be done without considerable knowledge of the history, physiography, and vegetation of the region as a whole. Prior to sampling, the community should have been observed repeatedly in different parts of its range and more particularly under the varying local conditions where it exists. Finally, the specific stand should be observed thoroughly to determine its obvious variations, its extent, limits, and transitions to contiguous communities. Then, knowing all this, together with the size of individual plants, the strata present, and the purposes for which the sampling is to be done, one may plan his procedure in terms of the desired results, the necessary degree of accuracy, and the time available for doing the work.

Ecologists call a sample area or plot a *quadrat*, and the method of sampling by the use of plots is commonly called the *quadrat method*. The use of the sample plot is by no means restricted to ecology, but its application in the sampling of natural vegetation has led to methods peculiarly adapted to the ecologist's needs. The quadrat has almost unlimited applications and has been used in a great variety of ways.

Kinds of Quadrats.—The *list-count* quadrat is probably most commonly used. With this the species are recorded and their num-

FIG. 11.   A small quadrat laid out with meter sticks, which are pinned at corners. Ready for list-count. This is a permanent quadrat that can be relocated by paint markings on boulders. At Glacier Bay, Alaska, for the study of early development of vegetation on raw morainic soil.[75] Ice covered this area thirty-seven years before picture was taken.—*Photo by W. S. Cooper.*

bers determined by count. This method is subject to many modifications depending upon circumstances. For trees, the individual diameters might be recorded and later used for segregating size classes, or perhaps for computing basal area (indicative of dominance) for species. Bunch grasses, too, are often measured across the base to obtain a basal area figure, which, combined with the count, will give a better expression of the relative importance of species. With herbs it is sometimes desirable to have additional information on the weight of tops, which must, therefore, be removed for each species. In any event, the species are listed and tabulated by number, weight, or size.

A *chart* quadrat is a more detailed record of the individuals

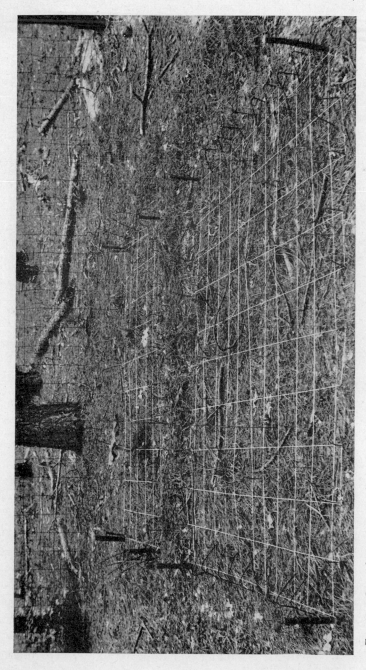

FIG. 12. One of a series of permanent experimental plots treated as chart quadrats. Note iron pipes used as markers and the grid pattern of string to facilitate accurate charting. One of controls in background.—*Photo by C. F. Korstian.*

TRENCHING STUDY #2, SHORTLEAF PINE TYPE

CONTROL PLOT   9 -12 - 34

A = Andropogon ternarius	E = Eupatorium hyssopifolium	*Pe = Pinus echinata
Ad = Aster dumosus	G = Grass seedling	Pq = Psedera quinquefolia
Ca = Catherina angustifolia	H = Herbaceous seedling	*Q = Quercus velutina
Cp = Cladonia pyxidata	L = Lespedeza repens	Sb = Smilax bona-nox
C = Cladonia sylvatica	Oe = Oenothera longipedicellata	S = Solidago nemoralis
D = Dicranum scoparium	Ox = Oxalis stricta	T = Thuidium delicatulum
Ds = Dicranum spurium	P = Panicum sphaerocarpon	*U = Ulmus alata
*Dv = Diospyros virginiana	Scale	V = Viburnum affine

0.66 feet

FIG. 13.   The system of mapping used in the study illustrated in Figure 12. Such a procedure is adaptable to many situations.[146]

present, giving their size and distribution within the area. This is usually time-consuming, even on small quadrats with a relatively simple arrangement and few species. It does, however, permit study at a later date—an advantage not to be ignored under many circumstances. Small quadrats may be photographed with considerable success if proper equipment can be brought to them conveniently. Camera stands of various sorts have been designed that permit vertical views, and the photographs can be studied at leisure. Fairly accurate coverage for individual species can be determined from the prints with a planimeter (a mechanical device for determining the area of a surface with irregular boundaries). Such records are particularly useful when the areas are to be studied over a period of time and when they are subject to treatment.

FIG. 14. Mapping a quadrat by the use of a pantograph, which reduces all details to scale.—*U. S. Forest Service.*

When a high degree of accuracy is desired for small plots, a pantograph[193] can be used with a drawing board, or sketching on coordinate paper may be quite satisfactory, especially if the quadrat itself is marked off into a grid pattern, as with strings. For small quadrats of low or matted vegetation, a rigid frame permanently rigged with fine cross wires to form a grid (see Fig. 12) can be used to advantage since it can be moved from place to place, thus saving the time of marking off each new quadrat.[25] Small quadrats in relatively tall herbaceous vegetation or among shrubs and saplings can be laid out more easily with rods or wooden strips cut to proper length than with tapes (see Fig. 11). There are times when the accurate measurement or recording of cover is too time-consuming or is not actually necessary. Estimation of cover merely by inspection of each plot can be done with considerable accuracy after only a little experience, and such an estimate may be sufficient for the objectives.

The use of *permanent quadrats* has been advocated by many ecologists, but few have followed their own excellent advice. Whenever there is a remote possibility that a sampling area may again be visited for further study, the quadrats should be marked with permanent markers, for surprisingly worth-while results may

Fig. 15.   Paired pictures illustrating slow development of vegetation on rocks on Isle Royale. Lower picture taken seventeen years after upper.— *Photos by W. S. Cooper.*[14]

be obtained by restudying identical areas after a period of years. Such results are often valuable out of all proportion to the effort required, especially when compared to the initial study. Most quadrat studies are planned for immediate results and to help solve problems of the moment, but with little extra effort they could be used to yield returns over a period of years. Actually it would be well to consider the possibility of making every quadrat permanent. When Dr. W. S. Cooper made his now widely known study of vegetation on Isle Royale in Lake Superior, he photographed his sampling areas and carefully marked the spots even though he had no definite plan for restudying the area. Seventeen years later he was able to relocate these points exactly, and he obtained a striking series of matched pictures illustrating the development of each of the vegetation types on the island.[74] A number of similar illustrations could be mentioned, but they are far too few.

Marking such plots when far afield may be something of a problem, but by forehanded thoughtfulness combined with ingenuity an adequate plan can usually be devised. A small can of paint is no great burden when added to regular field equipment, and its judicious use in conjunction with blazed trees, rock cairns, or the like will usually suffice (see Fig. 11). It should be added that experience indicates the advisability of recording in one's notes a careful description of the markers and their exact position with reference to landmarks of a permanent nature.

Quadrats originally set up for permanent study are usually of an experimental nature. Perhaps they are to be subject to a treatment of some sort, as, for example, different degrees of grazing, watering, or thinning. For acceptable results these must always be laid out in pairs so that an untreated plot can be used as a check or control on the treated area. Usually it is desirable to replicate the pairs one or more times, and this must be given serious thought in terms of the extent of the stand and uniformity of conditions. Such experimental areas are often established near at hand and in easily accessible places, for they are to be visited regularly. With plans made in advance, materials for permanent marking are among the first equipment to be assembled. Substantial lengths of old pipe or scrap metal, when driven into the ground leaving a few inches protruding, are permanent and very satisfactory markers. If they are painted conspicuously and marked with numbers, there can be no confusion.

Experimental quadrats are of many types. Studies of competition and survival may involve thinning of stands, eliminating undesirable species, or introducing other species, either by seeding or planting seedlings, the object being to observe effects on the community or the introduced species. Newly exposed bare areas may be studied to follow the natural development of vegetation, or areas may be denuded and attempts made to produce artificial communities. Perhaps the quadrats are used to evaluate the effects of some controlled factor such as artificial watering or shading or

FIG. 16. A large grassland exclosure (left), which shows range recovery in absence of grazing such as has continued on deteriorated grassland (right) where burroweed and snakeweed predominate.—*U. S. Forest Service.*

the application of a fertilizer. Again, animals may be the factor under consideration, and then exclosures of the vegetation or the animals will be necessary, depending upon objectives.[84] Exclosures should not be considered lightly, for their installation may require considerable time and labor. Also certain types of materials may be surprisingly expensive, especially if plots are replicated. If the effects of grazing are to be studied, a barbed-wire fence will keep out cattle, but rabbits must also be considered. They may be attracted by the very things that flourish within the exclosure after the cattle are kept out. Again, small plots may be fenced for rabbits and yet permit squirrels or birds to come in over the top. Then the entire plot must be covered. Lesser rodents may go through or tunnel under the wire, and suitable precautions must be taken to check them.

The effects of the exclosure itself upon the vegetation should not be ignored since it may serve as a windbreak, which may reduce transpiration and intercept snow, soil, and seeds. Small plots completely screened over will have quite a different micro-climate from unscreened areas. To hold constant a single variable within an exclosure is difficult, but it can be approached by having exclosures as large as possible, by insuring a liberal transition or isolation strip around the margin, which will not be used in sampling, and by having the barriers as low and as open as possible within the limitations of the experiment.

Quadrat Methods—Actually the unit sampling area can be any shape or size, and any number can be used in a variety of ways, depending upon circumstances and objectives. As one soon learns, the major concern is to get adequate data with a minimum of effort. Because vegetation is so variable, generalizations cannot be made to fit all situations. Because objectives are rarely the same, methods quite satisfactory in one instance may not be so in another. Set rules are not advisable for sampling, but certain generalizations may well be considered in the light of experience.

Shape of Quadrat.—The term, *quadrat*, implies a square, and this shape is undoubtedly more commonly used by ecologists than any other. This is probably a matter of habit, for other shapes are just as usable and sometimes more efficient. When Raunkiaer[202] was making his pioneer studies of frequency, he at first used a square frame for marking his sample areas but later used a circle exclusively because of its convenience. He wished to have data from many small quadrats that were randomly distributed. For marking, he used a rod to which a stick was attached at right angles to form the desired radius. The rod was thrust into the ground at the sampling point and rotated so that the stick marked the limits of the circle to be sampled. He said, "The most convenient forms and sizes of the unit areas are the best." With low vegetation, circular plots are sometimes a distinct advantage. An efficient means of laying out circular plots is to use a set of hoops or rings of proper size tossed in all directions from a central point. These cannot be used in tall vegetation of any kind since they may be obstructed when thrown or may be suspended above the ground. Larger circular plots can be quickly and accurately marked with a string attached to a free-turning ring on a central axis. Again, this method will not be found satisfactory where vegetation is more than waist high.

It has been demonstrated that a rectangular plot is significantly more efficient in sampling than a square one of equal area since it will tend to include a better representation of the variation in the stand. Clapham,[55] who worked with low herbaceous vegetation in his study of this problem, concluded that plots ¼ x 4m. were the most efficient in size and that to secure the same amount of information with squares as with strips nearly twice as large an area would have to be observed. Short strips (1:4) gave less variable data than squares but more variable than long strips (1:16). The same general conclusions were reached after studies of certain types of sagebrush-grass range sampling.[194]

Size and Number of Quadrats.—A community is rarely homogeneous throughout as to species and their distribution. Newly formed habitats, such as sandbars or tidal flats where often only a single species is a pioneer, may support a nearly homogeneous stand, but the usual community will have some variation. If there were no variation, a single relatively small sample would always be sufficient. Since variation is the rule, it becomes necessary to have samples large enough or numerous enough to include the variation and to have it fairly represented in the data. There is thus always a question of how large and how numerous the quadrats should be for adequate sampling.

The literature dealing with this problem is far too extensive to review here. Agreement has not been reached on all phases of sampling methods, and probably different methods will be advocated for some time to come. Several recent papers summarize ideas and analyze the problem in detail. Their extensive bibliographies will soon lead one to the conclusions of a variety of workers. Cain's publications [43, 49] have done much to clarify methods of determining sample sizes and numbers both through his own contributions of methods and their applications as well as through his summaries of the literature. Penfound[196] has brought together and analyzed the usefulness of several currently favored procedures.

Species : area curves have been used in a variety of ways. Originally used by European ecologists to determine the "minimal area" to be recognized as an "association individual" (stand), they have been equally useful in arriving at numbers or sizes of plots to be used in sampling individual stands. A characteristic curve will result from plotting the number of species obtained against the area sampled. The accumulated number of species found may be expressed as a percentage of the total or as an absolute number and plotted on the y axis. When the corresponding numbers of plots, or sizes of area sampled, are plotted on the x axis, the curve formed by the joined points will rise abruptly with first increases in area, but will soon level off, and tend to rise only slightly thereafter with increase of sampling area. It is assumed that the added information represented in the slight rise of the curve is not sufficient to justify the time and effort needed for the extra sampling. Therefore, for this same type of vegetation, the sampling is assumed to be adequate when the size of the sample somewhat exceeds the area plotted against the point at which the curve flattens strongly.

It is of interest that, when the ratio of the x to the y axis is shifted, it will result in a change in the form of the curve and a consequent shift in the position where the curve tends to flatten. This suggested the desirability of some means other than inspection for determining this point. Cain[46] suggests that, in terms of his experience, sampling is adequate when a 10 percent increase in sample area results in an increase of species equaling 10 percent of the total present. He suggests a mechanical means of determining this point on the curve regardless of the ratio of the x and y axes. When a triangle is placed so that one edge passes through the zero point and the point representing 10 percent of the area and 10 percent of the species, the triangle can be pushed upward along a ruler placed at the right until its lower edge describes a tangent to the curve. The point of the tangent is the center of the region where the 10 percent relationship holds. If greater accuracy is desired, the minimal area could be placed at the point of 5 percent rise for a 10 percent increase in sampling.

By another procedure,[49] the ratio of the *x-y* axes can be ignored, a sample size or number can be selected, and a value set upon the sampling. If the total number of species obtained in the sampling is divided by the total number of sample units, the average increment of new species per additional sample unit is obtained. The point on the curve is located (point *A*), in the region of which addition of a unit sample produces an increment of species equal to

FIG. 17. Species : area curves for an oak-hickory forest, (A) indicating a minimum of six 10 by 10 m. quadrats for sampling the arborescent strata, and (B) a minimum of ten 4 by 4 m. quadrats for sampling the transgressive and shrub strata. (C) A dune grassland community required a quadrat of not less

the average increment. Beyond this point addition of samples will yield progressively less than the average. In the region of point B a sample yields only one-half the information and at point C only one-quarter the information obtained by a sample at point A. Used in combination with the tangent procedure, this should be helpful in interpretation of the species : area curve and the selection of numbers or sizes of plots most suited to a vegetation type.

If a series of quadrats of an arbitrarily set size is run in a stand, a species : area curve constructed from the data will indicate how many such quadrats would have been necessary for sampling to achieve a desired accuracy. The most efficient size of plot to be used can likewise be determined from the same preliminary series

than ⅛ sq. m. and (D) a minimum of six such samples. The lines tangent to the curves were put in using Cain's triangle method described on page 45. In (B), point a is equivalent to the average increment per sample, at point b the yield is only one-half this increment, and at point c only one-quarter the increment.

of data if each quadrat is subdivided into successively smaller plots
(e.g. : 1, ½, ¼, ⅛ sq. m.) for which the records are kept separately. The data obtained from the smallest area then become a
part of those for the next larger area, and so on. When the number
of species is plotted against increase in area sampled, the usual
curve is formed. The information regarding numbers and sizes of

FIG. 18.   Nested quadrats. (A) shows a plan used successfully for sampling
the several strata in forest stands. (B) and (C) show systems of dividing plots
of any size for accumulating data to be used in determining the desirable size
of plot by means of species : area curves.

plots is then applied to sampling of similar or closely related communities. The procedure for determination of numbers and sizes
of plots is well illustrated by Cain's study of sample-plot techniques applied to alpine vegetation in Wyoming.[49]

When vegetation is stratified, a series of sample plots large
enough to include the trees will certainly be large enough for all
plants and strata. The work involved in measuring or counting the
lesser vegetation in such plots, however, would be unnecessarily
great. It, therefore, becomes advisable to sample each stratum separately with an appropriate size of plot for each. These plots can
be "nested" one within the other and the work thus materially
reduced. Sampling forest vegetation in the Piedmont area of North
Carolina has been done satisfactorily by using 10 x 10 m. plots for
trees, 4 x 4 m. plots for all other woody vegetation up to ten feet
tall, and 1 x 1 m. plots for herbs.[183] By separating the data for
trees into overstory and understory individuals and by recording
separately those woody plants less than one foot tall and those
from one to ten feet tall, five strata were distinguished. More
might be necessary or advisable under other conditions.

In general, it may be said that small plots require less work than large plots, both in the laying out and in the obtaining of data, even though more small plots than large ones are needed for complete sampling. At the same time, there is a further saving of effort in that the total area sampled by small plots may usually be less than that sampled by large plots and yet give comparably valuable information.

Distribution of Quadrats.—When the size, shape, and numbers of quadrats have been determined, there still remains the question of how they are to be placed efficiently and in such a fashion that they will give representative data for the stand as a whole. If a stand had a perfectly homogeneous composition, it would make no difference where the sampling was done, but this is rarely, if ever, true. Differences in the soil, drainage, and topography are usually present and are reflected in the vegetation. These variations must be fairly represented in the sample. It becomes necessary, there-

FIG. 19. The distribution of quadrats in a stand according to three different systems. (A) Random distribution as determined by Tippett's numbers.[252a] (B) Spaced as widely and evenly as possible by survey and measurement. (C) Distributed evenly along lines run by compass or sighting; spacing determined by pacing.

fore, to distribute the quadrats throughout the stand, and a plan that will eliminate the human factor in placing the individual plots is desirable.

The statistician prefers a sampling system that gives him data obtained at random.[216] This demands a division of the entire stand into possible sampling areas and then a selection of actual sampling areas determined strictly by chance. Under such conditions, the statistician is able to express mathematically how good his sampling may be. Such a method frequently brings several sampling areas into close proximity at the same time that wide areas are left unsampled. Within these wide areas, there are very likely to occur a number of infrequent or unusual species in small numbers, which would be of little concern in a statistical treatment but whose presence could be of great interest to the ecologist. For him, it is usually desirable to have as many of the variations as possible represented in his data because they are subject to interpretation in terms of experience and the nature of related communities. For such purposes, statistical methods are often of little help. It is, therefore, probable that quadrats distributed systematically throughout the stand as evenly and widely as possible are quite satisfactory for most ecological sampling. In fact, systematic sampling is likely to be better than random sampling for certain ecological purposes.

Any method that will insure wide and even distribution of samples should be satisfactory. The limits and extent of the stand must first be ascertained, and sampling plans made accordingly. Once the plan is made, it should be followed rigidly unless some previously unknown irregularity, like a swamp or an outcrop of rock, should fall within a sample.

In small stands it is possible to plan a grid pattern and to sample at regular intervals in this pattern. When stands are large but of reasonable uniformity, it is common practice to run one or more lines across the greatest extent and to space the quadrats evenly along these lines. It would appear that the more widely the plots are spaced in an area to be sampled the greater the efficiency of the sampling unit, provided the spacing is not so great as to make correlation negligible between adjacent plots.[194] Under some conditions, it may be desirable to run the lines with a surveyor's transit, although a compass line will usually suffice, and in open country it is possible to run them by sighting on some landmark. The spacing may sometimes require accurate measurement, but pacing may serve quite satisfactorily. The important thing is to avoid any method bordering on personal judgment in placing the plots once the sampling is under way. This should be remembered particularly when the sampling is being done to prove or disprove a point. Under such conditions, there is often a strong temptation to shift a plot a few feet or more to include or exclude a desired or undesired species or condition.

FIG. 20. Diagrammatic profile along a transect on the dunes at Ft. Macon, N. C. Physiographic-vegetational zones are indicated. Transect was 110 meters long and horizontal scale is one-half the vertical.[188]

FIG. 21. Portion of field-mapped transect along profile shown in Figure 20 from 97 m. through 104 m. across the transition from Zone 4 to Zone 5, where dominance changes from *Andropogon* to *Uniola*. The symbols indicate *A—Andropogon, U—Uniola, H—Heterotheca, C—Cenchrus, Oe—Oenothera, L—Leptilon.* Such a map gives accurate quantitative data for each species as well as a visual record of changes in vegetation associated with habitat. See Table 1.

Transects.—A *transect* is a sampling strip extending across a stand or several stands. It is most often used when differences in vegetation are apparent and are to be correlated with one or more factors that differ between two points. From a flood plain of a river to the adjacent upland there would be marked changes in moisture conditions, and in such a place a transect can be useful for determining the range of moisture requirements of individual

TABLE 1.   Average density (D) and cover (C), by zones, of principal species mapped on a transect from high tide to the crest of the rear dune at Ft. Macon, N. C. (see Fig. 20). Both cover and density values show the predominance of *Uniola* in exposed zones; *Andropogon* in protected ones. Correlated with amount of salt spray reaching the plants from the open sea.[188]

		Transect I					
	Zones	I	II	III	IIIa	IV	V
Uniola paniculata L.	D	11.8	7.5	3.3	0.4	4.0	10.6
	C	2.7	6.9	0.3	0.03	9.1	18.9
Andropogon littoralis Nash	D	2.1	2.5	5.7	6.6	4.1	0.9
	C	2.2	7.1	7.3	15.4	5.5	2.3
Oenothera humifusa Nutt.	D	1.1	1.8	7.2	1.8	6.5	4.5
	C	0.06				0.9	
Heterotheca subaxillaris (Lam.)	D	4.3	0.5	0.5	0.2	1.1	0.8
Britt. and Rose	C	0.5	0.1				
Leptilon canadense (L.) Britton	D	0.4	1.2	15.1	0.06	6.2	5.1
Euphorbia polygonifolia L.	D	0.1	0.3	0.3		0.2	
Fimbristylis castanea (Michx.)	D			1.4	11.6	1.9	
Vahl	C			0.2	16.6	0.1	
Myrica cerifera L.	D				0.5		
	C				14.7		

species. Transects are also useful in altitudinal studies and in any situation where transitions between communities occur.

Sizes of transects, just as sizes of quadrats, will be determined by conditions. A transect reaching from one small community to another, across a transition zone, might need to be only a few meters long and perhaps a meter or less in width. Transects from lake margins across the several marginal girdles of vegetation that are usually present might be much longer. One reaching from high-tide mark across seaside dunes might be several hundred meters long. A study of the zonation of vegetation on the Sierra Nevada was made by mapping a transect seven miles wide and extending across the mountain range for a distance of eighty miles.[144]

When it seems desirable to map an entire transect in detail, it is advisable to do so by blocks. Values for each block may then be conveniently used as quadrat data, an additional means of analysis and expression of results. A variation of the transect is the method of sampling a unit area at regular intervals along a line. These intervals may be determined by distance or altitude. Such records taken on several lines are particularly helpful in mapping several vegetation types that intergrade irregularly over an extensive area. In the early land surveys of the northern and midwestern states, it was required that the characteristic trees be listed in the records for definite intervals along the lines run by the surveyors. Since the county and township lines they established still stand, it has been possible to reconstruct with considerable accuracy the composition of the forests as they then existed as well as the limits of

FIG. 22. Forest associations of southwestern Michigan as reconstructed from the field notes of the old land survey. Unshaded areas, marked B, beech-maple forest; X = hemlocks, constituting, along lake shore, a codominant with beech and maple; O = white pines (a mark for each locality of occurrence noted in the survey); horizontally shaded areas, oak-hickory forest; obliquely shaded areas, oak-pine forest; stippled areas, dry prairies; and vertically shaded areas, swamp associations.—*From Kenoyer*.[139]

forest and grassland.[139] These surveyors' "transects" were some of the first and longest ever run.

Sometimes there is an advantage in the use of "line transects," in which the species are tabulated as they occur along a line. The method is adaptable to the determination of numerical abundance, frequency, coverage, and other characteristics. It has the advantage of speed and apparently gives accurate information, considering the time it requires. It is particularly useful in dense stands of scrubby vegetation, which would be very difficult to sample with quadrats. Determinations of cover in dense chaparral using line transects gave results that compared very favorably with those obtained by complete charting, although the transects were made in a small fraction of the time required for the detailed procedure.[13]

Rain Forest   Swamp Forest

FIG. 23. Profile diagrams (bisects) of two types of tropical forest. Note that difference in height of trees and in form of trunk is well shown and that rain forest has three distinct strata of trees but swamp forest has essentially one.—*After Beard.*[15]

Bisects.—These are variations of transects in that they are sample strips aiming to show the vertical distribution of vegetation. Thus they may include stratification and layer communities from dominant trees to seedlings on the forest floor and, in addition, show the stratification and root distribution of these same plants below ground.

GENERAL REFERENCES

S. A. CAIN. The Species-Area Curve.
S. A. CAIN. Sample-Plot Technique Applied to Alpine Vegetation in Wyo.
F. X. SCHUMACHER and R. A. CHAPMAN. *Sampling Methods in Forestry and Range Management.*

CHAPTER IV

VEGETATIONAL ANALYSIS
PHYTOSOCIOLOGICAL OBJECTIVES

The interest of European workers in community structure, their desire to describe communities precisely, and their concern with systems of classifying communities resulted in the development of a phase of ecology known as *phytosociology*. Its development was paralleled by (1), the growth of systems of terminology with which the characteristics of a community could be adequately expressed, and (2), the testing and refinement of methods for obtaining quantitative data on the structure and composition of a community to support the systems of description.

Phytosociological methods and terminology have become progressively more standardized, but, as yet, there is not complete agreement among workers. The problems to be resolved are still of the same nature as those of earlier days as is illustrated by a recent characterization,[196] which groups them into two categories : *(a)* the size and number of quadrats to be utilized and *(b)* the conditions to be investigated. The first we have discussed at some length as a part of quantitative methods in community analysis. It should be remembered that the development of these methods has been strongly influenced by phytosociological interests. Although the quadrat method in ecology had its origins in America, its adaptation and refinement for complete analysis and description of communities must be largely credited to European workers.

What phytosociological values are necessary for an adequate characterization of a community would hardly be agreed upon by all workers even today. Through the years this has been the subject of much debate. Some early workers attempted to describe communities on the basis of a single value (e.g., frequency) for each species. Today such a simple system would not be recommended by anyone, and, regardless of objectives, several values are now used in all phytosociological analyses. Methods of sampling and objectives have always influenced each other, and, therefore, it is not surprising that early European workers had widely different

55

approaches, which led to somewhat different conclusions. Several centers of thought and research naturally grew up, which still influence our thinking and procedure. The ideas of the so-called Zurich-Montpellier school have gained rather wide favor, largely through the influence of Dr. J. Braun-Blanquet,[34] and they will be summarized in the remaining section of the chapter.[42]

Before proceeding with this summary, it seems entirely appropriate to point out the unfortunate fact that Americans have been slow to adopt the phytosociological approach, probably because of a lack of appreciation of the usefulness of sociological data. Although phytosociology is, in itself, only a phase of ecology, its methods are useful far beyond the field for which they were developed. Whenever communities must be described or the significance of individual species in a community must be evaluated, phytosociological concepts and methods are applicable and usually with distinct advantages. This means that the methods are useful in experimental studies of communities, for comparing one community with another, for showing changes in a community from year to year, and, in fact, whenever precise information is needed about community structure and the part contributed by various species. Its possible applications are almost unlimited. To illustrate, various of its methods have been used to advantage in such diverse problems as correlating the progressive changes of vegetation and soil on abandoned fields,[20] showing the effects of different intensities of fire on the structure of pine stands,[184] and for demonstrating differences in virgin forest with changes of topography.[187]

STRUCTURAL CHARACTERISTICS

The sociological characters of an individual stand or concrete community may be conveniently grouped in two categories: quantitative and qualitative. Quantitative characters, obtained by quadrat methods, indicate numbers of individuals, their sizes, and the space they occupy. Qualitative characters indicate how species are grouped or distributed, or describe stratification, periodicity, and similar conditions, and are based upon the knowledge derived from long familiarity and observation of the community.

Quantitative Characters. — *Numbers of Individuals.* — Under some circumstances, it may not be practicable to make actual

TABLE 2. Portion of a list of species occurring on the east coast of Greenland at fourteen localities ranging from (A) 70° N latitude, southward to (N) 65° N latitude. Both presence and degree of importance of the species in each locality is indicated by the field-assigned numbers according to the following scale:
5—very common (important constituent of several closed communities); 4—common (more scattered occurrence); 3—here and there; 2—uncommon; 1—rare; + —present.
The listed species were selected to show how the system of values indicates range limits and progressive changes of importance with latitude. *From Böcher.*[24a]

| | Localities | | | | | | | | | | | | | |
	A	B	C	D	E	F	G	H	I	J	K	L	M	N
Cystopteris fragilis	4	+	3		4	+	3	4	4	4	4	?	4	4
Cerastium alpinum	4	4	5	4	5	+	4	4	5	4	4	4	4	5
Minuartia biflora	4	4	4	4	4	+	4	4	4	4	4	4	4	4
Silene acaulis	5	4	4	4	4	+	4	5	4	4	5	4	5	5
Sedum roseum	4	+	4	2	4	+	1	5	5	4	3	4	5	5
Oxyria digyna	5	5	5	4	4	4	4	5	5	5	5	5	5	5
Polygonum viviparum	5	5	5	5	5	5	5	5	5	5	5	5	5	5
Salix herbacea	5	5	5	5	5	5	5	5	5	5	5	5	5	5
Potentilla tridentata										1		3	?	3
Polystichum lonchitis								1					2	3
Alchemilla filicaulis				1				3	5	4		?	5	5
Sagina intermedia		+				+	3	3	4		4	+	3	3
Draba rupestris	?		3				3	3	4	4	4	4	4	4
Empetrum nigrum	3	2	2	1	2	+	5	5	5	5	5	5	5	5
Salix arctophila	+	+	+	+	+	+	4	4	5	5	5	5	5	5
Epilobium arcticum	3													
Potentilla pulchella	3	+												
Ranunculus sulphureus	3		2											
Draba lactea	4	+	+	+	+									
Dryas octopetala	5	+	2		2									
Draba alpina	4	4	4	4	3		3							
Cassiope tetragona	5	5	5	5	4				1	1	4			1

counts, but plentifulness may rapidly be estimated according to some scale of abundance similar to the following :

1. very rare
2. rare
3. infrequent
4. abundant
5. very abundant

Such estimates are particularly useful when several similar stands of uniform composition are to be surveyed within a limited time. Assuming the sampling is adequate, the determination of actual numbers by counting is of greater value because it permits the expression of *density*, which is abundance on a unit-area basis.

Density is the average number of individuals per area sampled. Since it is an absolute expression, the significance of density in interpretation may be overemphasized unless one remembers that it is an average value. Not all species with equal densities are of equal importance in a community, or need they be similarly distributed. If ten individuals of a species are counted on a series of ten plots, the density is "one" regardless of whether they are all found in one plot or one in each of the ten plots. It becomes necessary, therefore, to interpret density values or to specify other characters that, combined with density, serve to complete the picture. One such value is *frequency*.

Frequency.—This value is an expression of the percentage of sample plots in which a species occurs. In the example above, the plants that were all found on a single plot would have a frequency value of 10 percent, whereas, if they had occurred in every plot, the value would be 100 percent. Thus frequency becomes a very useful value, when used in combination with density, for then not only the number of individuals is known but also how they are distributed in the stand. These two characters are of prime importance in determining community structure and, taken together, have a variety of uses far beyond those of other quantitative values. The use of frequency as a single determination in analytic procedure has proven unsatisfactory, although numerous attempts have been made to show its adequacy.

It should be emphasized that frequency values cannot be com-

PINE HARDWOODS

Density-Frequency

Basal Area

Overstory

Understory

FIG. 24. Bar diagrams of density, frequency, and basal area to compare pine and hardwood development in an unburned pine stand (A), with portions previously subjected to surface fire (B), and crown fire (C). Densities are indicated by the height of the columns above the zero line and frequencies by the width of the columns. Basal areas in square feet are indicated by the length of the columns below the zero line, and the width of these columns indicates percent of total basal area in the stand. Values for density and absolute basal area were modified by the factor $2 \sqrt{y}$ because of their wide range.[184]

pared unless determined with plots of equal size. The larger the plots, the higher the frequency.

Frequencies may conveniently be grouped into classes, for example, A 1-20%, B 21-40%, C 41-60%, D 61-80%, E 81-100%.

Raunkiaer[202] used these five classes and, on the basis of more than eight thousand frequency percentages, found that Class A included 53 percent of the species; B, 14 percent; C, 9 percent; D, 8 percent; and E, 16 percent. From these data he drew his "Law of Frequency," which states that Class $A > B > C \gtreqless D < E$. This led to numerous investigations to check on the validity and univer-

TABLE 3. The effect on frequency of increasing size of quadrat as illustrated by data on Alpine fell-field vegetation in the Rockies. Quadrat sizes in sq. m. From[49].

	1/10	*1/4*	*1/2*	*1/1*
Arenaria sajanensis	100	100	100	100
Selaginella densa	100	100	100	100
Trifolium dasyphyllum	80	100	100	100
Eritrichium argenteum	80	80	90	90
Sieversia turbinata	50	50	60	80
Polemonium confertum	40	40	40	50
Phlox caespitosa	30	50	50	60
Sedum stenopetalum	30	50	50	60
Paronychia pulvinata	30	30	50	50
Silene acaulis	20	30	30	70
Potentilla nelsoniana	20	20	30	30
Potentilla quinquefolia	20	20	20	30
Potentilla sp.	10	20	30	30
Polygonum bistortoides	10	20	20	20
Artemisia scopulorum	10	10	20	20
Sieversia ciliata		10	20	30
Arenaria macrantha				10
Erigeron compositus				10
Total species	15	16	16	18
Average frequencies	42	45.6	48.7	52.2

sality of the principle of frequency distributions in plant communities.[137] The results have been in essential agreement regardless of the vegetation type. Class A will normally be very high because of the numerous sporadic species to be found with low frequency in most stands. Class E, and to a lesser extent D, must always be relatively high because of the species that dominate the community. If quadrats are enlarged, classes A and E will enlarge and the lesser classes will decrease accordingly. Frequency classes, therefore, are comparable only when based upon samples of the same size.

A frequency diagram is useful in indicating the homogeneity of a stand since floristic uniformity varies directly with the values for

FIG. 25. Frequency diagrams of pine stands of different ages and of virgin red fir stands compared with Raunkiaer's and Kenoyer's normals. The pine stands were all relatively homogeneous but became slightly less so with age as the total number of species increased by 25 percent and the accidentals declined. Class E, the dominants, remained essentially constant throughout the series. All the virgin red fir stands were extremely homogeneous in spite of a high proportion of incidentals occurring sporadically. The stands were also similar to each other although widely distributed along the Sierra.

classes A and E. When classes B, C, and D are relatively high, the stand is not homogeneous. In general, the higher Class E may be, the greater the homogeneity.

Cover and Space.—Although density and frequency indicate numbers and distribution, they do not indicate size, volume of space occupied, or amount of ground covered or shaded. These characteristics are desirable additional values that contribute materially to an understanding of the importance of a species in a stand, since they are closely related to dominance.

As suggested under Quadrat Methods (Chap. 3), cover can be

estimated with some success or may be accurately determined by various devices for measurement and recording. When vegetation is stratified, the cover must be considered in terms of the stratum to which the species belongs. For rapid estimation, as well as for analysis of results, there is a distinct advantage at times in using several cover classes. Braun-Blanquet recommends five :

1. covering less than 5% of the ground surface
2. covering 5% to 25%
3. covering 25% to 50%
4. covering 50% to 75%
5. covering 75% to 100%

In studies of grassland, estimates and measurements of cover are extremely useful because the variations in size and form of grasses make counts difficult and of little value. For expressing cover, sometimes as area of coverage, sometimes as basal area of clumps, range ecologists frequently use the term, *density*. This usage is, of course, at variance with the phytosociological application and, consequently, leads to confusion of interpretation unless it is known, for example, that a "density list"[96] applied to grassland, refers to area or cover for each species, and that "square foot density"[247] also indicates coverage evaluated by a different method.

Determination of the volume of space occupied by species is difficult and has not been widely done. When all plants are small, cover alone serves very well, especially when strata are distinguished. With grasses, as in pasture studies, clipping and weighing the tops is sometimes necessary for accurate comparisons. In forest studies, the estimate of volume of standing timber as used by foresters can be used to advantage, but a more useful value is basal area. Diameters can be determined accurately and quickly with a diameter tape, and basal area, easily obtained from standard tables, can add much to an evaluation in terms of size and bulk that cannot be visualized through the other quantitative characters. This provides a particularly useful means of comparing the relative importance of species of trees and, in addition, permits analysis in terms of size or diameter classes among the sapling and understory individuals. Several quantitative characters can be advantageously combined in the form of phytographs (Fig. 26) for evaluation.

Fig. 26. Phytographs showing the relative importance of the dominant species of trees in four types of pulpwood forest in northwestern Maine. Radius 1, percentage of total dominant density; Radius 2, percentage frequency; Radius 3, percentage of total size classes represented; Radius 4, percentage of total dominant basal area. The inner end of each radius represents the absence of its assigned sociological value.[191]

Qualitative Characters.—These characters, which include sociability, vitality, stratification, and periodicity, are mostly not derived from quadrat studies but from observation of, and wide experience with, the community. They describe the plan and organization of its components, which have been evaluated previously in terms of measurements and counts. When the quantitative analysis has been fairly complete, especially including density or cover in conjunction with frequency, and when strata have been analyzed separately, the qualitative characters are already largely included in the quantitative picture.

Sociability.—This character evaluates the degree that individuals of a species are grouped or how they are distributed in a stand. It has also been expressed as *gregariousness* or *dispersion*. Each of the various scales used to indicate degree of sociability include expressions which range from plants occurring singly, as one extreme, through intermediate conditions (patches, colonies, or groups), to large colonies, mats, or pure stands at the opposite extreme.

The sociability of a species is not a constant, for it is determined by the habitat and the resulting competition of the species with which it is associated. Since habitat conditions are not constant and since communities change, especially in plant succession, the sociability of a species, even in the same locality, may change considerably.

Dispersion is a statistical expression that has been applied to sociability. If dispersion is normal, it implies a randomized distribution such as might be expected by chance. In hyperdispersion there is irregular distribution, which results in crowded individuals in some areas and their complete absence from others. Hypodispersion means that the arrangement is more regular than would be expected by chance, as, for instance, the plants in a cornfield. All of these conditions are recognizable in natural communities and, when density-frequency values have been determined, are noticeable in the data.

Vitality.—Not all species found in a given stand need belong to the community. Unless the plants are reproducing, they are not completely adapted to the conditions and may disappear entirely. Even species constantly present in a community may be derived from seeds produced elsewhere and transported by wind or some other agency. It becomes necessary, therefore, to know something of the vigor and prosperity of the species before classifying it as a true community member.

Vitality need not always be listed for all species, but it must be considered in evaluating their importance, whether it is done systematically or not. Vitality classes or degrees of vitality include : (1) ephemeral adventives, which germinate occasionally but cannot increase, (2) plants maintaining themselves by vegetative means but not completing the life cycle, (3) well-developed plants, which regularly complete the life cycle.

Changes in the vitality of species are often indicators of community change or plant succession. Dominants decreasing in numbers and reproducing feebly indicate future radical changes. Rapidly increasing numbers of a species previously of little importance may suggest the new dominants to come.

Stratification.—The necessity for recognizing the strata of a community becomes obvious when sampling is attempted. The several strata that may occur were described under sampling procedure. Diagrams of stratification combined with cover are often used effectively to show the relative significance of the several layers in a stand. The physical and physiological requirements of species in different strata can be appreciated fully only when the stratification both above and below ground is clearly worked out. Then the micro-environments of these strata may be considered in terms of cause and effect.

Periodicity.—The conspicuous rhythmic phenomena in plant communities are those related to seasonal climatic change, and, of these phenological changes, the obvious ones have been given most attention. Flowering and fruiting periods have been noted for so long that they are fairly well known; in fact, phenology is often thought of as referring only to these phenomena. In community studies the terms *aspect dominance* and *seasonal dominance* have been used to describe situations in which a species or group of species appears to be dominant for a portion of the year, usually because of conspicuous floral characters.

Of equal importance to the community is the seasonal development of vegetative parts. The seasonal aspect of the individual may proceed through several phases, including a leafy period, a leafless

FIG. 27. Coverage-stratification diagrams comparing types of hardwood forest. Number and height of strata are graphically shown as well as the coverage class and number of species involved in each stratum.—*Adapted from papers by S. A. Cain.*

period, a flowering period, a fruiting period, an embryo period, and perhaps others. Rarely will all the species of a community have these periods strictly coinciding. Consequently, in temperate climates, the community as a whole usually has seasonal aspects, which are termed *vernal, estival, autumnal,* and *hibernal.* The structure and species of a community are strongly influenced by

FIG. 28. Aspect dominance as illustrated by chandelier cactus *(Opuntia arborescens)* in a mixed prairie community (Bouteloua-Hilaria). El Paso County, Colo. The cactus makes up only 8.9 percent of the total cover.— *Photo by R. B. Livingston.*

the extent to which periodic phenomena in the individuals are adjusted to each other.

Light and moisture conditions on the floor of a deciduous forest during the vernal period permit the growth and maturation of numerous herbs before the estival period. When the trees and shrubs are in full leaf, these herbs are already declining to a fruiting or resting condition and are unaffected by the reduced light and moisture available to them. These vernal herbs are a part of the community and must be so considered.

Another illustration of a periodic phenomenon that may be important in sociological relations is the time of growth. Height growth has been systematically studied for numerous woody species, but the periods of root elongation are rarely known. Studies of loblolly pine[205] showed, surprisingly, that it makes some root growth in every month of the year. Even in the winter months, its roots are constantly coming in contact with new supplies of soil water, which fact may partially explain its ability to thrive in

FIG. 29.   Vernal aspect dominance of atamasco lily *(Zephyranthes atamasco)* in a low North Carolina meadow where only grasses, rushes, and sedges are visible a few weeks later.—*Photo by H. L. Blomquist.*

the southeastern states where transpiration may at times be fairly high during the winter.

Periodicity may be controlled by a variety of factors. Length of day affects the time of flowering, some species requiring long days, some short. The fall of leaves in autumn is a response not to temperature but to length of day. Desert vegetation may flower or not depending upon precipitation, and semidesert plants regularly flourish during the brief seasonal rains and exist in an almost dormant condition for the remainder of the year. Arctic and alpine areas usually receive little rain. The melting snow provides the moisture for vegetation. In situations where little snow accumulates or where it melts and disappears quickly, the vegetation is sparse and takes on a hibernal aspect very quickly. Where snow patches remain well into the summer and provide a water supply by melting gradually, the estival aspect may carry on for several weeks after plants in less favorable sites near by have gone to seed. Plants deeply buried under snow may not be exposed until so late in the season that conditions are unfavorable for flowering, and, as a result, they produce no fruit or seed.

SYNTHETIC CHARACTERISTICS

It has previously been pointed out that it is often desirable as well as practical to consider a community in the abstract as well as in the concrete sense. When a community is studied on this basis, it becomes necessary to observe numerous stands and to determine whether they actually do belong to the same community and to what extent they vary from each other. It is desirable also to know which species, singly or in combination, may be taken as indicators, which species are only incidental, which ones are always present, and which ones occur only when a stand develops under a given set of conditions.

Thus, for a complete synthetic analysis, it is desirable to have information on as many stands as possible, or at least enough stands to be representative of the whole. These should be distributed throughout the range of the community and under all the variety of conditions in which they develop. Again, to make a proper analysis, only those stands should be employed that are in a comparable stage of development or maturity and that are extensive enough to include all the important species and most of the anticipated variations.

Presence.—A most useful synthetic character involves merely the degree of regularity with which a species occurs in the stands observed. When the species present in each of the stands have been tabulated, the presence of each is expressed by the percentage of stands in which it occurred or by a five-degree scale of presence classes.

    1.—rare (1-20% of the stands)
    2.—seldom present (21-40%)
    3.—often present (41-60%)
    4.—mostly present (61-80%)
    5.—constantly present (81-100%)

The number of stands necessary for a study of presence as well as the necessary extent of stands cannot be arbitrarily stated. Ma-

TABLE 4

Species	1	2	3	4	5	6	7	8	9	10	11	12	13	14	15	16
TREES																
Abies magnifica	x	x	x	x	x	x	x	x	x	x	x	x	x	x	x	x
Pinus monticola	x	x	x	x	.	.	x	x	x	x	x	x	x	x	x	. .
Pinus contorta	.	.	x	.	.	.	x	x	x	x	x	x	x	x	x	x
Tsuga mertensiana	.	x	.	.	.	.	.	.	x	x	x	x	x	x	x	. .
Abies concolor	.	.	x	x	x	x	x	x	.	.	.	.	.	.	x	. . x
Acer glabrum	.	.	x	x	.	.	.	.	.	.	.	.	.	.	x	. .
SHRUBS																
Ribes viscosissimum	.	.	x	x	x	x	x	x	x	x	x	x	x	x	.	x
Symphoricarpos rotundifolius	.	.	x	.	.	x	.	.	.	x	x	.	.	x	.	. . x
Ribes montigenum	.	.	.	.	.	.	.	.	.	x	x	x	x	x	.	x
Sambucus racemosa	.	.	.	.	.	x	.	.	.	.	x	.	.	x	.	x
Ribes cereum	x	.	.	.	.	.	x	x	x	.	.	.	.	.	.	.
Spiraea densiflora	.	.	x	.	.	x	.	.	.	.	x	.	.	.	x	.
Arctostaphylos nevadensis	x	.	x	.	.	x	.	x	.	.	.	.	.	.	.	.
Symphoricarpos mollis	.	.	x	.	.	.	.	.	.	.	x	.	.	.	.	x
Lonicera conjugialis	.	.	.	.	.	.	.	x	.	.	x	x	.	.	.	.
Quercus vaccinifolia	.	.	.	.	x	.	.	.	.	.	x	.	.	.	.	.
Amelanchier alnifolia	.	.	x	x	.	.	.	.	.	.	.	.	.	.	.	.
Rubus parviflorus	.	.	.	.	x	.	.	.	.	.	.	.	.	.	.	.
HERBS																
Chrysopsis breweri	x	x	x	x	x	x	x	.	.	x	x	x	x	x	x	x
Monardella odoratissima	x	x	x	x	x	.	.	x	x	x	x	x	.	.	x	x	x
Gayophytum ramosissimum	.	.	x	x	.	.	x	x	x	x	x	x	x	x	x	x
Pedicularis semibarbata	.	.	x	x	x	x	x	x	x	x	x	x	x	x	x	x
Pirola picta	x	x	x	x	x	x	x	x	.	.	x	x	.	.	x	x	. . x
Phacelia hydrophylloides	.	.	x	x	x	.	.	x	x	x	.	x	x	x	x	x	x
Poa bolanderi	x	x	x	.	.	.	x	x	x	.	.	x	x	x	x	x	x
Arabis platysperma	x	.	x	x	x	.	x	x	x	.	.	x	x	.	x	x	. .
Corallorrhiza maculata	.	.	x	x	x	x	.	x	x	x	.	x	x	.	x	. . x
Thalictrum fendleri	.	.	x	x	.	x	x	x	x	.	x	x	x	x	.	. .
Kelloggia galioides	.	.	x	x	x	x	x	x	x	x	.	x	.	.	x	. .
Erigeron salsuginosus var.																
angustifolius	x	x	.	.	x	.	x	.	x	x	.	.	x	.	.	x	. . x
Hieracium albiflorum	.	.	x	.	.	x	x	x	.	.	x	.	.	x	x	.	x
Lupinus andersoni var. *fulcratus*	x	x	x	x	x	.	.	.	.	x	x	.	.	.	.	x
Viola purpurea	.	.	x	x	.	.	.	x	.	x	.	x	.	.	x	x	x
Chimaphila umbellata	x	x	x	x	x	x	x	x	.	.	.	.	.	.	.	.
Penstemon gracilentus	.	.	x	x	x	x	x	x	x	.	.	.	.	.	.	.
Plagiobothrys hispidus	.	x	.	.	.	.	x	x	.	.	x	.	.	.	x	x	. . x

ture, homogeneous, undisturbed stands of virgin forest would require the observation of only small portions of individual stands and a relatively small number of stands to give dependable information. In younger, less stable vegetation, more stands and a wider observation would be necessary so that variation would be repre-

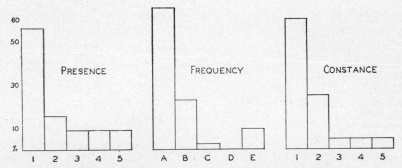

FIG. 30. Presence, frequency, and constance diagrams for Sierran red fir forest, based on sixteen stands. The presence diagram is normal, especially in the absence of a second maximum. The constance diagram is constructed from regular quadrat data rather than a constance sample. Compared to a frequency diagram it should show a material decrease in Class 1 because of the greater odds on discovery of a single plant of an accidental species in a restricted area. Surprisingly, with only forty species, it retains the same form as the presence diagram (ninety-seven species) although the high constance classes are reduced. The frequency graph is normal, and indicates stands of relatively great homogeneity.

sented and so that those species seldom present or rare would fall into their proper classes. What this minimal area should be and what the minimum number of species might be for the community must largely be determined by experience and familiarity with the community.

Constance.—When a unit area in each stand instead of the entire stand is used for listing species, as for presence, the values are termed *constance*. There is thus no fundamental difference be-

TABLE 4. Portion of a presence table compiled from sixteen stands of virgin red fir (*Abies magnifica*) forest in the Sierra Nevada. Only *Abies magnifica* and *Pinus monticola*, of the trees, are constantly present (Class 5). Only one shrub, *Ribes viscosissimum*, is a constant, others falling in Class 3 or lower. Five herbs are constants, eight are mostly present (Class 4), and five are often present (Class 3). Eleven herbs of Class 2 (seldom present) and 46 of Class 1 (rare) are not listed.[189]

tween presence and constance. The latter has the advantage of eliminating discrepancies resulting from sampling stands of unequal size. The lower classes of constance are more uniform than those of presence, for the larger the area examined the greater the number of incidental species encountered.

Constancy bears a relationship to the abstract community very similar to that of frequency in the concrete community. The problems of minimal area are similar and can to some extent be reduced by the use of species : area curves as used in frequency determinations. Both concepts are concerned with homogeneity, the one with that of the stand, the other with that of the abstract community. If constance values are divided into five classes and these are diagrammed as for frequency, the results are quite different. Instead of two maxima as in frequency, only the classes representing irregular occurrences are high, and each succeeding higher class is apt to include fewer species.

Fidelity.—This character is indicative of the degree with which a species is restricted to a particular kind of community. Species may be grouped into five fidelity classes.

Fid. 1.—Strangers, appearing accidentally
Fid. 2.—Indifferents, without pronounced affinity for any community
Fid. 3.—Preferents, present in several communities but predominantly in one of them
Fid. 4.—Selectives, found especially in one community but met with occasionally in others
Fid. 5.—Exclusives, found completely, or almost so, in only one community

Species with fidelities 3-5 are termed *characteristic species* in a community. Positive establishment of which species are characteristic is possible only after all communities of a region have been studied sociologically. Approximations can, of course, be made by those of wide experience, but even then the assigned values must be considered with skepticism. When fidelity values are accurately determined, they contribute strongly to the recognition and classification of a community. However, studies of this sort have been so few in the United States that it will be a long time before suf-

TABLE 5. A summary of sociological concepts that permits presentation of the important data for a community in a single tabulation. The quantitative data (1) are derived from quadrats; the analytic data (A) from the study of some one community; the synthetic data (B) from the study of several different examples (stands) of the same community.—*After Cain.*[42]

SPECIES LIST	SOCIOLOGICAL SUMMARY													
	I ORGANIZATION											II SYNECOLOGY (Physiognomy)		III GENETIC SOCIOLOGY
	A ANALYTIC								B SYNTHETIC					
	1 Quantitative				2 Qualitative									
	a	b	c	d	a	b	c	d	a	b	c	a	b	
	Abundance	Density	Dominance	Frequence	Sociability	Vitality	Periodicity	Stratification	Presence	Constance	Fidelity	Life Form	Leaf Size	Dynamic Behavior
Classes	1-5	—	1-5	1-5	1-5	1-3	1-4	1-4	1-5	1-5	1-5	1-10	1-6	1-5

ficient data have accumulated to permit accurate statements of fidelity for species of most communities. Under such conditions, it seems advisable to use constance, an absolute value determined within the community in question, as a means of fixing upon the sociologically important species. Some ecologists consider constance of greater significance than fidelity for this purpose. It should be noted that characteristic species are more responsive to habitat variations and are consequently of greater indicator significance than are, in general, the species of high constance. It would be desirable if we had both values available for all communities.

Coefficient of Community.—When comparing two communities or the vegetation of two regions, a mathematical expression of the similarity of lists of species may be useful. If community X is compared to Y, the number of species common to both, expressed as a percentage of the number for Y has been termed the *coefficient of community*. The same principle can be used for evaluating variation or similarity among several stands of an abstract community. Then, however, each must be compared with a standard or list of the characteristic species of the community as a whole.[130]

OBJECTIVES DETERMINE PROCEDURE

If these several sociological concepts are grouped systematically in tabular form, their relationships become clearer (Table 5). Such a grouping has the further usefulness of presenting tabulation of values obtained in the field in compact and logical order for interpretation.

When the objective is merely to describe a community as completely as possible, it might well be desirable to have such a table completely filled out. In studies involving the application of phytosociological methods to special problems it is frequently only necessary to use a few of the values. This does not mean that not all are of significance, or that some can be ignored entirely. Rather, it suggests that each has its uses and that some are applicable where others are not.

The limitations and possibilities of usefulness of the several concepts become increasingly understandable after one has had some experience with them. Nevertheless, selection of the most useful values for study and application to a particular problem always remains a matter for serious consideration. The concepts to be used must be selected in terms of their contribution to the object of the study, the time available, and the labor involved.

GENERAL REFERENCES

J. BRAUN-BLANQUET. *Plant Sociology : The Study of Plant Communities*.
S. A. CAIN. Concerning Certain Phytosociological Concepts.
C. RAUNKIAER. *The Life Forms of Plants and Statistical Plant Geography; Being the collected papers of C. Raunkiaer*.

Part 3 · Factors Controlling the Community: the Environment

Vegetational analysis gives the information necessary to describe and name a community and provides data that can be used to compare it with other communities or with itself after a lapse of time or an experimental treatment. This in itself is worth while, but the ecologist has the added objective of correlating the vegetational record so obtained with the environment. To interpret the vegetational statistics, and to explain them in terms of cause and effect, leads to an analysis of the environment and its relationships to the community.

Since the environment consists of many factors interacting upon each other and upon the vegetation, its complexity prohibits consideration of it as a whole. The interactions are by no means all clearly understood and the effects of a single factor upon an organism may be inadequately known; therefore, it is logical to approach the subject of environment through individual factors and their effects. With information as complete as possible on the operation of individual factors, explanations may often be found for plant responses among the interactions and effects of a few of the variable factors. The chapters of this section deal successively with climatic, physiographic, and biological factors as each may operate in the complex of factors termed *environment*.

CHAPTER V

CLIMATIC FACTORS: THE AIR

GASES OF THE ATMOSPHERE

The air surrounding the earth is made up of only a few gases in proportions that remain remarkably constant. The average volume percentages of dry air are : nitrogen, 78.09; oxygen, 20.95; carbon dioxide, 0.03; and argon, 0.93. In addition, there are minute but measurable quantities of several rare gases, which have no part in our discussion. Within the limits of the atmosphere that can affect plants directly, there is but slight variation in the proportions of these gases whether over the ocean or land, at sea level or on high mountains. Minor but rather consistent variations have been found over large industrial cities where quantities of carbon dioxide are constantly being produced.

Whenever an organism respires or a fire burns, oxygen is removed from the atmosphere and carbon dioxide is added to the air. Decomposition of organic matter also liberates carbon dioxide, and photosynthetic activity of plants removes carbon dioxide and liberates oxygen. When these processes are not in balance, there may be local variations in the composition of the air, but so long as the air is not strictly quiet, the least motion, combined with diffusion, is sufficient to eliminate gaseous differences almost at once.

Thus, regardless of its terrestrial environment, the organism is almost certain to be plentifully supplied with these gases that form a relatively constant part of the atmosphere; therefore, these need not be considered as variable factors in the environment.

GASES OF THE SOIL ATMOSPHERE

Although normally there is never a shortage of oxygen in the air above ground, such a shortage sometimes occurs in the soil. Air space in the soil is limited and is partially, or sometimes wholly, occupied by water. Any change in the composition of the soil atmosphere is only slowly readjusted from the atmosphere above, for here air movement and diffusion are relatively slow.

Since all living structures in the soil respire, and this includes small animals and other microorganisms as well as roots of large plants, the supply of oxygen is constantly reduced and carbon dioxide is released. As a result, the soil atmosphere always contains less oxygen and more carbon dioxide than the air above. Oxygen decreases with depth, and carbon dioxide increases. In the soil under closed stands of vegetation, carbon dioxide often equals 5 percent and has been found in much higher concentrations. The constant use of oxygen and its extremely slow rate of diffusion when soils are saturated soon result in oxygen deficiency. Temporary saturation may not be serious, but, when prolonged, it results in death of the vegetation through inhibition of root growth and absorption. Under these conditions, several soil organisms may carry on anaerobic respiration for a time, but such activity results in chemical changes of several kinds, which may affect fertility of the soil or actually inhibit plant growth.

Available oxygen in an aquatic habitat probably is somewhat higher than in a saturated soil because of the movement of the water and because the oxygen is more readily replaced by solution from the atmosphere. If, however, the water is solidly frozen over, it is not uncommon for the oxygen supply to fall so low that many of the fish die. When such conditions develop in well-stocked fishing lakes, it is now common practice to cut several holes through the ice and to pump air through the water until the depleted oxygen supply has been replaced. The mud at the bottom of a shallow pond is probably the least favorable habitat for plant roots. Most plants growing well in such places are of the emergent type, having at least part of their structure in the air and characterized by lacunar tissue, which permits gases to accumulate in, and move freely through, the plant.

WATER CONTENT OF THE ATMOSPHERE

In addition to the gases constituting the atmosphere, water is always present as vapor but in widely varying amounts. Since atmospheric moisture represents the indirect source of the plant's water and likewise controls the amount and rate at which water is lost by the plant, it is an environmental factor deserving considerable attention.

The capacity of air to hold water vapor increases as temperatures rise or pressure is reduced. The air is said to be saturated when it contains as much moisture as it can hold at a given temperature and pressure. If for any reason the temperature is raised or the pressure is decreased, the amount of water remaining constant, the air is no longer saturated. On the other hand, if the temperature of saturated air decreases, the capacity is reduced, and some of the vapor condenses as a liquid. Thus air that is not saturated will become so without change of vapor content if its temperature is lowered, and, when saturation is reached, the air is said to be at the "dew point." If the cooling continues, the vapor becomes a liquid, which may condense on objects near the surface of the earth as dew or frost or, if condensation takes place in the air, may result in precipitation.

Terminology of Atmospheric Moisture.—Several expressions are used to describe the moisture content of the air. *Absolute humidity* is commonly interpreted as the amount of water vapor per unit volume of air and can be expressed as grams per cubic meter or any other units of mass and volume. In itself the absolute humidity has little bearing on the life of a plant, for it is not the total atmospheric moisture that determines evaporation and transpiration, but rather the difference between the weight of vapor present and the maximum weight the air could hold at the time. Thus the *relative humidity*, which is an expression of percentage of saturation, is more nearly related to the rate of water loss from a free water surface or from a plant. Relative humidity depends upon temperature as well as the amount of moisture present, and, as a consequence, identical relative humidities do not indicate identical moisture conditions unless the temperatures are also the same. This means that every shift in temperature results in a change in relative humidity, regardless of moisture present, and a consequent change in rate of evaporation or transpiration.

Several authors have emphasized that, when considered independently of other factors, the actual amount of water vapor in the air has little if any influence upon evaporation. One illustration[7] especially serves to emphasize the ecological significance of this fact. Death Valley, California, is probably the most arid region in the United States, yet its "dry" atmosphere contains on the average in July almost exactly the same amount of water vapor per unit volume as does the "moist" atmosphere of Duluth, Minnesota, at the same time of the year.

An atmosphere 70 percent saturated at 60° F. will contain much less water vapor than an atmosphere 70 percent saturated at 80° F., and the capacity to hold more water will be less in the first than the second case. Evaporation will, therefore, normally be more rapid at 80° F. even though the relative humidities are the same. It can be seen that a statement of relative humidity alone gives little indication of atmospheric moisture conditions since a relative humidity of 80 percent may mean "dryness" if the temperature is high or "wetness" if the temperature is low.

It is desirable then to have a term indicating the amount of water that air can take up before it becomes saturated. Vapor pressure is a measure of the quantity of water vapor present, the temperature being constant, and is usually expressed in units of pressure (inches or mm. of Hg). Therefore, *vapor pressure deficit* is the difference between the amount of water vapor actually present and the amount that could exist without condensation at the same temperature. It is a direct indication of atmospheric moisture, quite independent of temperature and, therefore, compared to relative humidity, its values are much more indicative of the potential rate of evaporation.

When the relative humidity is 100 percent at 68° F., the vapor pressure is 17.54 mm. of mercury. If the relative humidity were 70 percent, the vapor pressure would equal 12.28 mm. (0.70 x 17.54), and the deficit would be 5.26 mm. (17.54—12.28). If the relative humidity were the same (70%) at 59° F., the vapor pressure would be 8.95 mm. (0.70 x 12.79) and the deficit would be only 3.84 mm. (12.79—8.95). Tables of saturation pressures (vapor pressures) are usually available in handbooks of chemistry, and it is possible to transform relative humidities to vapor pressure deficits quickly when the temperature is also known. The relationships are shown in Table 6.

Greater general use of the vapor pressure deficit in ecological work seems desirable, for in spite of certain limitations, its accuracy is much greater than that of relative humidity. The potential rate of evaporation cannot be indicated with a single simple expression of atmospheric moisture since the rate depends upon the vapor pressure gradient between evaporating surface and atmosphere. The gradient can be determined only when the temperature and vapor pressure of the liquid are known as well as those of the atmosphere. Vapor pressure deficit is directly related to evaporation only when the temperatures of the air and of the evaporating surface are equal.[252] Ecologists more often than not measure evaporation directly, but when evaporation is not known, in spite of the above, vapor pressure deficits could well be used instead of relative humidities.

TABLE 6. Vapor pressure deficit and vapor pressure as related to relative humidities at different temperatures.

Vapor pressure deficits (mm of Hg), reading down, at given relative humidities

| Temperature | | Relative Humidities | | | | | | | | | | |
C°	F°	0%	10%	20%	30%	40%	50%	60%	70%	80%	90%	100%
50	122	92.51	83.26	74.01	64.76	55.51	46.26	37.00	27.75	18.50	9.25	0
45	113	71.88	64.69	57.50	50.32	43.13	35.94	28.75	21.56	14.38	7.19	0
40	104	55.32	49.79	44.25	38.72	33.19	27.66	22.13	16.60	11.06	5.53	0
35	95	42.18	37.96	33.74	29.53	25.31	21.09	16.87	12.65	8.44	4.22	0
30	86	31.82	28.64	25.46	22.27	19.09	15.91	12.73	9.55	6.36	3.18	0
25	77	23.76	21.38	19.01	16.63	14.26	11.88	9.50	7.13	4.75	2.38	0
20	68	17.54	15.79	14.03	12.28	10.52	8.77	7.02	5.26	3.51	1.75	0
15	59	12.79	11.51	10.23	8.95	7.67	6.40	5.12	3.84	2.56	1.28	0
10	50	9.21	8.29	7.37	6.45	5.53	4.60	3.68	2.76	1.84	0.92	0
5	41	6.54	5.89	5.23	4.58	3.92	3.27	2.62	1.96	1.31	0.65	0
0	32	4.58	4.12	3.66	3.21	2.75	2.29	1.83	1.37	0.92	0.46	0
		100%	90%	80%	70%	60%	50%	40%	30%	20%	10%	0%

Vapor pressures (mm of Hg), reading up, at given relative humidities.

Measurement of Atmospheric Moisture.—The psychrometer and the hygrometer are the two instruments most useful to ecologists for this purpose. The former consists of two thermometers, one of which has the bulb wrapped with a wet piece of cloth, and both of which are aerated in some fashion, usually by whirling. Evaporation from the wet cloth is controlled by the moisture in the atmosphere, and the bulb is cooled in proportion to the evaporation. The dry bulb gives the temperature of the atmosphere,

FIG. 31. A sling type of psychrometer for determining relative humidity by the difference in temperature of the wet and dry bulb after whirling.—*Courtesy Friez Instrument Division, Bendix Aviation Corporation.*

and the difference between the dry and wet bulb readings gives the wet bulb depression. Knowing the barometric pressure and these two values, the relative humidity can be quickly determined from standard tables or from nomograms.[108] The necessity for aeration of the thermometers, usually accomplished by rapid rotation, has led to the design of several "sling" type psychrometers. Because these must be whirled, they require considerable space for operation. The "cog" psychrometer, functioning like an egg beater, can be used in much smaller spaces.

The hygrograph is usually a continuously recording instrument in which an arm marks on a rotating drum the stretching and contracting of a strand of hairs, which respond to relative humidity. The drum is so calibrated that relative humidity is recorded directly. Often the device is equipped to record the temperature simultaneously and is then called a hygrothermograph. Naturally, this automatic device is very convenient, particularly since it normally needs to be serviced but once a week. If, however, several stations are to be maintained, the necessary instruments may not be available, and the psychrometer is then the only solution.

With readings of the psychrometer and the hygrothermograph, the air temperature is also obtained, providing the means of calculating vapor pressure deficits with no extra determinations. A

FIG. 32. A hygrothermograph, which automatically gives a continuous record of relative humidity and temperature of the air.—*Courtesy Friez Instrument Division, Bendix Aviation Corporation.*

simple nomogram (Fig. 33) permits direct conversion from wet and dry bulb temperatures to vapor pressure deficit.

Evaporation and transpiration.—Measurement of transpiration under natural conditions is often practically out of the question. Although small plants may be potted or grown in cans and these may be weighed at regular intervals to determine water loss, only a limited number of plants can be used, and the labor involved can soon become prohibitive if a comprehensive study is to be made.

Relative rates of transpiration can be determined by the cobalt-chloride method, which is rapid and permits numerous determinations in a short time. Paper treated with cobalt-chloride is blue when dry and turns pink as it takes up moisture. Small squares of the dry paper can be attached to leaves between small glass plates by means of a wire clip. The time required for the paper to turn pink is taken as a basis of comparison. To get comparable values, the paper must be absolutely dry and care must be taken that the clip fits snuggly to the leaf. For increased accuracy, standard color strips are usually attached to the glass to be used for comparison with the sensitized strip. In spite of its simplicity, the method has definite limitations. The close-fitting clips exclude all outside air and thus eliminate air movement as a factor, while at the same time diffusion into the air is practically stopped by the glass. Thus the measurement is perhaps an indicator of the moisture in the internal atmosphere of the leaf. Rarely will two leaves on a plant give identical readings, for their water loss varies with their positions on the plant and their ages. Thus several determinations must be made simultaneously to evaluate a single plant, while to compare this plant with others necessitates a considerable number of readings. In spite of these limitations, it should not be assumed that the method is ineffectual, for under certain conditions, it has been used to great advantage.

These methods have their greatest utility in intensive studies of a few or of individual plants under experimental conditions in the laboratory or field. In studies of communities, it is often desirable to have a more generalized picture of transpiration conditions. Under those conditions, the rate of evaporation may be more useful than a limited number of measurements of transpiration. Perhaps the most desirable information is obtained by using plants as instruments (phytometers). Two or more habitats may be compared by setting up potted plants of the same species in each of these habitats and comparing their transpiration rates as indicated by loss of weight over the same period of time. Again the work involved is often prohibitive. As a result, ecologists have largely come to depend upon mechanical devices that measure evaporation over unit periods of time, and, since evaporation and transpiration

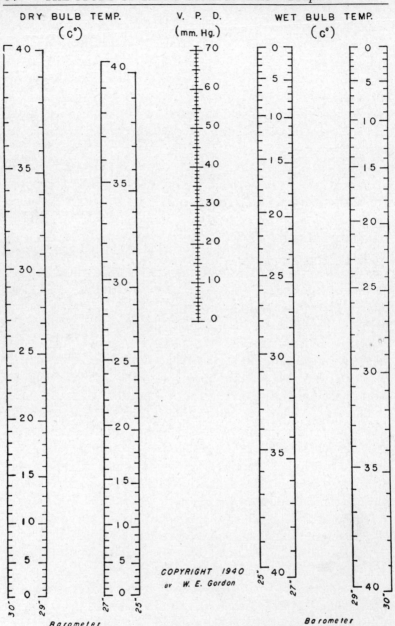

DRY BULB TEMP.
(c°)

V. P. D.
(mm. Hg.)

WET BULB TEMP.
(c°)

Barometer

Barometer

FIG. 33.   Nomogram for the direct conversion of wet and dry bulb temperatures to vapor pressure deficit, at barometric pressures of 30, 29, 27, and 25 inches. To use, lay a straight edge across the appropriate temperature values on the wet and dry bulb scales and read off V.P.D. directly. Because of the reduction necessary for this reproduction, extreme accuracy is not possible in its use.—*By permission W. E. Gordon.*[108]

respond similarly to the external factors affecting the latter, evaporation is taken as indicative of potential transpiration.

Evaporation is measured by the United States Weather Bureau by means of large open tanks of uniform size and depth, but this method is quite unsatisfactory for most ecological purposes. The bulkiness of the equipment, the necessity for frequent checking, and the probability of disturbance and of contamination are all against it.

Various compact evaporimeters have been devised primarily for ecological use. Of these the now well-known Livingston atmometer has been most widely used. It consists of a porous clay sphere or cup connected to a reservoir by means of a tube. Water evaporates from the clay surface and is constantly replaced from within. If the sphere and tube have been filled with distilled water so that no air bubbles are present (most easily done under water), the water will be drawn from the reservoir through the tube. An additional small-bored tube passed through the stopper of the reservoir will permit equalizing of pressure but negligible loss of water by evaporation. The reservoir is marked near the top and filled to this mark by lifting the stopper. Subsequent fillings made at regular intervals indicate water lost to the air by evaporation over the period of time involved.

The simplicity of this device has been in its favor, and it has other advantages. Before they are sold, all atmometer cups are checked against a standard and marked with a correction factor which, when applied, permits direct comparison of results obtained with every instrument wherever it is used. If, as is frequently true, the cups become dirty or accumulate a film of algae, they must be restandardized. If algae and fungi tend to accumulate in the reservoir or on the cup, they can usually be controlled by a small piece of copper sulfate in the water. The error produced by the solute is negligible as compared to that caused by a film of algae.

The spherical form of the atmometer cup gives it the advantage of exposing half its surface to the sun regardless of the sun's position. Other evaporimeters with different shapes have been less useful for this reason alone. Black cups can be used in combination with white and the increased evaporation resulting from their greater heat absorption may be used as a measure of relative light intensity in different habitats.

Since the cup permits evaporation, it also will absorb water during rainy spells. For field work, therefore, it is necessary to install one of the various mercury traps designed to permit water to rise in the tube but not to let it return to the reservoir. A simple but effective trap consists of a drop of mercury in the lower end of the tube, held in position between two plugs of pyrex glass wool.

FIG. 34. Two atmometers set up and in use in a study of grassland environment. The improvised shelter was used for max-min thermometers.— *Photo by R. B. Livingston.*

When temperatures fall below freezing, atmometers cannot be used because of the danger of breakage. A summary of the development, uses and limitations of atmometers is given by Livingston.[157]

Condensation of Atmospheric Moisture.—If air is sufficiently cooled, its relative humidity increases to 100 percent, or saturation. The slightest cooling beyond this point will result in condensation of the vapor to form a liquid. The temperature at which condensation occurs (dew point) will, of course, vary with the moisture content of the air.

Cooling of air masses is commonly caused by their expansion when air rises in convection currents or when moving air is forced to rise, as when it strikes a mountain slope. Cooling also occurs cyclonically, for then masses of warm and cool air may meet, and, depending upon which is least stable, warm air moves up over the cool (a warm front) or the cold air underruns the warm (a cold front). Of considerable local ecological significance is the contact cooling resulting when relatively warm air moves over a cooler surface or when cold air moves in over a body of warm water. Under these conditions, fogs or clouds may form, which not only may result in precipitation but may also modify the effects of solar radiation.

Fog.—Any minute particles of matter in the atmosphere with hygroscopic properties may serve as condensation nuclei (there is disagreement as to their necessity) about which droplets of water form, the size of the droplets depending upon the speed of condensation. Contact cooling usually produces only small droplets, which remain in the air and are visible as fog. Coastal fogs are of this type when they are the result of prevailing winds coming off the warm ocean and striking a cooler land mass. Such fogs are usually dissipated as the day progresses, evaporating as the temperature rises. Coastal fogs may also be caused by winds blowing from areas of warm water across cool currents. In summer, along the Pacific coast, warm air moves in from far offshore across the cool California current flowing from the north. Fog forms over the cold current and is blown inland, where it disappears if the land is warm but persists at night when the land is cooler. Because they affect light, temperature, and moisture conditions, fogs may be of extreme importance in determining types of coastal vegetation and the agricultural possibilities of an area. The distribution of coastal redwoods of our Pacific coast forms a striking example of the effects of fog. In a region almost without summer rainfall, the coastal redwood and several associated species are almost precisely limited to the humid fog belt along the coast. Fogs inland are usually over low ground, swamps, or small bodies of water, and are common in valleys where air movement is reduced and radiation cooling is effective.

Clouds.—Clouds differ from fog only in their position. Both are made up of droplets of water suspended in the air because they are so minute that they do not settle out. Clouds are frequently formed when air is carried upward by convectional currents and is cooled to the dew point as it rises. Cooling and condensation with con-

Fig. 35.   Ocean fog pouring over crest of Coast Range, Oregon.—*Photo by W. S. Cooper.*

sequent cloud formation also result when air is forced upward over a mountain range and from cyclonic disturbances.

Clouds are classified on the basis of form and position, the terminology being derived from an early simple classification in which four types were recognized : cirrus (curly), cumulus (piled up), stratus (flat), and nimbus (rain or storm). Modern systems divide clouds into families, each with its own type of clouds distinguished by descriptive names that are combinations of the old terminology.[265] For details about clouds and cloud forms, an illustrated manual should be consulted.[261, 128]

Precipitation.—Fogs and clouds reduce intensity of solar radiation that reaches the earth and may thus be of constant, though minor, ecological significance in certain areas. But, of more general importance, they are the source of precipitation when, because of rapid condensation, their tiny droplets increase in size sufficiently to respond to gravity and fall to the earth. Not all clouds produce rain because convection may not be rapid enough or persistent enough to produce drops of sufficient size. Summer rains are frequently short and heavy because of local, vertically ascending air currents of high velocity. During cooler seasons, rain is more apt to result from the slow ascent of warm air currents along atmospheric fronts or great shifting air masses. In the vicinity of mountains the same effect is obtained by moist air being forced upward to altitudes of lower temperature and density. The highest precipitation records are usually found on windward slopes of mountains and are produced by such forced ascents of air. Tropical rains, although often very heavy, are usually convectional in origin.

Fig. 36. Coastal redwood forest in California, showing the characteristic fog that is a factor in its survival.—*U. S. Forest Service.*

Other forms of precipitation include snow, which is formed like rain but at temperatures below freezing and under conditions that permit the crystals to fall before they melt. Sleet is rain that falls through air strata of low temperature and then reaches the earth as clear pellets of ice. If rain falls on a cold surface and freezes, it is called glaze. Hail, which falls almost exclusively in

FIG. 37.   Northern hardwood stand of birch, hard maple, elm, and ash after a glaze storm in New York. Scarcely a tree escaped damage.—*U. S. Forest Service.*

summer because of its dependence on convectional storms, starts with a snow or ice nucleus, which falls to a stratum of sufficiently high temperature to be partially melted. When carried upward again, the moisture on the surface freezes, and condensation adds to the size. If the process of falling and being carried up again is repeated several times, the successive thawing, freezing, and condensation will form a concentrically layered mass of snow and ice of sufficient size to fall to the earth as a hailstone.

Since hail is primarily a summer phenomenon occurring only under exceptional conditions, it is of little consequence to plants as a source of water. It may, however, do serious physical damage, often stripping foliage completely from woody plants and damaging herbaceous structures beyond recovery. Sleet and glaze are in the same category. Glaze may be so heavy as to cause great damage to forest trees through breakage. Conifers are particularly susceptible to such damage because of the load of ice that can accumulate on their many needles. In young stands, the trees may be broken down so that they die, or they may be so bent and twisted that, should they grow to maturity, they form badly distorted trees.

FIG. 38. Average snow pack as it appears in March in the Sierra Nevada. Echo Summit, Calif.—*Courtesy of W. D. Billings.*

Snow is an important source of soil moisture and, in addition, may serve to modify the effects of low temperatures. Roughly ten inches of snow are equivalent to an inch of rain although the moisture content of snow is highly variable. Under average temperature conditions, water derived from melting snow might make up from 5 to 25 percent or more of the total precipitation, but its importance is not determined entirely by amount. Since conditions in the spring may be such that a heavy blanket of snow disappears in a few hours, the water may run off rapidly, especially if the soil is frozen, and be of no more significance than that of an extremely heavy rain of short duration. That same amount of snow, if it melts over a period of weeks, can release water so slowly that practically all of it will soak into the soil, to become a part of a reservoir to be drawn upon during dry periods weeks or months later. Again, under semidesert conditions where the vapor pressure deficit is high, this may not be true because, if the snow remains for long periods, much of it may be lost by evaporation or sublimation.

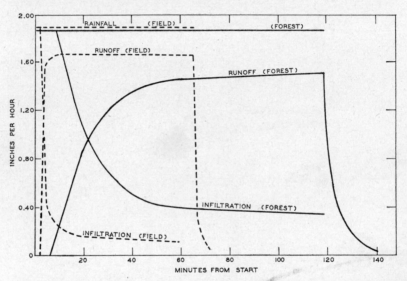

FIG. 39.   A comparison of surface runoff and infiltration on forested pineland (55 yr.) and on bare, abandoned land in Mississippi when precipitation was at essentially the same rate for both areas.—*Adapted from Sherman and Musgrave.*[232]

This reserve of ground water derived partly from snow becomes of greatest importance where the total precipitation is relatively low. The grasslands of our Middle West are much more dependent upon the reserve of ground water than are forested regions where the total precipitation is greater and is more evenly distributed throughout the year. The success of agriculture, especially wheat production in the mixed prairie region of the Dakotas, Nebraska, Colorado, and Wyoming, is, to a great extent, dependent upon the reserve of soil water derived

from snow. To be sure, where snowfall comprises a high percentage of the total precipitation, it must be of relatively greater
importance than elsewhere. Subalpine forests are often almost
completely dependent upon soil water derived from snow. The
red fir forest along the crest of the Sierra Nevada receives practically no rain throughout the growing season. However, the
cool summer days at these high altitudes do not create high water
losses, and since snowfalls of sixty feet have been recorded here,
the resulting water is adequate to maintain the forest and to pro
vide, as it runs off, an excess usable for agriculture at lower alti
tudes.

FIG. 40. A standard rain gauge and measuring stick. Cutaway view to
show funnel and inner tube.—*Courtesy Friez Instrument Division, Bendix
Aviation Corporation*

Snow water is of prime importance in those arctic and alpine regions where there is practically no rain. Here the plants are shallowly rooted, not uncommonly limited to the surface soil by perpetual frost a few inches below. Surface water must then be supplied continuously to maintain plant life. This is provided by the melting snow, some of which, in depressions or other pro-

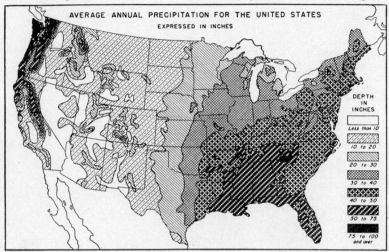

FIG. 41. Average annual precipitation for the United States.—*By permission, from Bernard,*[19] *in* Hydrology, *copyrighted 1942, McGraw-Hill Book Company.*

tected places, may remain throughout the growing season. The richest flora in best condition will usually be found at the margins of snow patches and in drainage lines below them. Ridges and raised ground are the first to be exposed at the beginning of the growing season, and there growth begins almost immediately. As the season progresses, more ground is exposed by melting snow, and plants there begin growth. Thus, at distances of a relatively few feet, may be found plants of the same species, that have flowered, fruited, and dried up, and, in the moist soil beside the snow, plants which have just begun their growth.

The total annual precipitation of an area is only a rough indication of moisture conditions for plant growth. A light rain of 0.15 inches usually does not affect soil moisture, for most of it will be intercepted by vegetation and will evaporate quickly. That which reaches the soil will wet only the surface and likewise be lost to the air. Several inches of the total rainfall may, therefore, be of no significance whatever except to raise the humidity temporarily and reduce transpiration for a short time. If rain falls heavily for short periods, say two or three inches in the same number of hours, much of it will be lost by runoff, the amount varying with steepness of slope, nature of the soil, and

FIG. 42. Annual precipitation patterns (based on averages) for several stations, which illustrate the relative amounts and distribution of precipitation throughout the year for areas supporting grassland, deciduous forest, and coniferous forest.—*Adapted from Transeau.*[256]

amount and kind of cover. Again, the seasonal distribution of rainfall may be of much more importance than the total amount. If rainfall is uniformly distributed throughout the growing season, moisture conditions may be far more favorable with twenty-five to thirty inches than they would be with forty to forty-five inches if the growing season is interrupted by one or more protracted dry spells. If precipitation is regularly seasonal, the type of vegetation may be definitely limited. For instance, grasslands characterize those areas where rainfall is rather light and concentrated in the spring and early summer. Winter rains with dry summers, characteristic of several coastal regions, support evergreen shrubby vegetation.

Measurement of Precipitation.—A standard rain gauge is a cylinder 8 inches in diameter and 20 inches high, which has a funnel built into the upper end that permits the water it catches to run into an inner cylinder with exactly one-tenth the cross-sectional area. The ratio of the outer to the inner cylinder being 10:1, the measurement of water collected in the tube must be divided by ten if taken directly, or it can be measured with a standard graduated rod. The 10:1 ratio makes accurate readings possible to 0.01 inch. Exceptionally heavy rains may overflow the tube, and the water in the large cylinder must then be poured over into the emptied tube for measurement. Two types of recording gauges are in use.[19] One registers increments of fall as a small bucket fills, tips, and records; the other, a weighing type, records accumulative precipitation as it falls.

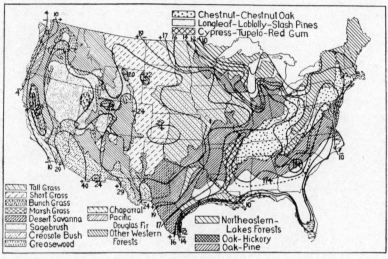

FIG. 43. Isoclimatic lines of vapor pressure deficits and vegetation areas of the United States.—*From Huffaker.*[125]

For generalized field studies, the precipitation records from the nearest weather station may be quite satisfactory. However, there may be wide local variations, especially if the topography is irregular, and, in mountainous regions, only local measurements have real significance. In addition, under forest stands, the precipitation reaching the soil will vary from stand to stand because of variation in interception. Thus, for intensive work, it is desirable to maintain rain gauges at each site of study. Although standard gauges are desirable, it is possible to obtain satisfactory records for comparison by using straight-walled jars or cans of equal diameter.

Snowfall is measured at a point where the wind has not caused drifting or disturbance, and the equivalent value in rain is computed from samples of the snow. Depending upon the density of the snow, the ratio may range from 5:1 to 50:1, but 10:1 is fairly average. Careful records of snowfall and water equivalents have not been generally kept until recently. In the western mountains, where melting snow may be the only source of water for distant low country, such records make possible forecasting of floods and, more particularly, the supply of water available for irrigation.[54]

FIG. 44. Precipitation-evaporation ratios for the United States calculated according to Transeau.[255]—*By permission from Jenny*, Factors of Soil Formation, *copyrighted 1941, McGraw-Hill Book Co.*

Atmospheric Moisture and Vegetation.—It should be clear that any single atmospheric factor is insufficient in itself to explain the distribution and survival of species or plant communities. Precipitation records are only suggestive, for they must be interpreted in terms of seasonal distribution, and they are not at all indicative of soil moisture conditions or of the evaporating power of the air to which a plant must be adjusted if it is to survive. The variation in the seasonal pattern of precipitation from place to place becomes particularly apparent when illustrated with twelve-point polygonal diagrams,[256] which make possible easy comparison of amount and time of rainfall by months. Evaporation alone is a poor criterion of ecological conditions since it does not take into account the amount of water supplied to the soil.

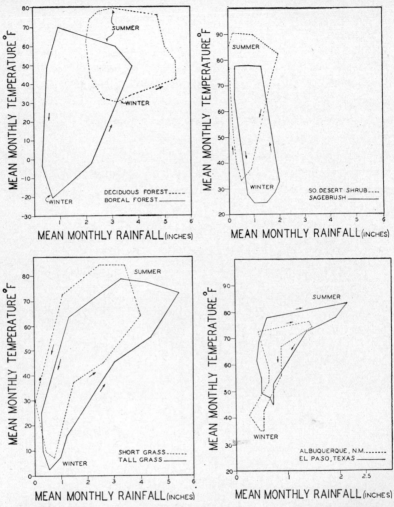

FIG. 45. Three sets of composite climographs, which permit comparison of forest, desert, and grassland climates, as well as differences within these general types of vegetation. The fourth set, which shows the similarity of climates at stations in New Mexico and Texas, has been used as support for classifying El Paso grassland as short grass, of which Albuquerque is representative, and not desert grassland as some have done.—*From Smith.*[243]

When points of equal vapor pressure deficits are connected by lines on a vegetation map,[125] the zones come nearer to matching the distribution of vegetation types on a regional basis than similar ones based on evaporation. Seeking a single comprehensive value that would include several factors operative in plant distribution, Transeau[255] used the ratio of precipitation to evaporation (P/E) for plotting climatic zones. These zones match the limits of vegetation types remarkably well, but the method is limited by the availability of adequate and comparable evaporation data.

A graphic method for distinguishing differences and similarities in atmospheric conditions is the climograph, in which mean temperature is plotted against mean relative humidity by months, and the points are connected to form highly distinctive twelve-pointed figures. Introduced by Ball[11] for indicating climate of

FIG. 46. Cup anemometer, Weather Bureau type, for relatively permanent operation, and a Biram type anemometer, convenient for short-time measurements.—*Courtesy Friez Instrument Division, Bendix Aviation Corporation.*

geographic areas, it has been variously used for comparing climates in studies of the distribution, migration, and success of populations of man, birds, and insects. The system is subject to modification and has been used also as a graph of temperature-precipitation (sometimes called a hythergraph). The latter method has been used[243] for characterizing climates of widely differing climax types in different parts of the world and for distinguishing grassland climates in North America.[52] The method probably has not been given the use it deserves in plant studies. Because temperature–relative humidity diagrams have been used with some success, it seems reasonable to suggest that similar graphs of temperature–vapor pressure deficit might give even more distinctive patterns and might, therefore, be even more useful in detailed studies.

WIND

Air moves from a region of high pressure to one of low pressure, and the differences in pressure are largely the result of unequal heating of the atmosphere. The equatorial regions receive more heat than regions to the north or south; consequently, low pressures normally exist in the lower latitudes. The tendency, then, is for air to move from the poles toward the Equator, there to rise and return toward the poles. This pattern, although true in general, is modified by the deflecting action of the earth's rotation and by differences in temperature resulting from oceans and land masses.

Continents in temperate zones tend to become very hot in summer, and the resulting low pressures produce winds that blow inland. The cold of winter reverses the pressure, and winds tend to be outblowing. In mountainous areas or along sea coasts these seasonal trends may have daily variations again produced by temperature-pressure differences. Mountain valleys and slopes, which are often warmed rapidly during the day, produce valley breezes blowing upward. At night, the rapid cooling of bare high ridges results in a flow of cold air down the valleys. The contrast between day and night temperatures of land and water results in an off-shore breeze at night as the land cools rapidly and higher pressures result. During the day, the land again heats up rapidly above the temperature of the sea, and an inshore breeze develops that may be noticeable for several miles inland. This brief summary of factors producing wind should serve to emphasize that air is almost constantly in motion and should suggest that, within limits, the general plan of motion is predictable for seasons and parts of the earth.

Measurement of Wind.—Wind velocity is measured with some form of *anemometer*. The cup anemometer used by the United States Weather Bureau has three or four hemispherical or conical cups, each attached to horizontal arms that rotate on a vertical axis and thus drive a gear system, which turns indicator dials. These are readable in miles per unit of time, usually expressed as miles per hour. More elaborate instruments may be equipped with automatic recording devices.

The cup anemometer is inconvenient to carry and operate in the field. In the Biram portable anemometer, a small fan drives the dial indicating air movement. The device is useful in small spaces and for short readings. Since it has no vane, it must be set to face the wind.

Physiological-Anatomical Effects of Wind.—The movement of air being in general characteristic of all environments, plants are largely unaffected by it under average conditions. In certain situations, however, wind may be an extremely important factor. Plants growing in habitats exposed to continuous winds of moderate velocity transpire more rapidly than unexposed individuals. If the prevailing winds are from one direction, the side of a plant toward the wind may be so desiccated that new growth is killed before it is well begun. Lateral buds taking over the growth may or may not survive, and a scrubby, matted growth develops on the windward side. To leeward, the new shoots are protected by the rest of the plant, and growth goes on there, resulting, over a period of years, in asymmetric growth forms of amazing shape. Such one-sided growth is commonly found in exposed places at high altitudes in the mountains where otherwise upright plants may be prostrate and form mats fitting into hollows or behind protecting rocks. Not uncommonly a forest stand on the protected side of a ridge or in a ravine may appear as though every tree had had its tip sheared to an exact height limit. Again, this is due to the desiccating effect of the prevailing wind.

Asymmetric growth, matted vegetation, and sheared tops as seen along the coast are likewise produced by wind to some extent, but here an added factor plays a part. The wind picks up spray as

FIG. 47.   Prostrate and matted, wind-sheared trees *(Pinus albicaulis, Tsuga mertensiana)* on a leeward slope near timber line, Mt. Hood, Ore. The twisted form is commonly termed *Krummholz.—U. S. Forest Service.*

it comes in over the breaking waves. The spray may be carried several miles inland, especially in severe storms, but its major effects are most noticeable near the coast. The spray that strikes any obstacle is dropped there and, of course, the salt from the spray accumulates on that object. Few dune and coastal plants are completely tolerant to salt spray, but, fortunately, most strong winds are accompanied by rain, which minimizes the effects by dilution and washing. If a severe windstorm is not accompanied by or soon followed by rain, much vegetation will be injured or killed by salt spray even for some distance inland.

Those plants growing near the beach are sprayed lightly almost daily and, as might be expected, show different degrees of tolerance. This results in zonation of vegetation associated with exposure to the wind.[188] Undoubtedly salt spray is one of the strong factors in determining the make-up and distribution of all plant communities on coastal dunes.[270]

When trees grow on one side only, they may become so heavy as to uproot themselves, but usually the eccentric growth is slow enough to permit compensating anatomical changes, particularly in the trunk. Secondary growth may cease completely on the windward side of the trunk and increase proportionately on the leeward side, thus forming a brace under the added top. An extreme illustration is a section of trunk taken* from a Monterey cypress that grew on Cypress Point, just south of Carmel Bay, California. It is 74 inches in the diameter that grew parallel to the prevailing wind but is only 9 inches in the opposite diameter. Only 50 growth rings were formed on the windward portion of the section, but the leeward portion (71 in.) has 304 rings. This section was taken 24 feet above the ground.

Other physiological effects might be mentioned, but they are largely brought about within the plants themselves through adaptations that serve to reduce the rate of transpiration through their effects on stomata. In the drier sections of the country, such as the plains and desert, the almost continuous dry winds increase transpiration rates materially and serve to accentuate the effects of low water supply.

Physical Effects on Plants.—Most people have seen the effects of a strong wind (25-38 miles per hour) upon vegetation. It is not uncommon for dead branches to be torn from trees; an occasional tree, especially if overmature and diseased, may be blown down.

FIG. 48. Asymmetric growth of a live oak *(Quercus virginiana)* exposed to ocean wind and salt spray from the right. North Carolina coast.—*U. S. Forest Service.*

*Collected by and in the possession of W. S. Cooper, University of Minnesota.

FIG. 49.   A white pine stand in New Hampshire after the storm of 1938. Such damage was prevalent over much of New England at the time.– *U. S. Forest Service.*

Closed forest stands usually suffer no major damage because the trees give support to each other. With greater velocities the wind becomes increasingly destructive. At gale velocities (39-54 m.p.h.) branches are broken, and a full gale uproots trees with ease.

Many of the destructive storms along the Gulf coast approach hurricane speeds, and it is fortunate that they infrequently reach the mainland. The most destructive hurricane in recent years (1938) moved northward along the Atlantic coast and struck inland at 70 miles per hour at Long Island and into west-central New England. The destruction in its path was extreme. Whole forests fell before the wind, the trees uprooted or broken off. An added factor in the destructiveness of this storm was the saturated soil, produced by a preceding period of heavy rain, which contributed to the ease and amount of uprooting and wind throw. Storms of such force and destructiveness are rare in North America, but lesser winds may cause considerable damage. When closed forest stands are thinned or selectively cut, the remaining trees are subject to wind throw for a number of years even though wind does not blow with great velocity.

In addition to physiologically-produced flag forms of woody vegetation, there are those resulting from purely physical effects of wind. A study of asymmetric trees in the Columbia River Gorge[152] showed that, when branches are continually bent in one direction by prevailing winds, the branches become "wind trained" and hold their positions permanently. Some grew completely around the trunk from the windward to the leeward side. Still another cause of asymmetry was found here. Severe winter storms, coming largely from one direction, cause much breakage, especially when accompanied by sleet, and almost complete pruning of branches on the windward side often results.

Transportation by Wind.—We have already indicated how important to precipitation are the vapor-laden winds moving inland

F IG. 50.   Wind throw often results when trees are uprooted, especially if on shallow or wet soil. Here is shown a giant Douglas fir in Washington whose torn-up root system had a spread of fifty feet.—*U. S. Forest Service.*

FIG. 51. Flag-form trees in the Columbia River Gorge, Ore. (1-2) Storm-pruned Douglas fir, deformed by breakage and killing due to glaze storms and strong east winds of midwinter. (3-4) Wind-trained Douglas fir shaped by long-continued pressure of strong west winds of late spring and summer.— *From Lawrence.*[152]

from large bodies of water and how transporting salt spray may be of local significance. Wind plays a more direct role in transporting pollen and in dissemination.

Wind-borne Pollen.—Many pollen grains are light and small or, as in conifers, have bladder-like wings, which increase their buoyancy. As a result, they may be carried for great distances by the wind. The chances that an individual pollen grain will accomplish its function must be extremely small. This uncertainty is compensated for in quantity of pollen produced. Erdtman[97] gives the pollen production for several wind-pollinated European species from which the following are selected : *Rumex acetosa* produces 30,000 grains per stamen, *Acer platanoides*, 1,000; pollen output per staminate cone of gymnosperms may be judged by *Pinus nigra*, 1,480,000; *Picea excelsa*, 590,000; and *Juniperus communis*, 400,-000; production per flower of angiosperms ranges from *Rumex acetosa*, 180,000, through *Tilia cordata*, 43,500, to *Acer platanoides*, 8,000. Such figures for single stamens and flowers serve to explain the continuous and enormous rain of conspicuous pollen that may fall in season, especially from conifers. Sidewalks, porches, floors, tables—everything in the vicinity of a coniferous forest—may be dusted with pollen.

Not all noticeable pollen is locally produced, and a great deal of evidence has been accumulated to show irregular and normal distributions. There is a story that, in the early days of the city of St. Louis, it was at one time continuously showered with a yellow dust, which gave residents some concern until botanists identified it as pollen of *Pinus palustris* transported from the coastal plain far to the south. Some quirk of pressure and wind was depositing the pollen upon St. Louis.

There are numerous records of pollen being transported long distances.[97] Spruce, pine, and birch pollen was collected on lightships in the Gulf of Bothnia thirty and fifty-five kilometers off the coast. Spruce pollen is carried from southern to northern Sweden. Peat samples taken in Greenland contained pollen of *Picea mariana* and *Pinus banksiana*, which must have originated on Labrador or southwestward. One of the most interesting studies of pollen transport was made by Erdtman as he crossed the Atlantic from Gothenburg to New York. Using a vacuum cleaner equipped with filters, he obtained a more or less continuous quantitative record of pollen in the air on the entire trip. Numbers of grains decreased with distance from land, but at no time did sampling fail to show some pollen. The evidence is to the effect that birch, pine, oak, willow, sedge, and grass pollen are carried in quantities for more than one thousand kilometers over the ocean.

The amount of pollen in the air and the distance it is transported is of significance to some plants but more so to many people who suffer from hay fever. Recently the kinds and numbers of pollen grains in the air in many sections of the country are determined daily and made publicly available for the use of hay-fever sufferers.

In general, wind-pollinated plants grow in the open or in exposed places. Even in a forest it is the trees of the upper strata that are characteristically wind pollinated; the flowers are small and inconspicuous, with simple or reduced structure. The corolla is often lacking, and there is an absence of bright colors, odor, and nectar. Stamens and pistils are commonly borne in different flowers, the stigmas are usually feathery, and the stamens are long and pendant. In spite of its apparent wastefulness, the system produces satisfactory results.

Dissemination.—Plants migrate from one point to another by means of spores, seeds, fruits, fragments of plants, or entire plants. The agent of transport may be water, animals, or wind, depending upon the various adaptations of the *disseminules*, which facilitate the movement.

Dissemination by spores is characteristic of all plants except spermatophytes. Wind-disseminated spores, like pollen, are small and dry and may be transported great distances. Everywhere that pollen is carried, spores are found too. Their transportation over long distances can be of great ecological and economic importance. A spore carried by a freak wind into distant territory may establish a species where it has never grown before, thus extending the range of the species and possibly necessitating adjustments within the community in which it develops.[275] The economic considerations are fairly obvious when it is remembered that fungi that produce diseases of both plants and animals are all propagated by spores. The fight against wheat rust is a case in point. Whenever a resistant strain of wheat is developed, it is immediately subject to attack by mutating strains of the rust, whether these strains are of local origin or not. There is evidence that strains of rust appearing in the Dakotas have come from wind-borne spores produced as far away as Mexico.[246]

Seeds, fruits, and fragments of plants are effective as disseminules in proportion to the devices that facilitate their transport. Wind dissemination is increased by the presence of winged structures, bladder-like protrusions, or plumose extensions of the

FIG. 52.   Approaching dust storm near Springfield, Colo. (1937), which was typical of conditions in the "dust bowl" during the drought of the 1930's. —*U. S. Forest Service.*

surface (see Fig. 93). Seeds, because of their small size, are apt to be carried farther than fruits, but for all, the kind of adaptation is an important factor in transport. The perfection of the parachute-like pappus is illustrated by the ubiquitous dandelion and related composites of field and roadside. Many winged fruits do not travel far because of their size, but often the wings (ash, elm, maple, basswood) are sufficient to assure transport beyond the shading and competitive effects of the parent tree.

The transport of entire plants is well illustrated by the tumbleweeds *(Salsola, Cycloloma)*. These have but a single main root, which, when broken at the ground surface, releases the spherical plant to roll before the wind until caught, perhaps in some fence corner. As it rolls, the seeds are gradually shed, sometimes miles from the place of growth.

The pioneers in a new habitat usually have effective means of dissemination and an abundance of seed. The same is true of weeds of cultivated fields and waste ground. The more common and

FIG. 53. Soil blowing out of a Kansas wheat field in the 1930's and piling up on highway, where fences and trees partially checked its movement.— *U. S. Forest Service.*

FIG. 54. Road cut through a deep deposit of loess in Missouri. The almost vertical banks have stood for eighteen years without eroding.—*U. S. Forest Service.*

FIG. 55. Extensive active sand dunes on the coast of Oregon showing transverse ridges that have typical form with gradual slope to windward and an abrupt drop to leeward.—*Photo by W. S. Cooper.*

FIG. 56. Blowout in Oregon coastal dune that was once completely stabilized by vegetation. This is a compound blowout as indicated by the partially stabilized surface of an earlier blowout (lower right), which was again excavated to a lower level by a later blowout.—*Photo by W. S. Cooper.*

widespread a species is, the more efficient are the mechanisms that facilitate its dispersal, regardless of whether the agent be wind, animals, water, ice, or gravity.

Wind and Soil.—The slightest air movement shifts dust particles from place to place, and increasing velocity results in the transport

FIG. 57. "Graveyard forest" near Florence, Oregon. Once a closed stand (probably mostly *Pinus contorta*) growing on the soil layer which is broken through in the foreground, the forest was completely buried by the dune now appearing in the rear which subsequently moved on to uncover it again. The view is to leeward.—*Photo by W. S. Cooper.*

of larger particles of soil in increasing amounts. Although fine materials are everywhere being shifted by wind, its greatest effects are noticeable in dry climates where there is a prevailing wind and a minimum of vegetation. During extended droughts, the cultivated, semiarid regions of our Midwest and Southwest have at times become shifting seas of drifting soil, and the clouds of fine materials carried about in the air have given rise to the term, "dust bowl."

Over an extended period of time great quantities of materials may be transported and deposited by wind, as is demonstrated by the enormous deposits of *loess* in various parts of the world. This

fine-grained, fertile soil occurs in deposits from a few to fifty feet
deep or more over thousands of square miles in the central Mississippi Valley region. Our richest farm lands in Iowa, Nebraska, and
Kansas are on loess soils. The deposits occur along the Rhine in
Europe and in the pampas of Argentina, and reach their greatest
extent in Asia, particularly in north-central China. Loess probably
originated during the glacial period as dust was swept up from

FIG. 58. Coastal sand dune moving inland and encroaching on evergreen
maritime forest near Kitty Hawk, N. C. Grasses in foreground have been
planted.—*Photo by C. F. Korstian.*

the barren flood plains of glacial rivers and carried high into the
air, from which it settled more or less uniformly over wide areas.

Sand beaches and desert regions are commonly dry, free of
vegetation, and swept by prevailing winds, which carry the soil
along near the earth's surface. Any obstacle that checks the velocity of the wind causes some of its load to be deposited and starts
a mound or ridge called a *dune*. Some dunes grow, by the deposit
of more sand, to a height of several hundred feet, but usually they
are much smaller. Most of the sand is deposited near the crest or
on the lee slope; this results in a characteristic gentle windward
slope and a sharp drop on the lee slope, the steepness of which is

determined by the angle of rest of the sand. Because wind frequently changes direction, dunes are rarely stable for long and present a constantly shifting pattern. Along sea coasts they tend to move inland as sand is carried from the windward side and dropped down the lee side.

FIG. 59.   Planted grasses and brush fences set up on shifting sand as part of a dune-stabilization program developed by the Civilian Conservation Corps. The attempt was partially successful but was not followed up with later work, which would have added to its success.—*Photo by C. F. Korstian.*

A dune is never completely stable unless covered with a continuous mat of vegetation. Should this mat be broken for any reason, a "blowout" results, which may enlarge and start again the shifting of the entire dune. Many cottage owners have learned this to their sorrow when—as has happened on Lake Michigan dunes—they have returned after a single year to find their summer homes almost completely buried under a shifting dune that had been stable for years. The encroachment of dunes on forest areas is not uncommon. Whole forest stands may be buried and subsequently, with shifting winds, be uncovered again to expose "graveyard" forests of dead trunks and branches.

The extensive dunes on the banks along the coast of the Carolinas have in recent years become increasingly active because their cover was broken or reduced by overgrazing and other disturbances by man. Acres of maritime forest have been buried, buildings have been destroyed, and channels in the waterways have been blocked. Here, as in the dust bowl, are problems that require drastic measures for solution, but such measures must take into consideration the ecological factors involved. Cover crops, strip cropping, mulching, and other modified methods of cultivation are now general practice in the dust bowl and promise to give some relief should an extended drought occur again. Long ago many European coastal dunes were planted with forests and effectively stabilized. The Carolina dunes, though, occupy thousands of acres with almost bare sand on which forests cannot be planted until some stability is attained. Kill Devil Hill, the dune from which the Wright brothers made their historic first flight, was stabilized with grasses by Army engineers, after much effort and considerable cost, through use of sodding, seeding, and watering. Such methods are impractical on thousands of acres. The efforts of the Civilian Conservation Corps were at least partially successful. Taking only the native dune grasses, they transplanted them according to several spacing systems and with some regard to habitat variation over several hundreds of acres. Combined with plantings, brush fences were installed at regular intervals across the largest blowouts. A considerable part of their work has proven effective.

GENERAL REFERENCES

R. F. DAUBENMIRE. *Plants and Environment.* New York : John Wiley and Sons Co., 1948. 424 pp.

W. J. HUMPHREYS. *Fogs and Clouds.*

O. E. MEINZER. (ed.) *Hydrology.* New York : McGraw-Hill Book Co., 1942. 712 pp.

C. W. THORNTHWAITE. Atmospheric Moisture in Relation to Ecological Problems.

G. T. TREWARTHA. *An Introduction to Weather and Climate.*

H. B. WARD and W. E. POWERS. *Weather and Climate.*

CHAPTER VI

CLIMATIC FACTORS: RADIANT ENERGY
TEMPERATURE AND LIGHT

The sun is the source of the earth's radiant energy (insolation). This energy, radiating as waves, includes those wave lengths of the visible spectrum that we term "light" and those that lie just beyond the visible spectrum, called "heat" if slightly longer, or "ultraviolet light" if shorter. The amount of insolation reaching the earth is always reduced because of absorption by the atmosphere (6-8 percent), and as much as 40 percent may be reflected by clouds. The remainder reaching soil or water on the earth may be further varied by such factors as distance from the sun at different seasons, duration of radiation, and the angle of the rays with the earth's surface. The last determines the amount of air through which the rays pass, modifies the amount of reflection and absorption, and likewise controls the amount of energy falling on a unit area simply by spreading or concentrating a given amount of energy over more or less space. With these things in mind, insolational variation with latitude and topography are more easily explained.

Insolation varies only slightly at the Equator because the angle of the sun's rays never exceeds 23½° from zenith, and the days are uniformly twelve hours long. Twice a year, on March 21 and September 21, called the equinoxes, the sun is at zenith at the Equator at noon and its circle of illumination exactly reaches the North and South poles simultaneously. After March 21, because of the tilt of the earth's axis, the North Pole comes progressively nearer to the sun until June 21, after which the shift is reversed to bring the pole back to the equinox position by September 21. The North Pole's movement away from the sun continues until December 21, after which it starts its shift back to the June position again. The shifting of the pole toward the sun causes the circle of illumination to extend far beyond the pole and results in continuous insolation at the pole during the June solstice, but, since the December solstice results in diametrically opposite conditions, it represents a period without insolation. Conditions in the Southern Hemisphere are, of course, always exactly reversed.

Thus, because of differences in insolation, we have seasons

FIG. 60.   Diagrammatic representation of the changing position of the earth with respect to the sun and its relationship to insolation and change of seasons in the Northern Hemisphere.—*Adapted from Trewartha.*[258]

marked by variation in length of day and temperature. Since the periodic differences in insolation become more marked with distance from the Equator, the seasons likewise become more distinct with increasing latitude. The greatest total insolation, however, occurs at the Equator and decreases with distance from the Equator in spite of the increasing length of day. Toward the poles, intensity of insolation is reduced because of the increasing angle of incidence.

These introductory statements refer to insolation as a whole. We may now more conveniently consider separately the visible portion of the spectrum known as light, and those longer, invisible wave lengths known as heat, whose presence or absence are expressed as temperature.

Fig. 61.   Circle of illumination, areas of daylight and darkness, angles of sun's rays at different latitudes, and differences in areas affected and thickness of atmosphere penetrated at time of summer solstice.—*Adapted from Ward and Powers.*[265]

TEMPERATURE

General Plant Relationships.—Each living thing is restricted to a definite temperature range, which may be quite dissimilar for different species and, depending largely upon the amount of water in the protoplasm, may vary for individuals of a species. The wide range of tolerance among species is illustrated, on the one hand, by subarctic conifer forests where −80° F. has been recorded and, on the other, by desert plants that withstand temperatures of 130-140° F. Dormant structures such as seeds and spores are practically without water and can, therefore, withstand the widest temperature variations and extremes.

Plant injuries from temperature changes are most often the result of freezing, which desiccates the tissues when the pure water on the cell walls crystallizes in the intercellular spaces and continues to crystallize as it is replaced from the vacuole and protoplasm. Injurious chemical changes, such as the precipitation of proteins, may accompany the desiccation. Some species, however—especially subtropical ones—are often killed before temperatures fall as low as freezing. Temperature injuries cannot always be explained in simple terms.

It is obvious that there must be seasonal and other adjustments in some plants, which permit their survival as cold weather comes on. It is known, in this connection, that the concentration of the cell sap of most conifers increases in the fall. Gardeners make use of this characteristic, for young plants grown in greenhouses are "hardened" before they are set out and subjected to early spring temperature fluctuations. Such plants are most liable to injury when temperature changes are abrupt and extreme. On the other hand, many arctic and alpine species can grow, flower and fruit during a period when they are subjected almost daily to alternate freezing and thawing.

Measurement of Temperature.—Accurate standardized glass thermometers are the most useful instruments for field studies. Air temperatures are usually taken in the shade with the thermometer exposed to the wind and away from the influence of one's body. Soil temperatures require a small well of some sort, or, when measurements are to be made periodically, a length of pipe may be permanently sunk to the desired depth. If the thermometer is suspended in the pipe by a string, it can be drawn up quickly and read before much change takes place. Soil temperatures at or very near the soil surface are difficult to obtain accurately with an ordinary thermometer because of the steep gradients from the surface downward, and upward into the air. The size of the thermometer bulb is sufficient to be affected by rather widely differing temperatures even when it is no thicker than 5 mm. Discrepancies have been observed as great as 11° C. between electrical (thermocouple) and ordinary thermometer readings at the surface. The errors are greatest in full sunlight and on dark soils.[86] It is under these conditions that the greatest care must be taken in placing the bulb.

Continuous temperature records are obtainable with thermographs. These usually consist of an expansion element attached by levers to a pen, which records on a graduated sheet revolving on a drum. Both air and soil thermographs are used and are also obtainable in the same instrument, thus giving parallel records. If cost of these instruments prohibits their use where a comparative study of numerous stations is to be made, maximum and minimum thermometers are the simplest solution. Placed in pairs and read and

FIG. 62.   Soil-air thermograph, which records the temperatures of soil and air continuously on a revolving drum. The cable at right is about six feet long and terminates in a sensitive bulb (not shown), which can be placed at any level in the soil.—*Courtesy Friez Instrument Division, Bendix Aviation Corporation.*

reset at regular intervals, they give the useful values of maximum and minimum temperatures for the period of exposure. Above the reservoir in a maximum thermometer is a constriction through which, because of the force and volume of mercury involved, expansion easily forces the liquid. Contraction, however, develops no pressure above the constriction, and the capillary column remains essentially at the level of its highest rise. As with a clinical thermometer, the column must be shaken or spun back down to the reservoir when a new reading is desired. The minimum thermometer has a small marker in its liquid, which, because of surface tension at the top of the column, is pulled down as the temperature is lowered but is not raised with increasing temperature. Tilting the thermometer will immediately bring the marker back to the top of the column in a new setting position.

Temperature Records.—Because temperature is so extremely variable, isolated or even numerous single determinations may be

FIG. 63. Maximum-minimum thermometers of a standard type for air temperatures. Installed in an instrument shelter, the holder permits whirling of the maximum thermometer for resetting.—*Courtesy Friez Instrument Division, Bendix Aviation Corporation.*

completely useless. A continuous record is most desirable because it gives the duration of extremes and variations. Although extremes may be important in the reaction of a plant, their duration is apt to be what determines the plant's response. Therefore, a thermograph is desirable for thoroughly satisfactory work. The "mean temperature" as computed by the United States Weather Bureau[141] is usually the average of the maximum and minimum for the day. This is not accurate or truly indicative of plant-temperature relations because it ignores duration and is likely to run too high. The true mean is more nearly approached by averaging the hourly temperatures for twenty-four-hour periods.

Annual mean temperatures are almost useless ecologically, for they do not indicate seasonal variation and duration. Temperate desert regions may have amazingly high annual mean temperatures and yet have winter frosts, which constitute an important limiting factor in the survival of certain species there. Subarctic areas may support forest vegetation because of the warm summers, yet mean temperatures may be so far below freezing that they suggest that little if any plant life would survive. It can be seen that mean monthly temperatures are desirable for evaluating ecological conditions, and this is equally true for monthly mean maximum and minimum values. Collectively, these indicate the extent of the growing season and the extremes to be expected during that time.

Temperature Variations.—Since fluctuations of insolation result in fluctuations of temperature, seasonal and daily temperature changes, as with insolation, can be expected to follow a general pattern for any region. The pattern follows that of insolation but with temperature responses lagging behind changes in radiation. A daily maximum of atmospheric temperatures usually comes in midafternoon, and minimum temperatures occur just before sunrise. Soil temperatures lag even more, for their maxima may not occur until 8:00-11:00 P.M. and minima may not be reached until 8:00-10:00 A.M. This is, of course, due to the fact that soil is a poor conductor of heat. For the same reason, the soil surface, if unshaded, produces the highest temperatures for an area and likewise has the widest range of temperatures. It is the subsoil temperature that follows the trend indicated above. With increasing depth, daily fluctuations are reduced until at two or three feet they are not apparent. Seasonal air temperatures also lag as is indicated by the usual hot days of July and the cold of January, both extremes coming after the June and December solstice. Soil temperatures follow seasonal atmospheric trends with a further lag.

Since the total insolation decreases with distance from the Equator, temperatures likewise decrease. Temperature zones, therefore, tend to run east and west, and the greater the latitude the lower the temperatures to be expected.

There are, however, local and generalized exceptions. Large

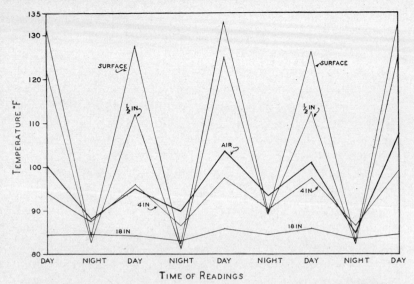

TIME OF READINGS

FIG. 64. Maximum day and night soil temperatures taken on a sand dune at Beaufort, N. C. in August, 1947. Readings were made on successive days at 7:00 A.M. and 7:00 P.M. for night and day maxima, respectively. Temperatures were greatest at the soil surface and were successively less with increasing depth by day, but, at all depths at night, dropped as low, or lower than the maximum at eighteen inches. Minimum temperatures fluctuated within the range of 72-85° F. (difficult to show accurately on so small a scale). At eighteen inches the minimum was never more than one degree below the maximum, but the difference between minimum and maximum increased upward to the surface where one minimum was as low as 72° F.

bodies of water are slower to warm up and slower to cool than land because of the higher specific heat of water. In addition, they reflect much of the insolation, and what heat is absorbed is distributed to much greater depths by water motion and convectional currents. As a result, temperature extremes are reduced around bodies of water as compared to those inland. The effect on plant distribution is particularly evident in the ranges of southeastern species, which often extend to the northern limits of the Atlantic coastal plain, where, undoubtedly, they are able to survive because of the maritime climate. The amelioration of temperatures is apparent about lakes as well as oceans, although to a lesser extent. The extremes of winter and summer temperature characteristic of the Dakotas are never experienced in lake-bounded Michigan, although latitudes are essentially the same.

The air near the earth's surface is warmed by absorption of insolation and reradiated heat from the earth. With increasing altitude the atmosphere becomes less dense and also contains less moisture and other heat-absorbing substances. Consequently, temperatures decline with altitude. Even the warm air rising from the earth is cooled by its expansion. Latitudinal temperature zones are, therefore, further disrupted by mountains where increasing altitude produces the same differences as increasing latitude. This is particularly noticeable on high mountains where, because of the combined effects of temperature and moisture, one may see zones of vegetation altitudinally arranged, which at lower altitudes are latitudinally distributed over hundreds of miles.

Just as latitudinal temperature zones are irregular, so are the altitudinal zones not perfect. Cold air drainage has been discussed. (p. 98.) It results in low night temperature in the valleys when tablelands and upper slopes are much warmer.[129] The areas may be distinctively marked by the vegetation they support. In mountainous country, orchards are frequently grown successfully at much higher altitudes on slopes than in valleys.[81] Slope and exposure disrupt mountain temperature zones even more. Since the maximum effectiveness of insolation comes only when it strikes a surface at right angles, the greater the variation from a ninety-degree angle, the less radiant energy will strike a unit area. In the Northern Hemisphere, therefore, a south-facing slope receives more insolation per unit area than a flat surface, and a north-facing slope receives less (see Fig. 67). Thus the same temperature conditions found on a tableland may occur at a higher altitude on a near-by south-facing slope and at a lower altitude on a north slope. The distribution of vegetation being correlated with temperature and the consequent moisture differences, a particular community will be found above its ordinary altitudinal range on south slopes and below it on north slopes, and the extent of this irregularity in zonation is affected both by the angle of the slope and its exposure. In Wyoming, Douglas fir from the montane zone may come down to 7,500 feet on north-facing slopes while mountain mahogany from the lower woodland zone may be found extending upward to better than 8,500 feet on south-facing slopes. In general, a vegetation zone extends higher on the south side of a mountain than on the north side.

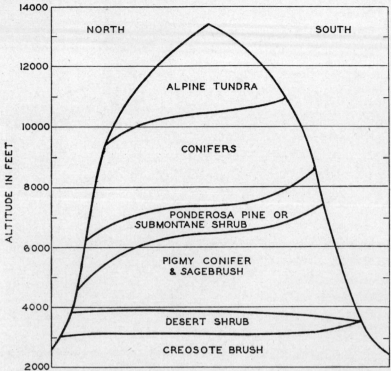

FIG. 65. A generalized profile of altitudinal zones of vegetation in the mountains of Utah, which illustrates the effects of northern and southern exposures.—*Adapted from Woodbury.*[276]

Cover and Temperature.—Anything that absorbs or reflects insolation before it reaches the earth will reduce both soil and atmospheric temperatures. Thus it is cooler in cloudy or foggy areas than in similar areas without clouds or fog, and any given area tends to be warmest on clear days. But, because heat radiated from the earth and clouds is held below a cloud blanket, the lowest temperatures also occur on clear days, and extremely low temperatures are not to be expected on cloudy days. Temperatures in and above bare soil, particularly dark soil, are higher than if that soil has some form of cover. Any type of vegetation must absorb some radiant energy and, consequently, reduce temperatures between itself and the soil, the reduction being proportionate to the closeness of the stand and how many strata compose it. Temperatures in forest stands in midsummer are usually ten degrees lower by day than in the open and ten degrees higher at night. Soil temperatures under forest are lower than in the open during the growing season and usually higher in winter. However, soil temperatures under deciduous forest are subject to considerable winter variation.

FIG. 66.   Effect of slope exposure is apparent in the desert, as elsewhere. Although species differences are not great, the south-facing slope at right supports a much sparser, more widely spaced stand of sagebrush than the opposite slope. Washoe County, Nev.—*Photo by W. D. Billings.*

Soil temperatures are further modified by dead or living cover on the surface. Any such cover reduces the range of extremes and the speed of variation. This amelioration of temperature may be important in the viability and germination of seeds and the survival of seedlings. Particularly affected are the physical and physiological processes involving water, its movement and availability in the soil, and its absorption and transpiration by the plant. Also, when soil is frozen, the runoff from heavy rains is much increased. Studies in Arizona[123] showed daily minimum soil temperatures to be five degrees higher under forest litter in the fall of the year than in bare ground and the daily maximum to be seven degrees lower. The average diurnal range was eighteen degrees in bare soil and only six degrees under litter. In North Carolina,[165] litter reduced the depth of frost penetration 40 percent, and, whereas the

TABLE 7. The average day and night temperatures (°F) in three upland forest communities in central Iowa. Air temperatures in contiguous prairie are higher than those in shrub by about 10° (day) and 4° (night). From[4].

Community	Time	April	May	July	August
Shrub...........	Day	58.8	65.1	76.7	73.9
	Night	45.3	52.8	64.0	61.1
Oak-hickory.....	Day	57.5	63.8	80.1	77.7
	Night	42.2	51.9	70.4	68.4
Maple-basswood..	Day	55.0	60.9	74.3	70.0
	Night	40.2	51.8	67.5	61.0

bare soil was frozen solidly, the soil under litter remained porous and loose, permitting deeper percolation during winter rains and thaws and causing very little runoff. The effects of snow as an insulator are much the same as are those of litter.

Temperature and Physiological Processes.—There is probably for every species an average optimum temperature at which it grows most successfully, other factors being equal. Likewise there must be a maximum and a minimum temperature that it can withstand. These limits may result from the temperature tolerances of the protoplasm peculiar to the species, but they may likewise result from responses of one or more physiological processes, which vary from species to species.

The temperatures affecting germination might alone limit the range of a species. Among our cultivated crops, the minimum-maximum range of temperature for germination is 35°-82° F. for flax and 49°-115° F. for corn. The optimum for each, respectively, is 70° and 93°. That the center of production for flax is considerably north of the center for corn is therefore not at all surprising.

Absorption of water is at a minimum when soil is frozen but increases, as do diffusion and capillary movement in the soil, with rising temperature. The optimum is surprisingly high as soil temperatures go, and the maximum approaches the boiling point in some instances. Absorption is reduced more at low temperatures for plants that grow normally in warm soil than for plants that grow, at least part of the year, in cold soil. For example, cotton absorbs only 20 percent as much water at 50° as at 77° F. while collards absorb 75 percent as much at 50° as at 77° F.[148]

Photosynthesis operates under a wide range of temperatures under natural conditions. Marine polar algae may live their entire lives at temperatures below 32° F. because the freezing point is depressed by the salts in the water. There is an often-quoted old report that spruce carries on photosynthesis at –22° F., but a recent study[99] using modern methods indicates that, although conifers do not lose their ability to carry on photosynthesis during midwinter, the species studied function only above 21° F. The process also goes on in desert plants at temperatures of 120° F. or more. The effective temperature range, however, is usually between 70° and 100° F. With increase in temperature the rate increases steadily to the optimum and then drops abruptly to the maximum, which is not much in excess of the optimum. The rate of respiration also increases with temperature until at high temperatures the process becomes destructive of life. Vant Hoff's Law, which states that the speed of a chemical reaction doubles or more than doubles with each 18° F. rise in temperature, is applicable within limits to reactions in organisms. In photosynthesis it holds reasonably well between about 41° F. and 77° F. Beyond these limits there is much variation.

Growth, being a product of chemical and physiological processes, follows the same pattern and is favored by relatively high temperatures. At temperatures near or above the maximum, the water balance is apt to be thrown off by excessive transpiration. Reproduction follows the same rule regarding temperature, but it is of interest that flowering and fruiting have higher optima than vegetative processes in the same plant.

LIGHT

That portion of the sun's radiant energy which forms the visible spectrum and which we commonly term "light" strikes the earth in quantities far in excess of the apparent needs of plants. Although green plants, with very few exceptions, are the only organisms that can directly convert this energy to their own use, they actually change to potential energy only about one percent of the light energy they receive. It has been estimated that, of the total solar energy falling upon a given field of corn during a growing season, only 0.13 percent can be "stored" as potential energy. However, this also suggests that, to function normally, plants require much more light energy than they actually use. Not all wave lengths are equally usable. Green light is reflected or transmitted, while the longer wave lengths, in the red end of the spectrum, are much more effective in photosynthesis than are the shorter lengths of yellow and blue. Not all species are equally efficient under equal illumination. Some require certain intensities and some need certain lengths of day or season to function normally. To add to the difficulties of interpreting plant-light relationships, it is not always possible to distinguish between light effects and those of total insolation, which include heat and its influence on physiological processes.

Light Measurements.—Ecological studies of light should not be casually undertaken in spite of the apparent simplicity of making measurements with modern instruments. As suggested above, plant responses and light values rarely bear a simple and direct relationship to each other. Whether or not these relationships can be interpreted may depend upon proper planning before making measurements. In addition, there are problems related to obtaining measurements for ecological purposes that must be considered.

Chemical, illuminating, electrical, and heating effects of light are measurable, and for each a different type of instrument is used.[233] Field ecologists have largely abandoned the first two approaches in favor of electrical measurements because of the recent perfection of compact, sturdy photoelectric apparatus with which accurate and rapid determinations can be made. These instruments are sensitive to approximately the same portion of the spectrum as is the human eye. Since they are selective instruments, there may

TABLE 8. Light measurements, in foot candles, made with a Weston photometer in a mixed pine–hardwood stand between 12:00 and 1:00 P.M. when full sunlight was 9,500 foot candles. Readings taken along three lines, at three-foot intervals, at a height of three feet. After completion of a line, the measurements were repeated at the same points. Note the great variation in readings at the same points at different times (sun flecks) and that some points are apparently much less shaded than others.

	Line *1*		Line *2*		Line *3*	
	300	500	500	400	100	100
	300	500	500	300	200	400
	200	300	300	400	300	100
	200	300	400	200	200	600
	300	300	300	200	200	200
	300	200	300	100	100	200
	200	200	400	3000	200	300
	100	200	3600	2400	200	400
	2400	200	4400	3600	300	300
	300	200	400	200	100	200
	300	200	2000	400	200	200
	200	2400	400	400	100	200
	500	200	400	300	100	200
	500	200	600	400	100	100
	500	200	1000	800	100	200
	300	200	200	300	200	200
	300	200	200	400	1600	200
	4200	200	300	200	100	100
	200	200	1200	5000	100	100
	200	2100	1600	2400	200	100
	200	600	300	4400	100	100
	300	300	300	300	100	100
	400	500	100	200	300	100
	200	200	300	200	200	200
	400	200	800	2000	200	100
Aver.	532	432	832	1140	224	200

Average for the stand = 560 ft. candles. 5.9% of full sunlight.

be some question of the advisability of generalizing as to plant responses in relation to the measurements they obtain. In most field studies this does not become a serious limitation because the usual objective is to compare relative intensities of light in two or more situations or habitats. For this purpose, the photoelectric method is quite usable.

The method has, however, other limitations, and its use requires certain precautions. Preferably two or more instruments should be available and the readings should be made simultaneously. Even so, readings should be made only on a clear day and, when periodic observations are made, at the same time of day. Results should be expressed as percentages of full sunlight at the time when each observation is made. At sea level this would be approximately ten thousand foot candles on a clear day at noon, but values as high as twelve thousand foot candles have been obtained in the clear air of high mountains. If for any reason the readings in the open are low on a given day, no further observations should be made.

Because of its flat sensitive surface, the instrument can be operated in only one plane at a time. If readings are made simultaneously at noon with the instrument in a horizontal plane, many complicating factors are automatically eliminated. The instruments are extremely sensitive to slight variations in light, and this necessitates numerous readings to arrive at average conditions. The slightest air movement shifts the position of leaves and permits bright sun flecks to come through a forest canopy. These flecks come and go, first at one point and then at another, and cannot be ignored in evaluating light in a stand. Their inclusion is best accomplished by making observations at a rather large number of uniformly or randomly distributed predetermined points and averaging the results. In all instances, the instrument should be in the same position relative to the observer and the ground.

A sensitive surface of spherical form is usually more desirable than a flat one. Where reflected light is appreciable, a sphere will record from all directions. If a continuous record is to be obtained, the sphere records accurately because one-half its surface always faces the sun regardless of its position. Several radiometers, which measure heat effects and are nonselective of wave lengths, are spherical in form and are advantageous in other respects. If a photoelectric cell is given more than a short exposure to strong light, the current it generates falls off because of solarization, but the radiometer can be exposed indefinitely without such effects.

It is, therefore, adaptable to continuous operation with a recording device.

Such equipment is not always available to the field ecologist, but, even so, some form of measurement is far more dependable than an estimate. Good approximations of light intensity may be obtained with photographic light meters even though they are not calibrated in foot candles. Useful values are obtainable by exposing black and white bulb atmometers in pairs. When one pair is exposed in the open and differences from pairs in near-by habitats are expressed as percentages of the value in full sunlight, the results may be quite as satisfactory as with more elaborate equipment. Since the atmometers would be operating continuously, they might even be more meaningful in terms of the vegetation.

Light Variations.—The biologically important variations of light are those in intensity and quality. These occur periodically, recurring seasonally and daily to a degree that is determined by latitude[140] as discussed under the general heading of insolation. Of course, altitude modifies the regional variations, and topography results in more localized variation through the effects of angle of slope and direction of exposure. Since the principles were previously discussed (p. 124), it should be sufficient here to present an illustration of how slope and exposure affect light in the southern Appalachian Mountains.[41]

Variation in quality of light is not so obvious as variation of intensity. Quality, however, is variable, largely because of the same factors that modify intensity, for the amount of absorption and diffusion by the atmosphere determines what wave lengths reach the earth. Clouds, fog, smoke, dust, or atmospheric moisture alone increase diffusion and absorption, and, as a consequence, dry regions receive more light than humid ones, and open country receives more light than smoky cities. The greater the diffusion, the higher the percentage of red light and the lower the percentage of blue reaching the earth.

A local variation of far greater general ecological importance is that produced by vegetation of one stratum upon that of a lesser stratum beneath it. Because plants growing in the shade of others receive only the light that is not absorbed or reflected, they must be adapted to functioning with reduced light intensity (often re-

FIG. 67.   Intensity of radiation received at different times of day on (A) south, (B) north, and (C) east slopes in the southern Appalachians, on June 21 and on December 21. For S. exposure, in summer, the 20 percent slope receives greatest radiation because it forms an angle of almost 90° with the sun's rays at noon. In winter, when the sun is low, the 100 percent slope receives more radiation than the 20 or the 40 percent slope. For N. exposures, in summer, 20 percent slopes receive almost as much radiation as 20 percent south slopes. In December, 100 percent N. slopes are in complete topographic shade but 100 percent S. slopes receive 48 percent of maximum radiation at noon. Curves for west slopes would be mirror images of those for east slopes. —*From Byram and Jemison.*[41]

duced to 15 percent or less) of somewhat different quality (reduced red and blue light) than those in full sunlight receive. Consequently, there are species representing a wide range of tolerance to shade, for no forest is so dense that nothing can grow beneath it, even when there is a reduction to 1 percent or less of full sunlight, as under some tropical forests. The reduction of light intensity under a forest canopy is probably of more ecological importance than the change in quality.

Shade Tolerance.—The ability or inability of certain plants to grow normally when shaded, as on the forest floor, has several practical considerations. When a forest stand is thinned or clearcut, the new stand that appears will, in general, be determined by the kinds of seedlings and saplings already present at the time of cutting. These species may or may not be desirable, and the question of how to encourage or inhibit them, depending upon circumstances, has led to much study and theorizing on the causes of *shade tolerance*.

Since light is obviously reduced under a forest stand, it was once assumed rather generally that light is the controlling factor. Studies of "trenched plots" under forest stands gave results interpreted by many workers as indicating a greater significance for water since, within these plots, shade-intolerant species for a time grew well when root competition for water and nutrients was eliminated by cutting off the roots of the dominant trees.[146, 253] Extensive investigations of conifer reproduction in the Lake States indicate that, for each light intensity, growth could be increased by reducing root competition and that at each level of root competition growth could be increased by increasing light.[234] Observations of the reproduction of certain southern pines[190] indicate that these shade-intolerant species may successfully meet extreme root competition if light is sufficient. It would seem that the successful growth of a seedling under a forest canopy may depend upon its ability to manufacture enough food with the light available to grow enough roots to meet the competition of the trees established there. Undoubtedly, shade tolerance cannot be explained on the basis of a single factor.

Physiological Responses.—When the supply of food in an organism falls and remains below what is required for respiration and assimilation, the organism cannot continue to function normally and must eventually die. Since a green plant produces its carbohydrates through photosynthesis, the process must proceed at a rate sufficient at least to satisfy the immediate needs of the plant if growth is to be normal. Light, which provides the energy for photosynthesis, is sufficient during the growing season to supply plant needs anywhere on the earth. In fact, light intensities may be too high for some plants to grow in full sunlight, their seedlings being especially subject to injury. Such plants might well be restricted to habitats with partial shade; if their photosynthetic

FIG. 68.   Trenched plot in a loblolly pine stand (40-50 yr.) four years after initiation (see Fig. 12). Contrast vegetation on trenched plot with floor of surrounding forest and control plot in foreground.—*Photo by C. F. Korstian.*[146]

efficiency is insufficient to maintain them in forest shade, they might thrive in regions where light intensity is reduced by cloudiness or fog. Probably the range of a species is rarely determined by light intensity alone, however, for it must be remembered that light effects are apparent in several processes and activities, which can rarely be considered independently. The production of chlorophyll, the opening and closing of stomata, and the formation of auxins are examples of light-conditioned phenomena with widely differing effects, but these activities must be considered in relation to each other when interpreting plant responses.

The production of chlorophyll, although (with a very few exceptions) accomplished only in the presence of light, is perhaps more apt to become limiting or significant in high than in low light intensities. Available evidence indicates a greater production of chlorophyll with decreasing light intensity and an ability of. most plants to produce chlorophyll at light intensities considerably below those necessary for effective photosynthesis.

The opening and closing of stomata can usually be correlated with light, but there are enough exceptions to give warning against generalizations or interpretations based on the principle of alternate opening and closing with light and darkness. In some plants, stomata may open at night; in others, light seems not to be a controlling factor. Where stomatal movement seems directly responsive to light, other factors may at any time become more important and modify or counteract the effects of light, as when stomata close during the day if the water supply is insufficient. However, stomatal movement is usually correlated with light changes and, when other conditions are favorable, is apparently caused by turgidity changes in the guard cells resulting from metabolic activity, which varies with light. The opening and closing in turn may modify effects of light by varying gas exchange related to photosynthesis and rate of loss of water by transpiration.

The production of certain auxins or growth-controlling substances in plants is inhibited by light. As a result, through them, size, shape, movements, and orientation of parts may be influenced by light. A plant grown in complete darkness, since it produces a maximum of auxins, elongates excessively, with poorly differentiated tissues throughout and with almost no supporting structure. These characteristics in an intermediate condition are often recognizable in plants grown in heavy shade, as under a forest canopy or in close stands where plants shade each other. Such plants tend to be tall and spindly with widely spaced nodes and relatively few leaves. The better the light, the stouter and more compact the individual will be.

Should illumination be one-sided, the increased production of auxins on the shaded side usually stimulates sufficient extra elongation on that side to turn the growing portion of the stem toward the light. Some species—sunflower, for instance—are so sensitive to such differences of light that the floral portions shift from east to west with the sun daily as differential elongation in the stem progresses from one shaded side to the other.

The orientation of vegetative parts is such that every leaf receives a portion of the light available. Genetic differences determine whether the leaves are exposed in the form of a rosette or in a mosaic pattern, or whether they are supported by a spirelike central axis or several spreading branches, each of about equal size. The variations within such a general plan probably result from effects of auxins on growth of petioles and secondary branches.

Leaves normally become arranged with their broadest surface exposed outward and upward on the side of the plant where they grow. This results in a maximum exposure to the available light at that point. However, plants growing under conditions of excessive light, especially where there is reflection from light-colored soil, not uncommonly have their leaves in a profile position, which, of course, reduces the light to which they are exposed. Turkey oak *(Quercus catesbaei)*, which grows on sand dunes in the southeastern United States, regularly develops a twist in the petiole that turns every blade vertically. The leaves of wild lettuce *(Lactuca scariola)* are vertical when grown in full sunlight but do not change from a horizontal position in the shade. Several so-called compass plants have leaves that are not only vertical but that also face east and west, exposing only their edges to the sun's rays at midday.

Plants growing in close stands characteristically lose leaves and usually branches from below when the light penetrates insufficiently to maintain necessary photosynthesis. Most monocots with grasslike leaves and underground stems are unaffected because their upright linear leaves permit light to penetrate to their bases. In forest stands, this self-pruning may be economically important. Conifers that self-prune grow tall and straight with few knots and smooth grain. In contrast, those with dead branches down to their bases are difficult to handle and produce much less valuable wood when finally cut.

Leaves grown in full sunlight tend to be smaller, thicker, and tougher than leaves grown in the shade. This is particularly noticeable in plants of the same species and may also be observed on the same plant. A forest-grown tree may have sun leaves at the top and shade leaves near the base, or in the interior of its crown. Certain structural differences are associated with the two types of leaves. Intense light results in elongated palisade cells and often the production of two or more layers of them. Conversely, weak illumination favors the production of sponge cells. A leaf that, with average illumination, has a single layer of palisade and several

FIG. 69.   Seedling of turkey oak *(Quercus catesbaei)*, a sandhill species, whose leaves have already assumed the vertical position they maintain throughout life.

layers of sponge cells might have had, in intense light, two or three layers of palisade and a proportionate reduction in sponge tissue. In reduced light the sponge tissue is increased at the expense of the palisade. In extreme cases there may be no palisade or no sponge tissue. The thickness of cutin and the amount of supporting tissue in the veins are likewise greater or less depending upon light intensity. These characters affect the relative toughness of the leaf.

What forces cause a developing cell to elongate at right angles to the leaf surface to form palisade or parallel to the surface to form sponge tissues, cannot be stated with any certainty. The causes may not be entirely controlled by light, for unfavorable moisture conditions favor palisade production as does poor aeration. Sucker sprouts from stumps often produce leaves of the shade type in full sunlight, probably because of the favorable water balance maintained by the extensive root system of the tree. Certain advantages of shade leaf development are more obvious than the causes.

In strong light, cells elongate parallel to the light source. The

FIG. 70.   The anatomical characteristics associated with so-called sun and shade leaves of two chaparral species. (A) *Arctostaphylos tomentosa* from normal xeric habitat, (B) from mesic habitat. (C) *Adenostoma fasciculatum* from normal xeric habitat, (D) from stump sprout. Note differences in thickness of leaf and cuticle, and proportion of palisade to sponge tissue.—*From Cooper.*[72]

more intense the light, the deeper its penetration into the leaf and the more layers of palisade there will be. Desert and alpine plants may have the mesophyll entirely made up of palisade cells. Leaves subject to reflected light from below commonly have palisade on the lower surface as well as the upper, and leaves growing vertically regularly have palisade on both sides.

When illumination is intense, chloroplasts arrange themselves along the side walls, and thus in palisade cells they receive a minimum of direct insolation. On the other hand, with weak light the chloroplasts tend to appear along the walls at right angles to the light source, and the form of sponge cells permits exposure of more chloroplasts to the greatest effectiveness of available light.

There are added advantages in the thinness and greater area of the shade leaf since both maximum exposure under conditions of reduced light and penetration of light to a high proportion of internal cells are thus assured.

Since reduced light favors elongation, vegetative growth, and delicacy of structure, it can readily be understood why several

A   B   C

FIG. 71.   Structure of leaves of broad sclerophyll forest trees (A) *Castanopsis chrysophylla*, (B) *Quercus agrifolia*, (C) *Quercus durata*. Note compact structure, multiple layers of palisade, and tendency for all mesophyll to be palisade-like. Note also struts of mechanical tissue from epidermis to epidermis.—*From Cooper.*[72]

garden crops used either for leaves or roots are best grown in spring and fall or in regions with many cloudy days. A number of leaf crops are grown under artificial shade. The point is well illustrated by the production under artificial shading of the large thin leaves of tobacco needed for cigar wrappers.

Since intense light inhibits vegetative growth and favors, or is actually necessary for, flowering and fruiting, it is not surprising that centers of grain and fruit production characteristically have much clear, cloudless weather during the growing season. Here, too, is a partial explanation of the reduced size of alpine and arctic plants, which produce large and numerous flowers. Likewise it helps explain why trees in the open often fruit more prolifically than those in a closed stand, where overtopped individuals rarely produce a seed crop.

Photoperiod.—A number of seasonal biological phenomena long have been accepted as such, without much concern as to causes. Violets, trilliums, bellworts and many other wildflowers blossom in the spring, but asters, goldenrods, and chrysanthemums are expected to flower in late summer or fall. When a fruit tree occasionally blossoms in the fall, the occurrence is considered unusual. The controlling factor in such periodic phenomena was not recognized until Garner and Allard[104] published results of their studies of *photoperiodism*, or responses of organisms to the relative length of day and night. Their investigations developed from difficulties

FIG. 72. The effect of long day (15 hours), left, and short day (9 hours), right, on flowering of henbane *(Hyoscyamus niger)*, a long-day plant. All plants received 9 hours of natural radiation. The supplemental light of the 15-hour lot was obtained from 100-watt incandescent lamps, which gave an intensity of only about 30 foot candles.—*Photo by courtesy of H. A. Borthwick, Bureau of Plant Industry, U. S. Dept. Agr.*

experienced in growing new varieties of tobacco and soy beans in the vicinity of Washington, D. C. The tobacco grew vigorously and did not flower under field conditions, but in the greenhouse, during the winter months, it flowered and fruited abundantly. The soy beans flowered and set fruit at about the same date in late summer regardless of how long they had been in the vegetative condition, as determined by plantings spaced at wide intervals during the spring and early summer. When the length of daylight period was shortened for these plants by enclosing them in a dark chamber for a few hours each day, the tobacco flowered very soon and the formation of seeds in the soy beans was hastened materially.

Some Applications.—It can readily be seen why garden plants grown for vegetative parts, if they are long-day species, develop best in spring and late fall and, if grown in summer, bolt to form

FIG. 73.   An *Abelia* hedge in late fall that (left) ceased growth and hardened normally everywhere except section under boulevard light. Here, because of the extended photoperiod, the plants continued to grow and put out new shoots, which were killed by the first heavy frost (right).—*From Kramer.*[147]

flowering structures. The differences in photoperiodic response between varieties may be the sole reason for success or failure of a crop at a particular latitude and is an excellent reason for knowing one's seed stock and its potentialities. Flowering shrubs and herbs, too, if grown beyond their normal latitudinal range, may be pampered and kept alive but often fail to flower because the length of day is unsuitable, or may invariably flower too early in the spring or too late in the fall.

The cessation of growth and subsequent "hardening" of evergreen woody plants are initiated in response to length of day. If plants are put out within range of street lamps, some winter-killing may be anticipated. Street trees of several species retain their leaves on the side illuminated by street lamps long after dormancy and complete leaf fall on the opposite side, which does not have supplemental light.[171] On the Duke University Campus, lamp posts are regularly spaced in a long Abelia hedge, and every winter frost injury results within a certain distance of each lamp because the plants here do not go into dormancy.[147]

Commercial greenhouses are making use of supplementary lighting and controlled period of illumination to bring crops into flower on special days or to produce maximum vegetative growth. Growing a crop for its vegetative parts in one latitude for which seeds must be produced in another latitude is now common practice.

Ecological Significance.[5]—It is thus apparent why many plants in the tropics, where the light period is almost constantly twelve hours, flower throughout the year and, likewise, why so few plants in the United States, even in the South, have this characteristic. It is apparent, too, that arctic species must be long-day plants and why they rarely flower when brought farther south. Also, long-day species could not survive in the tropics since they would not reproduce. Species requiring high temperatures and long days to mature are definitely limited in their northern range. The formation of abscission layers in leaves of trees and their decline in physiological activity are initiated in response to shortening days, not to reduced temperature. Therefore, at or beyond the northern limits of their range, trees may be killed by frost because they are not yet sufficiently dormant to withstand low temperatures when they occur.

It should not be assumed that plant distribution is primarily determined by length of day. Many species are little affected by it. Also temperature fluctuations have been shown to modify photoperiodic requirements and responses in several species. Photoperiod is just another factor, which may operate with temperature, moisture, and light to determine the range and distribution of a species.

GENERAL REFERENCES

H. A. ALLARD. Length of Day in Relation to the Natural and Artificial Distribution of Plants.

P. BURKHOLDER. The Role of Light in the Life of Plants.

R. F. DAUBENMIRE. *Plants and Environment.* New York : John Wiley and Sons Co., 1948. 424 pp.

W. J. HUMPHREYS. *Ways of the Weather.*

H. L. SHIRLEY. Light as an Ecological Factor and Its Measurement.

U. S. DEPT. AGR. *Climate and Man.*

H. B. WARD and W. E. POWERS. *Weather and Climate.*

CHAPTER VII

PHYSIOGRAPHIC FACTORS

SOIL

Land masses of the earth are covered by an unconsolidated surface mantle of mineral particles derived from parent rock by processes collectively called *weathering*. The depth of the mantle is variable depending upon disturbances and time, while its physical and chemical properties depend upon the nature of the parent rock and the weathering agencies that may have affected it. This inorganic material may be termed *soil* but is usually not so considered until organic materials have accumulated from organisms that have lived in or upon it.

Soil Formation.—Weathering may result in purely physical change, as when rock masses are broken into smaller and smaller sizes, or may be of a chemical nature, producing changes in composition of the material. The two processes function together normally. Disintegration is largely accomplished by physical agents, such as water, wind, ice, and gravity, and by expansion and contraction resulting from temperature changes. The first four agents are functional through the erosive action of the load of cutting material they transport and are, therefore, effective in proportion to speed of movement or to force and pressure. The effects of temperature are the most widespread although not always conspicuous. Differential expansion and contraction of rock materials result in cracking, which is especially marked when temperature changes are abrupt. The widest temperature fluctuations occur in arid regions and at high altitudes where their effectiveness is indicated by consistently coarse and angular soil particles. To a lesser extent the process goes on everywhere. Prying action of plant roots and excavating or burrowing by animals may contribute to disintegration, but these activities are certainly of greater importance in their facilitating of chemical processes. Openings in the soil increase aeration and the percolation of water. Shifting the

FIG. 74. Wind-swept alpine habitat in Utah with typical coarse, angular soil particles and little organic material. *Krummholz* at left is of *Picea engelmanni* and *Pinus flexilis* (see also Fig. 47).—*U. S. Forest Service.*

soil about exposes new particles to chemical action and likewise helps to incorporate organic matter.

The chemical or decomposing processes all tend to result in increased solubility of soil materials, which, in solution, may then be available for the use of plants but are also subject to leaching, or washing out, of the surface layers by rain water. Both oxidation and hydration, the addition of oxygen or water to a compound, are common and result in softening of rock. Carbonation, or the taking up of carbon dioxide, produces carbonic acid merely by union with water, and the acid is an effective solvent of many rocks. Water itself is a weak solvent, and, with the addition of carbonic acid, which is always present, its action is much increased. Decaying vegetation, when present, also contributes acids that facilitate solution. In solution, salts ionize and the relative effective concentrations of the basic and the acid radicals thus formed determine whether the soil solution will be alkaline or acid in reaction.

These and other chemical processes operating more or less continuously, together with physical processes, constitute weathering, which produces soil material that retains few characteristics of parent rock. However, soil is not a product of these processes alone, for biological activity also contributes to its formation. Organic material is an essential part of soil, and its decomposition and incorporation are accomplished largely by microorganisms, whose

FIG. 75.   A soil well that illustrates a soil profile (White Store sandy loam) in which the A_0 horizon is very thin, the sandy gray-white A horizon is sharply distinguished from the plastic red clay of the B horizon, and the rocky C horizon shows in the bottom.—*Photo by C. F. Korstian.*

numbers and activities increase as more complex organisms, particularly higher plants, gradually occupy the surface.

Soil Profile.—Processes resulting in the formation of soil material also contribute to soil development. As weathering proceeds, fine materials in suspension and solution are carried downward by percolating water to a lower level, where they gradually accumulate. As a soil develops, therefore, a rough stratification becomes apparent in which the horizons characteristically have different physical and chemical properties. These horizons, collectively called the *soil profile*, are designated and recognized as follows:

A Horizon. The upper layer of soil material from which substances have been removed by percolating water.

B Horizon. The layer below the A Horizon in which these materials have been deposited. Layer of accumulation.

C Horizon. The underlying parent material, relatively unweathered and not affected as above.

Litter accumulated on the surface of the mineral soil may be termed the A_0 Horizon. It is often convenient to subdivide the

ROOT DISTRIBUTION ON OUTSIDE WALL OF SOUTH TRENCH
TRENCHED PLOT NO 2 JUNE 10, 1932.

LEGEND
· = root .0˝- 0.1˝   ● = root 0.2˝- 0.3˝   SCALE
● = root 0.1˝- 0.2˝   ● = root 0.3˝- 0.4˝   1 foot

FIG. 76. An illustration of root distribution in soil horizons and of a method for mapping roots in the wall of a soil well.—*From Korstian and Coile.*[146]

major horizons as A_1 and A_2, B_1 and B_2, etc. A_1 is a particularly useful subdivision, for it is applied to the portion of the A horizon, distinguishable by its darker color, in which organic material has become incorporated.

Soil profiles may be observed in any fresh road cut. When studied in connection with vegetation, a rectangular pit is usually dug some four to six feet long, and wide enough to stand in comfortably. One face is kept vertical and cut cleanly to observe the horizons—and possibly the root distribution. Depth of the pit is, of course, determined by local conditions and position of the parent material.

Soil-Plant Relationships.—Soil must provide plants with anchorage, a supply of water, mineral nutrients, and aeration of their roots. Not all plants require these essentials to the same degree, but unless all are present to some extent the average plant cannot become established. On this basis, soil has four major components : (1) mineral material derived from parent rock, (2) organic substances added by plants and animals, (3) water, and (4) soil air. These components vary in amount and proportion from place to place, and the variation may be a significant factor in determining the distribution of species and vegetation types.

Local Soil Variations.—Size of soil particles *(soil texture)* and shape of particles, which determines how they fit together *(soil structure)*, may vary markedly within short distances. Texture and structure primarily affect the plant through their influences on air and water in the soil. Organic materials, in addition to modifying soil structure, are the source of plant nutrients that may be quite unavailable from mineral sources.

These variables are a product of the manner in which the soil originated and the time involved in its development. Great areas of the earth are covered with soils that overlie the parent rock from which they were formed. These are *sedentary* soils, whose materials are termed *residual*, if of mineral origin, or *cumulose*, when deposited as organic matter. If soil material has been brought to its present location by some agency such as wind, water, gravity, or ice, it is said to be *transported* and will accordingly have distinguishing characteristics.

Soils Formed in Place.—Residual materials are most weathered at the surface and become progressively more like the parent rock with increasing depth. Where parent rocks differ in hardness or solubility, the resulting soils will differ. Fine-textured clayey soils may represent the leached residue of easily soluble rock, such as limestone, or may be the individual particles that made up a fine-grained hard rock. When the parent rock contains a high proportion of hard, insoluble material like quartz, its soils will be sandy or even coarser.

Cumulose materials may be mixed with mineral soils in any proportion or may have accumulated as almost pure organic masses. The latter are illustrated by peat bogs, which are common-

FIG. 77. A wide flood plain in an old river valley whose alluvial soils constitute the best farming land in the region. Hiawassee River, Tenn.—*U. S. Forest Service.*

ly made up of plant remains that only partially decayed and were added to year after year until the lake or pond in which they grew was completely filled. Found most abundantly in lakes produced by glacial topography, the peat accumulations are likewise greatest where temperatures are low enough to limit the activities of organisms that produce decay.

Transported Soils.—On the great part of the earth's surface covered with residual soil, the effects of transporting agents are commonly noticeable only locally. But, to the ecologist, these localities are of interest because the soil conditions are usually different enough to cause vegetational differences too.

Except for loess, discussed elsewhere (p. 112), soils of aeolian origin are usually sandy deposits, which wind picked up from wide exposed beaches of lakes or oceans. Normally occurring as dunes, they usually form unfavorable habitats because of the low water-holding ability of sand, its relative sterility, and because the dunes are subject to blowouts should the surface cover of vegetation be incomplete (see Figs. 55, 56). In contrast, stabilized dunes of arid or semiarid regions form relatively favorable habitats because almost all the water that falls upon them is available for plant use.

Alluvial soils have been deposited by streams, which, as transporting agents, are effective in proportion to their velocity and the size of particles involved. Since currents are rarely constant, the size of transported particles varies, and deposits are always noticeably stratified. Alluvial soils are characteristic of lowlands that formed as deltas in or at the mouths of streams or as flood plains along streams that periodically overflow their banks. The greater the distance from the main channel of the stream, the finer the texture of the soil materials deposited. Alluvial deposits usually make desirable agricultural land if properly drained, and, because of favorable moisture conditions, they usually support the richest natural flora of a region.

Colluvial materials are transported by gravity. Except in regions of rugged topography or in mountainous areas, they are rarely ex-

FIG. 78. Colluvial cones, still in formation in Colorado. Only in such rugged mountain topography is gravity of direct significance in soil transport.—*U. S. Forest Service.*

tensive. Generally they occur as talus slopes at the bases of cliffs from which the material has fallen. They are usually potentially good soils because they are mixtures of coarse and fine materials, often originating from several kinds of rocks, and organic matter is likewise mixed with the mineral components. The favorableness of the habitat is primarily determined by the moisture supply, which is strongly variable, depending upon exposure.

Glacial ice plucks and gouges quantities of soil material from whatever surface it traverses. Carried in the ice, these materials are ground, pulverized, and mixed until they are deposited as moraines at the limit of advance or dropped as the ice recedes.

FIG. 79. Shrinkage upon drying as illustrated by some Piedmont soils. Samples obtained in place (see Fig. 83), then initially saturated with water and oven-dried. B horizon clays—(1) Orange, (2) White Store, (3) Tirzah; A horizon sandy loam—(4) White Store. Such shrinking and swelling in the B horizon affects soil aeration and water movement.—*From Coile.*[64]

The glacial debris is heterogeneous in composition and texture, and the depth of its deposit is highly variable. Drainage is imperfect, but melt water from the receding ice is plentiful. Its early, rapid, and haphazard flow results in the transporting and assorting of a large amount of soil material, which, as drainage lines become established, is deposited to form topographic and soil features associated with glacio-fluvial activity. The water-assorted soils deposited in the valleys of glacial streams or carried from terminal moraines to form outwash plains are characteristic.

Although glacial deposits may include weathered rock and some organic material, these are usually not abundant in the beginning. Weathering and the establishment of vegetation at first proceed slowly on glacial soil, but as they progress, a generally good, productive soil is formed. The soils of the northeastern United States and most of Canada are almost entirely of glacial origin.

Soil Texture.—One of the most useful bases for classifying soils is that of size of particles. The local variations discussed above are all reflected in soil texture, which in turn has much to do with soil moisture, aeration, and productivity.

The standard classification in the United States is that of the United States Department of Agriculture, which recognizes the following sizes of soil particles by name:

Name	Diameter, mm.
Fine gravel	2.00 —1.00
Coarse sand	1.00 —0.50
Medium sand	0.50 —0.25
Fine sand	0.25 —0.10
Very fine sand	0.10 —0.05
Silt	0.05 —0.002
Clay	< 0.002

The percentage weight of these size classes in a soil sample is determined by mechanical analysis. The larger classes may be separated satisfactorily by means of sieves, but the fractions of small size are determined by the pipette method[182] or, better still, the use of a hydrometer.[26, 27, 28] Both methods are based upon the differential rate of settling of particles in water.

After mechanical analysis, accurate textural description is pos-

sible by using the names for the fractions singly or in combination. The soil classes are named primarily for the predominating
size fraction,[87] but when many sizes are present, the term, *loam*,
is introduced. Thus a soil may be termed *gravel* or *clay* if either
of these sizes is present almost exclusively, but if gravel or clay
merely predominates and is mixed with several other size classes,
the soil is called *gravelly loam* or *clay loam*.

A knowledge of the textural grade of a soil suggests numerous
other characteristics of that soil. With experience, even a rough
estimate determined by "feel" is useful, for texture indicates other
physical properties, particularly those affecting moisture, aeration, and workability.

Soil Structure.—The arrangement of soil particles becomes especially important when small size classes are involved. Sands have
single-grain structure, but silts, and more particularly clays, tend
to have particles aggregated in clumps. Aggregation is largely
caused by the colloidal portion, less than 0.001 mm., of the clay.
Just as clay soils with their tremendous internal surface swell when
wet, they also contract as they dry. The minute particles are
drawn together by cohesive forces in large or small aggregates
whose size and shape affect drainage, percolation, erosion, and
aeration (Fig. 79).

If the granular structure is lacking or destroyed by mismanagement, as when trampled by livestock or worked too wet, the soil
puddles or bakes into hard solid masses, and shrinkage results in
the formation of deep cracks. In a loam soil or one with a high
organic content, these undesirable features are reduced while the
desirable characteristics produced by colloids are retained.

Organic Content.—The amount of organic material in soil may
greatly modify its physical characteristics as determined by the
mineral components. In addition, organic material is the major
source of certain plant nutrients, especially nitrogen, so that fertility and productiveness are usually correlated with it.

Under natural conditions, organic matter in soil is derived from
remains of plants and animals. Mostly these remains accumulate
on the surface of the mineral soil to form a layer of litter, which,
if sufficiently thick, may reduce the effects of insolation, check
erosion, and prevent compacting resulting from precipitation.

When decomposition of litter does not exceed accumulation, the A₀ horizon has a surface stratum of undecomposed twigs and leaves, which is termed the L layer. Beneath this is a stratum of decomposing but still identifiable plant remains, which is marked by fungal hyphae in abundance and is called the F or fermentation layer. In contact with the mineral soil there may be an H or humus layer if the climate is sufficiently cool and moist. The term, *humus,* is applied to material decomposed beyond obvious recognition. Soil animals and percolating water carry the humus into the soil where, through further decomposition, its chemical constituents are slowly released for use by succeeding generations of organisms.

When a distinct layer of humus (H layer) is present with a rather abrupt transition to mineral soil, the humus type may be designated as *mor.* If there is no distinct layer of humus but rather it is mixed with the surface mineral soil, the humus type is *mull.*[120]

Local variations in amount, nature, and rate of decomposition of humus are to be expected. Evergreen leaves do not decompose as readily as deciduous ones, nor do they have the same chemical composition.[264] Even the leaves of deciduous species do not all yield the same decomposition products. Organisms causing decomposition may be active and abundant in one habitat but quite incapable of living in another because of such factors as temperature, moisture, and aeration. Consequently, humus may be unequally effective in different habitats, and soils of similar origin may have quite different productive qualities.

Regional Soil Variations.—Climate, which varies with latitude and longitude, includes the important factors in soil formation, especially temperature and rainfall. Within a climatic area, differences in parent material and topographic position often are reflected in soil variations, which may be chemical or physical. Such variations are most pronounced where parent rock is newly exposed or where soil materials have weathered but slightly, as below a receding glacier. After longer exposure the developing soils become much more alike, and the longer the time involved, the less noticeable will be differences related to local conditions. Evidence is sufficient to indicate that, within a climatic area, soil development progresses toward a particular kind of soil and profile regardless of the origin or nature of the materials; likewise, that the ultimate soil group for similar climatic regions will be the same.

Since climatic conditions determine the activities and kinds of organisms of a region and these organisms in turn contribute to soil development, it is not surprising that vegetation types and soil types are closely related. The development of a soil is paralleled by vegetational changes, the vegetation contributing to soil maturation and the soil controlling the rate of progressive succession of plant communities, until a mature soil for a given climate supports a climax community of organisms. Mapping soils on the basis of mature profile and mapping vegetation on the basis of climax vegetation should produce closely similar results.

The recognition of climatic soil types originated in Russia. The approach is well illustrated by Glinka's (1927) grouping of the great soil groups of the world primarily on a climatic basis. Acceptance of the idea has become rather general although sometimes in modified form. The use of specific climatic factors, such as the relationship between precipitation and evaporation, for delimiting effective climate produces regions that correspond closely to the major soil groups.[131] In the United States,[169, 170] soils are most often grouped on the basis of mature profiles. Since only the mature profile is considered, it is a recognition of the same basic approach used by those determining regional limits through climate, although it requires that the profile must exist in reality, not as a potentiality.

Profile Development.—Three major processes of soil development are concerned in the production of the profiles characteristic of different climatic conditions.

Podsolization occurs typically in humid, cold temperate regions where rainfall exceeds evaporation and where vegetation produces acid humus. The acid decomposition products from the litter increase the solvent power of the plentiful percolating water so that soluble materials and colloids are almost completely removed from the surface soil, which is, therefore, of single grain structure at maturity. Although podsolization occurs under hardwood and pine forests, its strongest development takes place where spruce, fir, or hemlock are dominant. The process is partially a product of the vegetation, for the content of bases in the needles of these trees is notably low, and decomposition products of the litter they produce always give an acid reaction.

Laterization is characteristic of tropical conditions with high temperatures and abundant rainfall. It is essentially the leaching of silica from the surface soil. The low acidity produced by de-

FIG. 80. The layer of calcium accumulation in a pedocal soil under sagebrush desert as shown in a road cut in Nevada.—*Photo by W. D. Billings.*

composition of tropical litter promotes the solution of silica as well as alkaline materials. After laterization, the surface soil is high in iron and aluminum, which are not removed by the process.

Calcification may occur anywhere but is most important in regions with low rainfall unevenly distributed throughout the year and with temperatures producing a relatively high rate of evaporation. Under these conditions, a permanently dry stratum may develop in the profile below the depth to which rainwater penetrates. Carbonates produced by carbonation in the surface layers, as well as those that may be present in the original soil material, are carried downward in solution toward this dry layer.

When the water is removed by plants or evaporation, the carbonates are left behind, at or above the dry layer, depending upon the depth of penetration of the moisture at the time.

Climatic Soil Types.—On the basis of absence or presence of a lime carbonate layer formed by calcification, the mature profiles of all soils of North America fall into two groups : *pedalfers*, without the layer; *pedocals*, with the carbonate layer. The two conditions occur regardless of the nature of parent material or its geological origin, and their distribution is obviously controlled by climate. Soils of eastern North America are all pedalfers, for the unfavorable balance between rainfall and evaporation necessary to carbonate deposition does not occur here. West of a line (about the 99th meridian) running from the eastern Dakotas to the south-

FIG. 81. General distribution of the important zonal soil groups of the United States. *After Kellogg,*[136] *from Klages,* Ecological Crop Geography, *by permission of The Macmillan Company, publishers.*

ern tip of Texas, where annual precipitation is normally less than twenty inches a year, mature profiles almost invariably show pedocal characteristics except where climatic conditions are variable, notably in the mountains and in parts of California. Climate, vegetation, and soil have corresponding distributions. The pedalfers occur principally in association with forest regions, while the pedocals do not support forests but are typically covered with grassland or desert.

Pedalfers.—Although mature soils lying east of the line marking the western boundary of the prairie are usually of this type, they vary considerably. The range of temperatures within the area is so great that podsolization is characteristic in the north and laterization in the south with intermediate conditions represented between. The following zonal climatic soil groups, therefore, occur in eastern North America.

Tundra Soils : Far northern soils with shallow profiles and high proportions of undecomposed organic materials.

Podsol Soils : Northeastern United States and extending north and northwestward into Canada. Distinct horizons with a thick A_0, white or gray leached A over a brown B horizon with its accumulation of aluminum and iron.

Gray-Brown Podsolic Soils : A wide band across east-central United States. Like podsol but with thinner A_0 horizon and less leaching of the A, which is gray-brown over a brown B horizon.

Red and Yellow Soils : Southeastern United States where humid, warm climate produces both podsolization and laterization. Colors bright, low in organic matter, high in clay, strongly leached. Yellow soils in the sandy, poorly drained coastal plain; red soils in the well-drained Piedmont.

Prairie Soils : Western margin of the pedalfers. Intermediate between forest and grassland soils. Black or dark brown with brown subsoils that differ little in texture from the surface.

Lateritic and Laterite Soils : Subtropical and tropical. Represent extreme in mineral weathering. Leached of silica.

Pedocals.—Zonation of these soils from north to south has not been recognized as for pedalfers. Moisture being more effective than temperature in producing variation in pedocals, the conspicuous zones lie in a north-south position. Their location and brief characterization follow :

Chernozem Soils : A broad band extending from Canada into Mexico just west of the Prairie Soils. Rich in organic matter. Black soils with brown or reddish calcareous subsoils. Strong carbonate horizon but normal horizons indistinct.

Brown Soils (also known as Chestnut Soils) : Bordering Chernozems to the west and developed under successively drier conditions, they contain successively less organic matter westward and southward and become lighter in color, as indicated by their division into Dark Brown and Brown Soils. Occupy mainly the area usually called the Great Plains.

Gray Soils : Desert and semidesert soils largely in the Great Basin and southward. Gray with yellowish to reddish calcareous subsoils. Negligible organic content. Weathering largely physical.

Within these climatically determined soil regions, are local variations that, because of time and topography, bear no resemblance to the mature soil type. Swamps and bogs, islands and flood plains, salt and alkali flats, or merely immature soils on steep slopes—all are illustrations of local conditions that must be disregarded in considering the broad aspects of climatic control of soil development.

The climatic classification of soils is useful because it makes possible broad considerations of regional problems. It is logical because it bases the major categories upon mature conditions, which remain stable with the climate, and makes possible the explanation of local variations, which represent merely stages of profile development. Best of all, it has world-wide application. Enough investigations have now been made to show that the same general soil types are repeated in those parts of the world where climatic conditions are duplicated. Thus, it has been feasible to devise several schematic representations of the relationship of temperature and moisture to soil formation that are reasonably applicable anywhere. A relatively simple climatic system[251] is shown below, in which temperature-evaporation and precipitation-evaporation relationships are used as criteria of climatic control. It serves to emphasize the importance of moisture in pedocal development and grassland areas but shows that temperature is more effective where pedalfers develop with the forests they support.

Vegetation and Soil Development.—The close similarity between the distribution of major vegetation types and climatic soil

FIG. 82.   Schematic representation to show the interrelated distribution of climatic types, vegetational formations, and major zonal soil groups.—*After Blumenstock and Thornthwaite.*[24]

types has been mentioned. It has also been suggested that the characteristics of a mature profile are partially produced by the vegetation or that they are possible only because of the kind of vegetation supported by that soil in the given climate. This point should be further emphasized. Newly formed soil material has no profile and bears no resemblance to the mature soil of the region. It cannot support the vegetation that grows on a mature soil, but the plants that can grow upon it contribute to its development, probably most effectively through their decomposition products, and so, in time, the resulting soil changes permit other plants to grow. There results, sometimes over a long period, a succession of edaphically controlled vegetation types leading ultimately to a climatically controlled community. Paralleling the plant succession are changes in the soil—called *soil development*—which are primarily possible because of the plants and which lead to the mature profile, also controlled by climate. Soil development and vegetational development are intimately related and together are controlled by climate.

SOIL WATER*

Soil water probably affects plant growth much more commonly than any other soil factor. It follows, therefore, that a basic understanding of what causes differences in amounts and availability of soil moisture and what such differences may mean to a plant is knowledge necessary for an ecologist.

Classification of Soil Water.—A simple, arbitrary system of classification that divides soil water into four general categories is sufficient for most ecological purposes.

1. *Gravitational water* occupies the larger pores of the soil and drains away under the influence of gravity. For a short time after a heavy rain or irrigation, the soil may be completely saturated with water, the air in it having been displaced from the noncapillary pore spaces between the particles. Under the influence of gravity, the free water soon percolates downward through the soil toward the water table unless prevented by some barrier, such as a hardpan or other impermeable layer. Within two or three days after a rain, all the gravitational water usually drains out of at least the upper horizons of the soil, and the pore

---

*Much of this section is adapted from a review by Kramer,[149] which includes an extensive bibliography.

spaces become refilled with air. If the soil remains saturated with gravitational water for several days, serious injury to root systems may result from lack of oxygen and accumulation of excess carbon dioxide. Hence gravitational water is of little direct value to most plants and even may be detrimental.

2. *Capillary water* is held by surface forces as films around the particles, in angles between them and in capillary pores. Immediately after gravitational water has drained away the capillary water is at its peak, and a soil is then said to be at its *field capacity*. Much of this film water is held rather loosely and is readily available to plants, but some of it, which is held by colloidal material and which is in the smallest pores, is relatively unavailable. It is in this connection that the size of particles becomes important. A cubical sand grain one millimeter on the edge has a surface of only 6 square millimeters, but if it were divided into cubes of colloidal size, 0.1 micron on the edge, the total surface resulting would be 60,000 square millimeters. The increase in surface and angles between particles would thus increase tremendously the total capacity for holding capillary water. However, the water available to plants does not increase proportionally, for the greater curvature of the films and the sharper angles sufficiently increase the force with which water is held to materially increase unavailable water.

3. *Hygroscopic water* is held in a very thin film on the surface of particles by surface forces and moves only in the form of vapor. The moisture remaining in air-dry soil is usually considered as hygroscopic and is, in general, unavailable to plants. Distinction between this and capillary moisture is difficult, for exposure of soil to increasingly moist atmospheres may increase the water content even to saturation.

4. *Water vapor* occurs in the soil atmosphere and moves along vapor pressure gradients. It is probably not used directly by plants.

Origin of Soil Water.—Precipitation in the form of rain, hail, or snow is the ultimate source of water found in the soil, but not all precipitation becomes soil water. The steeper a slope, the more water will run off from its surface before it can enter the soil. Excessive precipitation in a short period of time results in greater runoff than that following a gentle rain, since infiltration cannot keep pace with the rate of fall. If soil becomes saturated and precipitation continues, little, if any, will enter the soil. A larger proportion of water from slowly melting snow is apt to enter the soil than from an equal amount of rain. Infiltration into a fine-textured, clayey soil is slower than into a coarse-textured, sandy soil, and a compact mineral soil absorbs water more slowly than a loose soil or one with a high organic content or heavy litter. The particles of a bare mineral soil tend to pack at the surface when rained upon for only a few minutes and thus reduce the rate of infiltration (see Fig. 39). Variation of local conditions may, therefore, modify the effectiveness of a given amount of precipitation.

Movement of Soil Water.—Water moves downward in quantity during and immediately after rain or irrigation. Later it may move upward or laterally to some extent when evaporation and use by plants reduces the amount near the surface. Its principal movement occurs as a liquid in capillary films or through noncapillary pores, but some movement also occurs in the form of vapor. Gravity, hydrostatic pressure, and capillary action are the forces involved, and movement may be the result of interaction of all three.

The rate at which infiltration takes place is at first determined by surface conditions. When they are favorable, practically all of a light rain is absorbed. Within a half hour or less, however, absorption declines and is then controlled by conditions in the lower horizons, where percolation may be very slow. Movement of gravitational water through the soil is controlled by the number, size, and continuity of the noncapillary pores through which it percolates. Drainage is rapid in coarse-textured soils, but in clays movement is slow since the pores are small and may be blocked by the swelling of colloidal gels or by trapped air. Channels left by earthworms or other animals and those left by dead roots greatly facilitate downward movement. If there is no impermeable hardpan layer and if the water table has not been raised too near the surface, all gravitational water drains from surface strata within two or three days after a rain leaving the soil water content at *field capacity*.

A simple explanation of the movement of capillary water may be entirely adequate for most ecological purposes. Since capillary water forms a continuous, thin film around soil particles and in the small spaces and angles between them, it is obvious that surface tension of the water creates inward pressure in the film and that water, therefore, tends to move from regions with thicker films to regions with thinner films. An explanation with broader applications considers the difference in attraction for water between two portions of soil having different moisture contents and expresses this attraction or force as *capillary potential*—that is, the force required to move a unit mass of water from a unit mass of soil. Various methods of measuring this force indicate that the potential is directly related to the water content and that there is no change in the state of water as moisture content is reduced from field capacity to an oven-dry condition, but merely an increase in energy required to move it. On this basis, the boundaries between gravitational, capillary, and hygroscopic water are too indistinct to be recognized. That these boundaries are indistinct is, in fact, true regardless of the point of view. Such relatively simple considerations seem entirely satisfactory for an adequate understanding of plant-water relationships, although recent studies of soil moisture by soil physicists have become increasingly technical.

Movement of capillary water is closely related to soil texture. In wet soils, it is rapid in sand and slow in clay, but the rate is reversed as soils dry out. Capillary rise, or the distance that capillary force will move water, is much greater in clay than in sand although the rate of movement is less in clay. The rate is surprisingly slow at all times and probably is quite insufficient to maintain an adequate film on the soil particles from which a root is removing water. The water coming to a root by capillary action does not at all equal the amount made available in new films that the root contacts because of its elongation and production of new root hairs. When soil water is below field capacity, capillary movement is probably insufficient to replace the film on particles from which roots of an actively transpiring plant are removing water. The continuous elongation of these roots with the production of new root hairs brings them in contact with new films and helps to keep up the supply of necessary available water.

Movement of water vapor is along vapor pressure gradients, which are affected by temperatures and vapor pressures of the air and the different soil horizons. There must, therefore, be some movement in all soils, but its effects are most noticeable in semiarid regions where there is no connection between the water table and capillary water near the surface. In winter or in any cool period, water vapor moves upward from the warmer subsoil and cools and condenses in the surface layers. When temperatures rise at the surface, evaporation takes place into the air, and the total ground water is reduced. Usually the surface soil is warmest in summer and results in downward movement of vapor with condensation at lower levels. If the surface soil is cooler than the air above it, water vapor may move into the soil and condense there in quantities sufficient to be of significance under semiarid conditions.

Water Lost to the Atmosphere.—The loss of water from soil to the air by evaporation varies with the factors affecting the steepness of the vapor pressure gradient. Temperature, humidity, and movement of the air, as well as temperature and moisture content of the soil, are factors, which in turn are modified by exposure, cover, and color of the soil. Probably the loss of water by evaporation is much less than is commonly supposed, for numerous studies indicate that there is little capillary rise to replace water lost by evaporation unless the water table is within a few feet of the surface. In those areas where water lost by evaporation might be critical, the water table lies so deep that precipitation rarely wets the soil down to it and, consequently, the upward rise is of no consequence. In general, the loss of water by evaporation seems mostly to be from the top foot of soil. Under natural conditions, this probably affects few species and is rarely of significance.

In agriculture, water lost by evaporation has been the subject of much argument, particularly with regard to the effects of cultivation. Evaporation from a dry soil surface is much less than from a moist one because diffusion through soil is very slow. Since a dry soil surface can be moistened only by an upward capillary movement of water if no rain falls, it has been maintained that cultivation of the surface must reduce loss by evaporation since it prevents capillary movement. It is now known that, unless the water table is very near the surface, capillary rise is negligible under any circumstances. This being true, the dust mulch, or cultivated surface, has little to support it. In fact, if the surface capillary water is not connected with the water table, as is frequently true under irrigation, cultivation for a mulch probably increases the loss of water. Organic mulches seem to be more effective in reducing water loss, probably because they shade the soil and reduce its temperatures, increase the distance of diffusion from soil to air, and protect the soil from the drying effects of wind.

Water lost to the atmosphere through transpiration far exceeds that lost by evaporation. Whereas evaporation seems to be effective only in the surface soil, plants remove water from considerable depths. Studies of orchard soils in different parts of the country indicate that all readily available water may be removed to a depth of three to six feet in three to six weeks, depending upon atmospheric conditions and the kind of soil. Sandy soils, of course, are exhausted more quickly than clayey soils. The relative losses by evaporation and transpiration are illustrated by experiments,[262] in which water was lost from a bare soil surface in a tank at the rate of 4.7 pounds per square foot during one growing season, while a four-year-old prune tree removed water from a similar tank at the rate of 416 pounds per square foot of soil surface. An acre of deciduous fruit near Davis, California, used eight acre-inches of water in six weeks in midsummer. Corn grown in Kansas requires some fifty-four gallons of water per plant to mature. If this were applied at one time, as by irrigation, it would cover a cornfield to a depth of about twelve to fifteen inches. Plants growing naturally have similar requirements. The knowledge that transpiration is the chief means of reducing capillary water in the soil has led to a consideration[142] of what kinds of plants on watersheds will least reduce the supply of water by transpiration and still prevent erosion.

Soil Moisture Constants.—To compare the moisture characteristics of soils or to discuss them with respect to plants, quantitative expressions of hydro-physical properties are a necessity. These properties, determined under fixed conditions, are called *constants*.

The *hygroscopic coefficient* is the moisture content, expressed as a percentage of the dry weight, of a soil in equilibrium with an atmosphere of known relative humidity. The value is difficult to obtain with accuracy and is of little use to plant scientists.

FIG. 83. Sampler for obtaining undisturbed soil for determining volume-weight, air space, and water holding capacity. A counter-sunk steel plate or a block of wood placed on the cylinder prevents it from being battered when driven into the soil with a sledge hammer. The inner cylinder (see Fig. 79) is removed with the sample (600 cc.) and is covered with tightly fitted lids for transportation.—*After Coile.*[63]

Maximum water holding capacity is the water held by a saturated soil. It may be determined by weighing a unit volume of soil before and after it has been immersed in water for twenty-four to forty-eight hours.

Field capacity is the amount of water a soil retains after all gravitational water is drained away. Soils in the field attain this condition within one to five days after a rain except when the water table is near the surface or saturation extends to a depth of many feet. After prolonged rain, soil may be assumed to be at field capacity if samples taken at eight- to twelve-hour intervals have essentially the same moisture content.

It is now common practice to express most soil moisture values on a volume basis. In addition, it is desirable that most of these values should apply to the soil as it lies in the field. It is, therefore, advisable to obtain undisturbed samples of a certain volume and to make all determinations without modifying the structure of the samples. Such samples may be obtained with metal cylinders,[63] which, when forced into the soil, cut a sample of exact volume, which is then enclosed with airtight lids. Rocky soils may make it impossible to obtain undisturbed samples. It then becomes necessary to use special techniques, which, although they give much the same results, require more time and pains than are ordinarily necessary.[163] Some investigators obtain all their samples only when the soil is at field capacity. This system has several advantages, such as eliminating the problems related to swelling on wetting, simplifying sampling, and giving a value for field capacity that is strictly determined by field conditions. When soils are dry, it is often possible to soak them, in place, and permit them to come to field capacity before sampling.

Capillary capacity (water holding capacity) is the water retained against the pull of gravity. Although this appears to be essentially what is meant by field capacity, it is a value determined under laboratory conditions and may run slightly higher than field capacity. The saturated samples of undisturbed soil used for determining maximum water holding capacity are permitted to drain over sand for a fixed time, usually two hours, and the weight of water retained, expressed as a percentage of the volume of the sample, is termed the capillary capacity.

When the maximum water holding capacity, the field capacity, or capillary capacity, and the dry weight of an undisturbed sample are known, it is relatively simple to calculate pore volume, air capacity, volume weight, and specific gravity of soil material.[162]

The *moisture equivalent* denotes the water content of soil that has been subjected, usually for thirty minutes, to a centrifugal force of one thousand times gravity in a soil centrifuge. Its determination is simple if equipment is available. Within limits, it bears a constant relationship to certain other soil moisture values or, at least, suggests what these values should be. Its ratio to field capacity is near unity, but the relationship is least constant with coarse-textured soils. In many soils the moisture equivalent is 1.84 times as great as the water left in those soils when plants wilt. Unavailable water can, therefore, be approximated from the moisture equivalent. The ratio of moisture content to moisture equivalent (relative wetness) can be used to make comparisons between soils or soil strata of different textures where moisture content alone would mean little in terms of plants because of variation in availability.

The *permanent wilting percentage* should be considered as the moisture content of the soil at the time when the leaves of plants growing in that soil first become permanently wilted. Because it has not always been so considered, there have been various other terms (wilting point, wilting coefficient, wilting percentage) applied to the concept, and not all investigations have produced the same results. Briggs and Shantz[35] first emphasized the importance of this soil moisture condition to plant growth and called it the "wilting coefficient." Their procedure was to grow seedlings in glass tumblers of soil sealed with a mixture of paraffin and vaseline. When the leaves wilted and did not recover overnight in a moist chamber, the moisture content of the soil was determined by oven drying at 105° C. and calculated as a percentage of the dry weight. It is generally agreed that permanent wilting marks the soil water content at which absorption becomes too slow to replace water lost by transpiration.

Briggs and Shantz came to the conclusion that soil texture alone determines moisture content at which plants wilt permanently, regardless of the species, their condition, or the environmental conditions. This conclusion was not immediately acceptable to everyone, and numerous studies were made to check its validity with different kinds of plants of different ages under a variety of conditions. It is now generally agreed that permanent wilting of any species occurs at the same water content of a soil of a certain texture regardless of the age of the plant or environmental conditions under which it grew. Uniformity of results is assured if noncutinized herbaceous plants are used and if permanent wilting of the lowest pair of leaves is used as an end point. This eliminates the problem of recognizing the onset of permanent wilting and variations related to the ability of some plants to live much longer than others after the onset of wilting.

Briggs and Shantz also concluded that it was possible to calculate the wilting point from the moisture equivalent because the following relationship held in their soils :

$$\text{wilting coefficient} = \frac{\text{moisture equivalent}}{1.84 \pm 0.013}$$

Although this often holds true, it does not apply to all soils. Studies in different parts of the country indicate that the ratio ranges at least from 1.4 to 5.65. Attempts to relate the moisture content at the time of wilting to other variables have been equally unsatisfactory, and it, therefore, appears that its determination is most reliable when observed directly. Because the expression, "wilting coefficient," has been so often associated with calculated values, it is logical to restrict it to that usage and to apply the term, "permanent wilting percentage," to determinations made by direct observation.

Readily available water is that which can be used by plants for growth and is, therefore, the moisture above the permanent wilting percentage. This includes gravitational water, but its rapid drainage makes it of little consequence. The remaining usable water is in the range from field capacity or moisture equivalent down to the permanent wilting percentage. This range is narrow in sand and wide in clay. Obviously, the wider the range, the longer plants can resist drought and, in cultivation, the less frequently irrigation is necessary. The rate at which water moves from soil to an absorbing surface is strongly indicative of plant-soil moisture relationships at the time. An indication of the availability of soil water to the plant may be obtained with porous soil point cones,[158] whose rate of absorption is taken as the basis for evaluating *water supplying power* of the soil.

Availability of Soil Moisture to Plants.—Gravitational water is readily available to plants only when present in a saturated soil, a condition that rarely continues long enough to be of importance. Normally, then, readily available water is that capillary water in the range between field capacity and the permanent wilting percentage. It is usually lowest in sand, and highest in clay. The following values for readily available water are found in some North Carolina soils :[149] sand, 2 percent, sandy loam, 14 percent, clay, 19 percent. However, this generalization does not always hold, for some clays may have high field capacities but also have high wilting percentages. A California clay with a moisture equivalent of 31 percent was found to have a wilting percentage of 25 percent, and, therefore, it could contain only 6 percent of available water. Such a soil would store less water for plant use than many sandy soils, and plants growing in it would suffer from drought much sooner than its soil texture would indicate. This also explains why, in contrast to the usual situation, sand dunes in deserts have more favorable moisture conditions than the surrounding clay soils. When both are at or near the wilting percentage, as they frequently are, a typically light rain provides little or no available water in the clay but does provide some in sand, in addition to penetrating more deeply, because of the lower wilting percentage of sand.

Whether or not all available water is equally available to plants is not entirely agreed upon. The evidence from a variety of sources seems to favor a decreasing availability as the supply is reduced toward the permanent wilting percentage and particularly in the lower half of the range of available water. Another factor affecting the availability of soil water is the concentration of the soil solution, which, if high, may have a toxic effect on plants and also modify their osmotic activity. Soil temperature, too, may be effective. Water supplying power may be reduced by half when soil temperature is lowered from 77° F. to 32° F. Probably the increase in viscosity of water at low temperatures reduces the rate of movement from soil to absorbing surface.

Measurement of Soil Moisture.—For ecological purposes, it is of prime importance to know how much soil water is available for plant use and often to be able to follow its variations from day to day throughout a growing season. Because of soil variation, it is usually desirable to have determinations from numerous places in a stand and usually from more than one stratum in the soil. It is undesirable to use sampling methods that disturb any considerable amount of the soil or injure roots in the experimental area, and, again, any expression of soil moisture should preferably refer to a unit volume of sample obtained in an undisturbed condition. The last qualification is advisable because interest is in the volume of water available to roots occupying a given volume of soil, rather than weight of water in a given weight of soil.

It should be clear from our previous discussion that, to interpret soil moisture conditions, several soil moisture constants are necessary and that some physical analyses of the soil may be desirable. A single collection of samples from each local area of study may suffice for these purposes. Thereafter, some method must be fixed upon, which, within the time available to the worker, will give as adequate a notion as possible of the variations in soil moisture content of the experimental areas. Finally, it must be possible to express the soil moisture data in terms of what is available to plants.

Methods currently in general use are of two types : (1) determining the actual content of water, (2) measuring the forces with which water is held or the rate at which it is supplied to an absorbing surface.

The actual content of water is determined by weighing samples before and after drying to constant weight in an oven at 105° C. The loss in weight, representing the water content, is expressed as a percentage of the dry weight or, if the samples are undisturbed, on a volume basis. The disadvantages of the method are numerous. Sampling takes time and disturbs the soil, the samples must be transported, weighing and drying are time-consuming, and a continuous record is impossible. However, the method has its uses, and, where only a few determinations are wanted, it is undoubtedly the procedure to use. Note, too, that it requires no equipment that is not ordinarily available.

Several electrometric methods have been adapted to the measurement of soil moisture. All require calibration in terms of the wilting percentage of the soil involved but thereafter permit rapid determinations at short or long intervals and direct translation of measurements into available water. The method that seems to be most in favor at present is the measurement of resistance between two electrodes imbedded in gypsum blocks and buried in the soil.[29] The resistance varies inversely with amount of soil water and also with soil temperature. Other methods measure dielectric constant, or electrical or thermal capacity of the soil, values that vary with changes in soil moisture.

Two physical measurements, making use of (1) tensiometers[207] and (2) soil point cones,[158] have been used successfully.

A tensiometer measures the tension existing between the soil and the soil water. It consists of a porous cup set in the soil and connected to a manometer by a tube of small diameter. Water in the instrument makes connection through the porous cup with the soil water, from which equilibrium tension is transmitted to the mercury of the manometer. Since the height of the mercury column indicates the tension in the soil, the manometer can be calibrated for a wide range of soil moisture values, and readings can be taken at any time and translated directly into values for avail-

TABLE 9—Percentage composition of oxygen and carbon dioxide in soil air extracted at different depths in a silty loam soil[30]. Note that the percentage of O_2 decreases and of CO_2 increases with depth both winter and summer but that subsoil aeration is far better when the soil is dry in summer than when it is wet in winter.

Depth (feet)	Oxygen		Carbon dioxide	
	Winter	Summer	Winter	Summer
1	19.4	19.0	1.2	2.4
2	11.6	17.4	2.4	3.7
3	3.5	16.7	6.6	5.0
4	0.7	15.25	9.6	8.55
5	2.4	12.95	10.4	11.85
6	0.2	11.85	15.5	11.9

able water. The instrument is accurate for values ranging from zero tension to approximately 0.85 atmosphere of tension, or from saturated soil to a reduction of 80 or 90 percent of available water.[217] Approaching the wilting percentage, its values cannot be wholly trusted.

Soil point cones are small, hollow cones of porous porcelain, which can be inserted into the soil with a minimum of disturbance so that each has an equal area of surface in contact with the soil. The amount of water absorbed by the cone is determined by weighing and is taken as a measure of the water supplying power of the soil. In some types of studies, this value alone is sufficient to make comparisons between soils without any further analyses being necessary. It is also indicative of moisture conditions, for, at the wilting percentage, it approximates 0.085 g. in two hours.

SOIL ATMOSPHERE

Organisms and Soil Atmosphere.—It was pointed out earlier that air is a component of soil (p. 148). Both the amount and composition of this air are of importance to plants. Most plants require a well-aerated soil for growth and even for survival. Many seeds will not germinate unless well aerated even though temperature and moisture are favorable. Healthy roots must carry on respiration continuously, which means that oxygen must be present in the soil. At the same time, their activity produces carbon dioxide and carbonic acid, which tend to accumulate. To some plants, the increase in the proportion of carbon dioxide is more injurious than the decrease of oxygen. Since all microorganisms present are likewise using oxygen and releasing carbon dioxide, the balance of the two cannot be maintained unless there is a free exchange of gases with the air above the soil. If aeration is good, this may be accomplished by diffusion from the air. However, in any soil the proportion of oxygen decreases and that of carbon dioxide increases with depth, and the proportion of oxygen is not as great in soil as in air even when conditions are most favorable. (Table 9.)

Relation to Growth and Distribution of Roots.—Since aeration becomes poorer and oxygen decreases with depth of soil, these conditions may limit the depths to which roots can grow. The deepest root penetration is in well-aerated soils. Species growing in wet lowlands are invariably shallow-rooted, for here aeration is poorest because the soil is periodically or continuously saturated and the only available oxygen may then be in solution. These shallow-rooted species will usually grow well in uplands, but, if the naturally deep-rooted species are moved to lowlands, they do not do well or may actually die. Thus aeration may determine the rate of growth, an element of importance in forest stands, and may be the factor controlling the type of vegetation.

Soil Aeration and Plant Adaptations.—Well-aerated soils may have an air capacity of 60 to 70 percent by volume, a condition determined primarily by structure and scarcely affected by texture. The amount of air varies, of course, with the water content of the soil, for air is forced from the spaces in the soil that become occupied by water.

Thus continuously saturated soil is poorly aerated, and the mud under a pond probably has the poorest aeration of any plant habi-

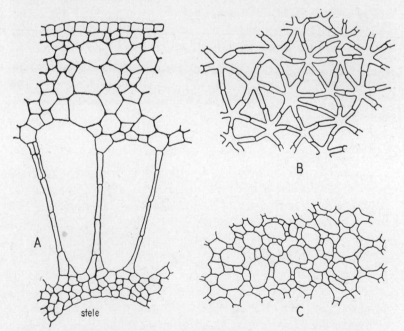

FIG. 84. Some types of lacunar tissue found in stems of emergent and other aquatic vascular plants. (A) Cortex of water milfoil *(Myriophyllum)*. (B) Ground parenchyma throughout stem of a rush *(Juncus)*. (C) Same for a sedge *(Cyperus)*.

tat. Most species growing in such habitats have adaptations that serve to counteract poor aeration. Many have large, continuous spaces—lacunar tissue—in their stems and roots permitting storage and free movement of gases within the plant. In emergent and floating-leaved species, these spaces are connected directly with the atmosphere through the stomata. Submerged leaves of aquatics are invariably finely dissected or extremely delicate, conditions

FIG. 85. Cypress swamp *(Taxodium distichum)* in the coastal plain of South Carolina. Note buttressed, somewhat planked bases of trees and an abundance of cypress knees, whose uniform height marks average high-water level.—*U. S. Forest Service.*

that bring a majority of the cells in contact with the water, from which they must obtain oxygen in dissolved form. A few submerged species produce pneumatophores, or special branches that extend above water and give direct connection with the air through lacunar tissues. In addition to shallow root systems, a number of swamp trees have other characteristics in common. Enlarged or buttressed bases and plank roots are frequent, especially in southern swamps, and the "knees" of cypress are in the same category. That these structures facilitate aeration has not been conclusively demonstrated, but their formation seems to be in response to alternate inundation and exposure to air.[150]

Determination of Volume and Composition.—Total pore space or pore volume (in c.c.) is equivalent to the weight of water (in g.) in the soil at saturation, for water then is assumed to occupy all the space in the soil. Actually not all air can be replaced by water, and the small amount of air remaining at saturation represents what is available to roots regardless of circumstances. Air capacity is the amount of air in soil that has been drained of all gravitational water. It is, therefore, equal to the difference between pore volume and the weight of water at field capacity. Since total water holding capacity and field capacity are constants, it follows that pore volume and air capacity are soil-air constants. The actual air content is not at all constant, for it varies inversely with the water content. Soils with a high air capacity are in general well aerated, but, after prolonged rain or flooding, they may for a time be poorly aerated because water fills so much of their internal space that actual air content is low.

TABLE 10—Porosity, field capacity, and air capacity of some soils with different textures. After[14] from Kopecky.

Character of soil	Particles smaller than 0.01 mm.	Total pore volume	Field capacity	Air capacity
Compact heavy clay........	86.7%	48.0%	47.6%	0.4%
Clay loam...............	67.2	46.1	41.1	5.0
Compact loam...........	46.5	41.1	34.9	6.2
Very fine sand...........	48.4	49.3	39.3	10.0
Friable loam............	42.6	49.3	37.1	12.2
Friable fine sandy loam....	39.6	49.5	34.6	14.9

The composition of soil air may be determined with a portable gas-analysis apparatus.[113] The sample of air can be pumped from the soil through a sampling tube[211] or some similar device,[30] or it can be withdrawn from a unit volume of undisturbed soil. The total percentage of oxygen and carbon dioxide in the soil is usually very nearly that found in air, and, in general, an increase of one results in a proportional decrease of the other.

SOME CHEMICAL FACTORS

Soil Acidity.—Regardless of the nature of their parent material, soils tend to become acid in reaction if precipitation is sufficient to cause downward percolation of water during much of the year. This is largely the result of leaching of soluble basic salts. To illustrate, calcium carbonate is relatively insoluble in water but reacts with carbonic acid, ever-present in soil water, to form readily soluble calcium bicarbonate. This, of course, is leached from the surface soil by percolating water. Although the leaching bicarbonates may be re-precipitated at any time the soil dries out, they, nevertheless, tend always to move downward. Thus the surface horizons tend to be low in basic materials and may have a highly acid reaction because of the acids produced by chemical and biological activity in progress there. The surface strata have the largest accumulation of organic matter, which yields acid products upon decomposition, the greatest numbers of soil organisms whose activities may produce acids, and the most active chemical changes in the mineral components, also contributing to acidity. Consequently, acidity is normally greatest at the surface and decreases in the lower horizons of the soil.

A solution is acid when the concentration of hydrogen ions (H^+) exceeds that of hydroxyl ions (OH^-), and it is alkaline if there are more OH^- ions than H^+ ions. If the two concentrations are equal, as in pure distilled water, the reaction is neutral. Since the concentration at neutrality is known, an expression of the H^+ ion concentration in a solution indicates its degree of either acidity or alkalinity.

Because H^+ ion concentration involves numbers too cumbersome for ordinary use, negative logarithms of the numbers are substituted and preceded by the expression pH. Neutrality is expressed as pH 7.0, indicating a solution that is 0.0000001 (or 10^{-7}) normal in H ions. A pH value below 7 indicates a greater concentration of H ions, or acidity, and a value larger than 7 indicates alkalinity. Since the pH values are logarithmic, the relationships between them are geometric and acidities at pH 5.0, 4.0 and 3.0 are respectively 10, 100, and 1000 times as great as at pH 6.0. The pH of most soils will normally fall between 3.0 and 9.0, and, in humid regions, the range to be expected is considerably less, perhaps no greater than pH 4.0 to 7.5.

Under ordinary conditions, the hydrogen ions themselves probably have little direct effect upon plants, but degree of acidity of the soil may have a regulatory effect upon chemical processes that do influence growth. Increased acidity may reduce availability of nutrients, as when phosphorus combines with aluminum and iron to form insoluble phosphates. High acidity may, apparently, produce toxic effects, but these are not caused by H ions. It is more likely that they result from soluble compounds of aluminum and iron, which form in increasing amounts as the H ion concentration rises. Since calcium is a required nutrient, its characteristically low content in acid soils may be of more importance than the degree of acidity. Numerous soil organisms are sensitive to changes of acidity, and, if their activities are inhibited, decomposition of organic matter may be retarded, nutrients may not be released, and nitrification and nitrogen-fixation may be checked.

With such a variety of things that may be affected by soil acidity, it should be suspected that a simple relationship between pH and plant responses does not exist. Studies of soil pH and plant distribution bear this out, for, in general, if the environment is favorable and necessary nutrients are available, most species can tolerate a rather wide range of pH. At the same time, many of these species reach their best development or are most abundant within a restricted portion of that range of pH. It should be clear that, even under such conditions, pH alone cannot be the limiting factor.

Determinations of pH may be made colorimetrically by the use of indicator solutions or electrometrically with a potentiometer and a glass electrode.[206] A very useful approximation may be made with a universal indicator, which, when placed in the soil solution, takes on a color corresponding to a particular pH value. This is handy in the field since it requires no more than a small bottle of indicator and a pocket-size porcelain plate on which permanent color standards are painted. More accurate colorimetric determinations require a series of indicators whose colors correspond to overlapping pH ranges. When electrometric equipment is available, it is preferable because of its accuracy.

Exchangeable Bases.—Ecologists have given relatively little attention to the ways in which the mineral nutrients of the soil affect plant distribution and growth of wild species. An important part of the mineral nutrition of native and cultivated vegetation is derived from the *exchangeable bases* or cations adsorbed on the surfaces of the soil colloids. When these vary considerably in amount or kind, there may be marked differences in the type of vegetation or at least in rate of growth. For example, it has been shown that, in soils derived from hydrothermally altered rocks in the Great Basin, sagebrush and its associated species fail to grow because of the very low percentage of exchangeable bases as compared with the normal brown soils of the sagebrush zone.[22]

The colloidal portion of the soil is composed primarily of alumino-silicates. These colloidal particles are almost always negatively charged, and upon their surfaces are adsorbed great numbers of cations. These cations are principally H^+, Ca^{++}, Mg^{++}, K^+, and Na^+, named in the decreasing order of tenacity with which the cations are held. The hydrogen ion is held more tightly than calcium and replaces calcium more readily than calcium will replace hydrogen. This same relationship holds between calcium and magnesium, and so on down the series. The displaced cation usually enters the soil solution. This phenomenon, in which one cation may replace another on the colloidal particle, is called *base exchange*.

Plants are almost entirely dependent on this process of base exchange for their supply of calcium, magnesium, and potassium. Of the anions, only PO_4^{---} is held to any extent by colloidal adsorption, the other anions, such as NO_3^-, being readily soluble in the soil solution and therefore, readily leached. One source of the H ions that can displace the bases and make them available is the carbonic acid formed when carbon dioxide from root respiration is released into the soil solution. This was shown experimentally for the calcium ion.[132] Another common source is the organic acids derived from humus.

Soils differ widely in their ability to supply cations because of the effects of climate, parent material, and vegetation. The maximum amount of exchangeable cations a soil can hold is called the *base exchange capacity* of the soil. Obviously, a soil high in colloids will have a high capacity as compared with one low in colloids, as, for example, a sand. Even the kind of clay may make a great difference in the base exchange capacity of a soil. For example, kaolinite has a very low capacity compared to clays of the montmorillonite group, which have relatively high capacities.

Since soils are constantly losing some of their adsorbed bases due to replacement by H ions, the soil is rarely, if ever, saturated with bases to its capacity. The degree of saturation at any given time is known as the percentage of base saturation of the soil. The base exchange capacity of a soil minus the percentage of base saturation is theoretically equivalent to the percentage hydrogen saturation of the soil, since hydrogen is the replacing ion.

Both climate and vegetation have great effects upon the amounts of exchangeable bases present in soils. On soils derived from the same parent material, sugar maple–beech–yellow birch forest maintains a soil at a higher percentage of base saturation than that under a red spruce forest.[53] This seems to be due largely to the ability of the hardwoods to absorb calcium from the subsoil and to add it to the surface soil by leaf fall.

Arid region	Transition zone	Humid region
Desert soils	Chernozems	Gray-brown-
Arid brown soils		podsolic soils
Chestnut soils		Podsols

Many investigators have shown the relation between precipitation, percentage base saturation, and pH. In brief, it may be stated that, in regions of high precipitation, the bases are readily replaced by hydrogen ions and then leached from the soil. The excess of hydrogen ions results in lowering the pH and creating an acid soil. Such conditions prevail in the cool, moist, coniferous forests of the north. Just the opposite conditions prevail in the soils of arid regions where low precipitation and scanty vegetation combine to allow the bases to remain on the colloids, thus maintaining a high percentage saturation and pH. These relationships are represented schematically on page 181.[131]

Inhibition of Growth by Plant Products.—That certain plants produce soil conditions inhibiting the growth of other plants is probably true.[273] Over a hundred years ago it was argued that crop rotation was necessary for this reason and that fallowing of land favored the next crop because it permitted the leaching of harmful excretions or by-products of decomposition resulting from the previous crops. Today we cannot entirely ignore this line of reasoning, for explanations of the benefits of rotation and fallowing based upon nutrient deficiencies are not always adequate. Likewise, there is some evidence that toxic substances are released in the soil as excretions,[215] or when external root cells are sloughed and decompose,[209] or when the plants disintegrate after death.

A number of grasses inhibit growth of other plants. In lawns, certain strains of bluegrass almost completely check the growth of white clover.[1] Walnut inhibits the growth of a number of herbs. Fairy rings of both fungi and higher plants may be the result of toxic products produced by the plants, for other explanations do not always suffice. If water, supplied in excess to flats of experimental plants, is permitted to percolate through the soil and is then used as the water supply for other plants, the latter are frequently inhibited in growth even under the most favorable conditions.[17] Extracts from decomposing plant remains have produced similar results. Apparently toxic or growth-inhibiting substances are produced by a number of plants, which may affect germination of seeds and growth of seedlings, or even of mature plants of the same or other species. Some species are affected, others are not. Whether higher plants are affected directly is not always clear. Perhaps effects upon soil organisms and their activity in turn affect the higher plants.

The subject is controversial, and some evidence is conflicting. The limited information that is available is often derived from observation of agricultural soils and cultivated plants. Cultivation, probably because of better aeration, reduces the effectiveness of inhibiting substances, and the problem is practically eliminated by crop rotation and the compensating effect of fertilizer. It is, therefore, not surprising that investigators have turned to other things.

In natural soil, however, these artificial modifications are absent, and, consequently, in view of the possible implications in interpreting associations of species or the causes of succession, it is surprising that the subject has not been given more attention.

Alkalinity.—Soils with an alkaline reaction have usually originated from limestone, dolomite, or marble in which calcium carbonate is the basic mineral. The $CaCO_3$ tends to neutralize acids that appear in the soil, and the degree of alkalinity is proportional to the solubility of the limestone. Dolomite contains more $MgCO_3$ than $CaCO_3$, and gypsum is largely $CaSO_4$, but the soils they form contain $CaCO_3$, and their floras are essentially similar to that of limestone. In our arid West, soils are often alkaline in reaction because of the sodium ions, which accumulate as sodium hydroxide ($NaOH$).

Neutral or alkaline soils favor the activities of most soil organisms and the availability of nutrients for higher plants. At the same time, the tendency of soil colloids to aggregate and produce crumb structure in the presence of lime results in soil structure with water, air, and temperature conditions favorable to plant growth. Thus most cultivated crops do best on soils with a pH ranging close to neutrality. Native plants, in general, respond similarly, but there are exceptions, which require, on the one hand, high concentrations of $CaCO_3$ or, on the other, extremely acid conditions regardless of other factors.

Not all species found growing in calcareous soils are *calciphiles*. The distribution and occurrence of many show no correlation with alkalinity of the soil. A considerable number of these widely distributed species may, however, grow more luxuriantly when on calcareous soil. Some, although not restricted to the habitat, will be found there characteristically. These are true calciphiles. There are, in addition, obligate calciphiles, which grow only in calcareous habitats.

The exceptional vigor on calcareous soils of otherwise widespread species may result simply from the improved aeration, moisture, or nutrient conditions produced by lime. Calciphiles may grow on other than alkaline soils if competition from noncalciphiles is not too great. The less favorable are the general conditions for growth, the more the calciphiles are restricted to their alkaline habitat, and, as a result, at or near the limits of their ranges they often appear as obligate calciphiles.

Salinity.—Under conditions of poor drainage and high temperature, much of the water deposited in low places evaporates and leaves behind the salts it has carried from the soil of surrounding slopes. If precipitation is seasonal and alternates with extreme drought, there is insufficient leaching to prevent accumulation of these soluble salts, which then form *alkali soils*, so called regardless of the salt involved. Alkali soils of various kinds occur in all parts of the world and are common in the arid portions of western North America. Lowlands bordering the oceans are subject to periodic inundation with sea water and, consequently, contain relatively high concentrations of salts.

Plants that can tolerate the concentrations of salts found in saline soils are termed *halophytes*. How they survive where ordinary plants have little chance has been the subject of much debate. If not actually dry, these saline habitats may be termed "physiologically dry" because of the high concentrations of salts, which would limit osmotic activity and, consequently, absorption of water by the ordinary plant. The morphological and anatomical characteristics usually appearing in plants of arid regions are common in plants of saline habitats. Succulence is particularly general. Yet these xeromorphic characters have been shown to be relatively ineffectual in maintaining low transpiration rates in halophytes. They must then be able to absorb water in spite of the high salt concentrations, and this is possible because of their own high salt contents.

Not all species are equally tolerant, and, therefore, they will often be found in zones adjusted to the concentrations of salts in the soil and the plant. Flat areas with uniform salt concentration may support a constant group of species over their entire extent. The number of species tolerant to salinity is not great and many of the same genera are found in all parts of the world where similar conditions occur (e.g., several Chenopodiaceae). Because certain species in alkali areas are tolerant to definite ranges of salt concentration and, in addition, to particular salts, they may be rather positive indicators of soil conditions. There are other species that are not so limited. In some, the concentration of the cell sap adjusts itself to changes in the soil and permits growth under a variety of conditions. Some can tolerate only small amounts of salt and do better in its absence, while a few others absolutely require

FIG. 86. Margin of a saline flat in the Smoke Creek Desert, Nev. The shrub at the margin is the relatively salt-tolerant greasewood *(Sarcobatus vermiculatus)*. Extending farther into the playa is salt grass *(Distichlis stricta)*, which is more tolerant but soon also fades out until nothing grows over most of the area.—*Photo by W. D. Billings.*

salt to survive, some even requiring a fairly high concentration. The extreme in salinity is illustrated by portions of the Great Salt Lake area in Utah where salt concentrations are so great that no vascular plants can grow.

TOPOGRAPHY

Although topography affects vegetation indirectly by modifying other factors of the environment, it has nevertheless a significant influence upon all plant communities. If an area is so level that topographic variations are practically nonexistent, then, other factors being equal, uniform vegetation may be anticipated throughout. Normally, however, such areas of any extent are rare, and slopes, bluffs, and ridges with different exposures, lowlands, drainage lines, and depressions are present.

Such irregularities in topography produce light, temperature, and moisture conditions that differ greatly between north and south slopes or ridges and depressions. The effect of exposure on these individual factors having been previously discussed (p. 124, 132), it is necessary here only to emphasize that vegetation on slopes is the resultant of interaction of light, temperature, and moisture differences. South-facing slopes receive more light, have higher temperatures, and are drier than the average site in the area, while north-facing slopes receive less light, are cooler and moister than the average. Of course, these differences vary with degree and extent of slope, but, in general, the environment of north and south slopes differs sufficiently to maintain distinctive vegetative types.

Apart from the interaction of the factors mentioned above, slopes affect runoff and the amount of soil water and, likewise, the possibility of erosion.

Since water always moves toward depressions, these are invariably moister than uplands and usually support distinctive vegetation. If topography is immature, as in the northeastern United States, drainage is relatively poor and depressions contain ponds or lakes supporting aquatic vegetation. Some lakes fill with sediment, marl, and organic materials to form bogs, which likewise have their characteristic species. With more mature topography, depressions are connected by streams, which make drainage far more effective. Even so, the streams are usually bordered by flood plains supporting vegetation requiring more favorable moisture conditions than obtain upon the uplands.

The greatest differences in vegetation associated with local variations in topography can usually be correlated with moisture, either in respect to an excess or to a deficiency. If the latter, adaptations that facilitate absorption or restrict transpiration are likely to characterize the plants. In a region where moisture is rarely a critical factor, slope and exposure produce scarcely noticeable differences in vegetation. This occurs only under conditions where a combination of fog, clouds, or rain maintains a humid atmosphere, low transpiration rates, and a plentiful supply of water.

In addition to local topographic effects are those of a regional nature associated with mountains. The increase in precipitation and decrease in temperature with increasing altitude result in vegetational zonation. Within these zones, the local effects of topography again become apparent so that zones lie at higher altitudes on a south than on a north slope and the species of a particular zone will be found extending downward in ravines and upward on ridges.

A mountain may affect conditions for growth at some distance from itself. Some mountains are centers over which rain clouds form and from which they often move to provide moisture for surrounding lowlands. At the same time, streams starting in mountains and fed by precipitation there, flow down to valleys below. Other mountains act as barriers when they lie at right angles to the prevailing winds, for so much moisture may fall upon the mountain that little is left for the area beyond. This explains the lack of moisture in the Great Basin. The prevailing winds coming from the Pacific lose their moisture over the Coast Ranges and the Sierra Nevada.

Finally, it is probable that mountains act as barriers to the natural migration of some species that are unable to compete with the flora upon the mountain or to withstand the successive changes of environment associated with increasing altitude.

GENERAL REFERENCES

L. D. BAVER. *Soil Physics.*
K. D. GLINKA. *The Great Soil Groups of the World and Their Development.*
H. JENNY. *Factors of Soil Formation.*
C. E. KELLOGG. *Development and Significance of the Great Soil Groups of the United States.*
P. J. KRAMER. Soil Moisture in Relation to Plant Growth.
C. F. MARBUT. Soils of the United States, in *Atlas of American Agriculture.*
U. S. DEPT. AGR. *Soils and Men.*

CHAPTER VIII

BIOLOGICAL FACTORS

Associated organisms having mutual relationships to each other and to their environment are recognized as a community. Many, if not all, of the organisms in a community are thus not only a part of the community but also a part of the environment of every other organism there. The dominants obviously compete with each other and with subordinate individuals. At the same time, they provide conditions that permit the survival of lesser organisms, which, though quite inconspicuous, may yet markedly affect the permanence of the community as a whole. Both plants and animals are factors of the environment of any community, and man is not the least of these factors.

PLANTS AS FACTORS

Competition.—It has been shown that, within a community, competition occurs between individuals of the same species, or between different species, whenever some requirement of the organisms is available in amounts insufficient to supply all demands adequately. Each organism involved in competition is a factor in the environment of all other organisms so involved. The effects of competing organisms upon each other are more apt to result from their influence upon physical or physiological conditions of the environment (such as available water or nutrients, light, temperature, humidity, and air movement) than they are from direct action. An extreme example of direct competition as a factor is that of the strangling fig, an epiphyte of tropical forests, whose roots grow down, envelop the tree trunks and eventually kill the trees as pressure is increased. When the tree falls, it may pull down numerous others over which the fig has sprawled. The community, however, is only locally disturbed and soon readjusts itself, for the forest is climax and these giant epiphytes are a part of it.

The introduction of new species into a community, by man or

188

other agents, usually results in failure because the plant cannot meet the competition of the normal species, which are adapted to each other and their environment. However, an occasional species reverses the rule, establishes itself as a part of the community, and often produces community changes. Japanese honeysuckle was introduced in the southeastern states many years ago and has

FIG. 87. Japanese honeysuckle in bottomland hardwood forest. When the vine is as dense as this, few tree seedlings come up through it. If they do, they are soon pulled over and the honeysuckle forms mounds upon them, as at the left.—*Photo by L. E. Anderson.*

spread widely. In lowland woods particularly, it sprawls over all the low vegetation and climbs well up into the trees. Under favorable conditions, it almost excludes low herbs and shrubs. When a tree seedling grows through it, the vine climbs upon it and bends down the slender stem, which, under the mass of honeysuckle, soon dies. Such lowland stands frequently have practically no tree reproduction beneath them. It is a matter of ecological interest as to how the natural development of these stands will progress. An economic aspect must be considered by the forester who is interested in regeneration of trees or planting these areas after cutting,

FIG. 88.   Dead chestnut, killed by blight, in a forest stand of which they once were important members. Cherokee National Forest, Tenn.—*U. S. Forest Service.*

for, unless the land is cultivated, the honeysuckle cannot be eliminated without considerable trouble.

Parasites.—A parasite is completely dependent upon its host for its existence and thereby becomes a factor in the environment of a community. When conditions are favorable for the host, a certain amount of parasitism can be tolerated with little apparent effect. Parasitic fungi and bacteria are almost constantly present but cause no serious disturbance of a community unless conditions become unusually favorable for their increase. Then they may cause death of enough hosts to produce a change in dominance or to destroy the community. Such occurrences are usually local and may be followed by gradual recovery of the original community. However, when a parasite is introduced from afar, it may be so effective in its new environment that disaster results.[166] Chestnut blight[9] has practically eliminated chestnut in the eastern United States, and oak is now dominant where oak-chestnut occurred before. Dutch elm disease[62] is gradually spreading from New England, where it first appeared, although its spread has been somewhat retarded by the drastic procedures used to check it.

Parasitic seed plants are not usually of much ecological significance, but they are always of interest because of their peculiarities and relatively local distribution. A considerable range of degree of parasitism is possible.[78] The common dodder *(Cuscuta)* is representative of those parasites *(holoparasites)* completely dependent upon their hosts, but the mistletoes and others are termed partial parasites because they are green and can manufacture food. Some species are attached to their hosts at a single point of contact, often by roots. A number of Scrophulariaceae are of this type. Others twine or sprawl over the host plant and are connected to it at intervals by absorbing structures called haustoria, whose conducting systems may be in intimate contact with xylem and phloem of the host. Still others may be contained within the host and show only their reproductive structures externally. Effects upon the host are obviously physiological, and reduction of growth and vitality are usually apparent. Abnormal growth is also common in the presence of a parasite. It is often manifested as bushy masses, called "witches'-brooms," or is occasionally found in twisted, flattened, or distorted branches. Parasitic seed plants have little effect upon

FIG. 89. A stand of scrubby oak infested with mistletoe *(Phoradendron flavescens).—U S. Forest Service.*

FIG. 90.   A striking witches'-broom on a young red pine in Michigan.—
U. S. Forest Service.

community structure in comparison with the drastic changes that may result from infestation with pathogenic fungi or bacteria.

Epiphytes.—These include a wide variety of plants, all of which depend upon larger plants for physical support only. Algae, fungi, mosses, liverworts and lichens may be found growing on bark or, in some instances, even on leaves. Often their occurrence seems correlated only with the general humidity of the atmosphere in particular habitats, but they are frequently associated with certain communities and not with others, and, within a community, they may be distributed systematically. Some may grow only on the bark of certain trees and, even more specifically, only in patterns related to drainage of water down that bark.[200] Others may be found only at the base, middle, or top of a tree trunk, and this may be correlated with moisture content of the bark.[23] The occurrence of the moss *Tortula pagorum*[8] illustrates how specific a habitat may be required by some epiphytes. This moss has been found only in close proximity to man's habitations and then almost exclusively on the trunks of elm trees. The epiphytic lichens associated with evergreen forests of boreal and alpine regions are distinctive and characteristic.

In and near the tropics, higher and less variable humidity permits a greater variety of epiphytes to survive, and vascular species increase. In temperate regions, drought-resistant species, such as polypody ferns, are found occasionally, but farther south, first on swamp trees only and then almost anywhere, epiphytic vascular plants become the rule. Orchids, bromeliads, and ferns are especially abundant. Structures that catch or conserve water are characteristic of many of these species. Stratification at different levels in the forest, as controlled by light, air movement, and water supply, is common, and succession of epiphytic communities may be observed as organic "soil" is accumulated.[181] Occasionally their weight may increase sufficiently to break down the branches supporting them. Such massive growths as are produced by the well-known Spanish "moss" *(Tillandsia)* of the southeastern United States must reduce the normal foliage and its functioning (see Fig. 8). In general, however, the epiphytes and their "hosts" seem surprisingly well adapted to their relationship.

Symbiosis.—The most generally accepted concept of symbiosis includes only the relationship of intimately associated, dissimilar organisms that live together to their mutual advantage. By appending descriptive adjectives, the concept has been expanded by some to include almost any relationship between organisms whether actually in contact or merely in competition with each other (e.g., cattle grazing in a meadow would illustrate antagonistic nutritive disjunctive symbiosis[167]). But the conservative interpretation recognizes only a few plant symbionts as significant in community life. The intimate association of unicellular blue-green algae with a fungus mycelium, termed a lichen, is an example of plant symbionts that is familiar to all who have any botanical interest. Lichens, however, can hardly be considered of general importance in community relationships. Although they often play a part in the establishment of communities on bare rock, they probably influence mature, stable communities very little. Fungi and bacteria living symbiotically on plant roots are less noticeable but of far more importance.

Mycorhizas.—When a root and the mycelium of a fungus grow together, the fungus may form a feltlike layer around the root

FIG. 91.   Transverse sections of mycorhizal roots of forest trees : (1) endotrophic, (3) ecto-endotrophic, others all ectotrophic. (1 and 4) *Pseudotsuga mucronata*, (2 and 3) *Pinus murrayana*, (5) *Populus tremuloides*, (6) *Picea rubens.—After McDougall and Jacobs.*[168]

and penetrate the spaces between cells (ectotrophic mycorhiza), or the fungus may occur within the cortical cells of the root only (endotrophic mycorhiza). Such root-fungus relationships are far more common than was once supposed. It is known that they occur on most forest trees and shrubs and that many herbaceous plants may have them. They form during periods favorable to root growth and are practically restricted to the young roots in the surface strata of the soil.

Whether mycorhizas represent a mutualistic relationship or merely parasitism on the part of the fungus has been strongly argued by numerous investigators. The conflicting evidence makes interesting, if somewhat confusing, reading. However, the evidence that mycorhiza must be present for the successful growth of many species, particularly forest species, is sufficient to suggest that the mycorhizal condition is desirable under most situations even though the reasons are not too obvious.

Pot cultures of certain tree seedlings in poor soil have been unsatisfactory until inoculated with mycorhizal fungi. On a larger scale, unsuccessful forest nurseries on prairie soil or long deforested agricultural soil have been saved by bringing in small amounts of forest soil, which started the formation of mycorhiza. Tree seedlings transplanted without mycorhiza to treeless areas have been saved from gradual death by the application of small amounts of soil containing mycorhizal fungi.

Several members of the heath family (azalea, rhododendron, blueberry) are dependent upon the presence of mycorhiza that cannot tolerate alkaline conditions. Disappearance of mycorhiza leads to death of the plants, and consequently, the soil must be acid for successful propagation of these species.

Many orchid seeds germinate normally only in the presence of mycorhizal fungi and were difficult to propagate until it was found that proper nutrient media could compensate for the absence of the fungus. Such evidence indicates that, regardless of what the fungus may take from the root, the vascular plant is benefited by the presence of the mycorhiza or may actually be dependent upon it. Probably the benefit is derived through some nutritional improvement provided by activities of the fungus.

Nodules.—Certain saprophytic bacteria, living free in many soils,

FIG. 92. Two seedlings of *Psychotria punctata*, about three and one-half months old. The plant on the right is normal both as to growth and the presence of bacterial nodules dotting every leaf. The one on the left, grown bacteria-free, has reached its maximum development.—*From Humm.*[127]

enter the root hairs of most legumes when available and produce a proliferation of cortical cells sufficient to appear as a small nodule on the root. Although the plant provides food for the bacteria and produces the nodule in which the bacteria multiply, the relationship is truly symbiotic. These nitrogen-fixing bacteria are able to take free nitrogen from the air, unavailable to most plants, and to combine it with other elements to form compounds that can be used by the plant during its lifetime. After death of the plant, the accumulated nitrogenous compounds are released in the soil and are used by other plants growing there. Legumes and nitrogen-fixing bacteria are, therefore, important factors in maintaining soil fertility in natural or cultivated soils. Plant communities becoming established on poor sites, such as eroded slopes, invariably include a number of legumes, which are, of course, particularly adapted to colonizing sterile or nitrate-depleted soils and contributing to their improvement. Agricultural practice includes legumes in most crop rotations, and worn-out lands are rebuilt by cropping with legumes of some sort.

Nodules produced by bacteria are found on the roots of a few plants in families other than Leguminosae, but they are not of the same type. Nodules containing bacteria are also formed on leaves of a number of tropical plants, mostly in the family Rubiaceae.

These bacteria are associated with the plant tissues in all stages of development from seed to maturity, but nodules form only on leaves. Although these bacteria have been credited with nitrogen-fixing ability, it is certain that the plants are not dependent upon them for their nitrates. Certain products of their presence are necessary, however, for without the bacteria, seedlings do not mature.[127] The relationship is, therefore, truly symbiotic (Fig. 92).

Other Soil Flora.—In addition to the symbiotic fungi and bacteria, great numbers of bacteria, fungi, and algae occur free in the soil. Their importance to natural plant communities cannot be evaluated accurately, but their significance is indicated by their general functions of making nitrogen available by fixing it, or releasing it with other nutrients through their activities in decomposing organic matter.

The fixation of nitrogen as nitrates by free soil organisms is known to be accomplished by a number of bacteria under both aerobic and anaerobic conditions and even in practically sterile soils. Some are inhibited by acidity or chemical constituents of the soil, and temperature ranges may affect their activity, but, in general, some are present almost everywhere. Certain algae are also thought to be capable of nitrogen fixation.

All nitrates appearing in the soil from sources other than fixation are the products of organic decomposition, particularly of proteins. The breakdown involves a series of chemical changes accomplished by a succession of bacteria and fungi. The first of these causes the proteins to break down into the less complex proteoses, peptones, and amino acids. This digestive process allows the bacteria and fungi to use a part of the nitrogen for themselves, and, in so doing, they release ammonia as a waste. Few plants can use ammonia directly, and many are injured by its accumulation in the soil. Ammonification is followed by nitrification, in which a group of nitrite bacteria convert the ammonia to nitrites by partial oxidation. Subsequently, the activities of nitrate bacteria cause further oxidation and the formation of nitrates. Now, finally, the nitrogen is usable by higher plants. Digestion of proteins, ammonification, and nitrification must all take place before organic nitrogen can be used by plants, and the succession of bacteria must be present if the processes are to occur.

The activities resulting in available nitrates produce partial breakdown of organic materials, which are further decomposed by other bacteria and fungi acting upon the remaining nonprotein plant materials. The partially decomposed plant remains, or humus, may be broken down completely in a single season if relatively high temperatures and sufficient moisture occur most of the year and permit more or less continuous functioning of the organisms. If the organisms can operate for only a few summer months, the deposition of litter usually exceeds the rate of decomposition, and humus tends to accumulate.

ANIMALS AS FACTORS

Pollination.—Insects are by far the most important animals involved in pollination, and bees, wasps, moths, and butterflies are particularly concerned. A few birds, especially hummingbirds, contribute to pollen transport, and even some small crawling animals may be effective at times. Most animal-pollinated flowers have certain characteristics in common, such as conspicuousness in size and color and the production of an odor as well as nectar. It has been shown that all of these characters serve more or less to attract insects. In general, the flowers are more elaborate than those of wind-pollinated plants, and they have characters usually interpreted as of more modern origin.

Devices that insure insect pollination are common and often of intricate design. Adaptations may occur in both insect and flower limiting pollination of a particular species to a single type of insect. Some adaptations are so extreme as to produce complete dependence of plant and insect upon each other.

Dissemination.—Plant parts, called disseminules, give rise to new individuals in new places. Their food content is an attraction to various animals, which, consequently, often act as agents of dissemination. Many seeds that are eaten are indigestible and retain their viability after they are dropped at considerable distances from their sources. Others, not immediately eaten, are carried by birds, rodents and even ants to places of storage or concealment, where they may germinate. Of course, great numbers of seeds are eaten or destroyed by animals, but dissemination is effective nevertheless.

Vegetative structures may be effective in the same way. Aquatic animals, such as muskrat, tear up rhizomes and bulbs, some of which float free and establish new communities elsewhere. In this connection, it is worth mentioning the importance of water as an agent of dissemination, especially of floating propagules, even though they do not retain their viability for long when saturated.

Finally, the hooks, spines, and other devices characteristic of many seeds and fruits insure their attachment to almost any animal contacting them and thus make possible their transport for

FIG. 93. Structural modifications of seeds and fruits that facilitate dissemination by wind or animals. (1) The parachute fruit of common dandelion (*Taraxacum*); (2) winged fruit of dock (*Rumex pulcher*); (3) the silky-haired seed of milkweed (*Asclepias mexicana*); spiny, hooked, and awned fruits of (4) sandbur (*Cenchrus pauciflorus*), (5) cocklebur (*Xanthium canadense*), (6) red-stem filaree (*Erodium cicutarium*), (7) beggar's-tick (*Bidens frondosa*).— *By permission, from* Weed Control *by Robbins, Crafts, and Raynor, copyrighted 1942, McGraw-Hill Book Company.*

some distance. Animals with long, soft hair are the most effective agents. The clothing of man is likewise well adapted to such transport, as anyone knows who spends time in the field during late summer and fall. Some of these devices are simple hooks, effective because of sharpness or strength; others are elaborate structures with several features insuring their transport. The fruits of awn and needle grasses are illustrative, since they have sharp-pointed, retrorsely-barbed fruits, which easily penetrate cloth, fur, or wool, and an awn which twists with changes of moisture and thus pushes the fruit forward to a secure anchorage. These may cause severe damage to grazing animals by penetrating skin, lips, or even internal organs.

Soil Animals.—The microfauna of the soil, concentrated in the upper strata, consists of great numbers of protozoa, nematodes, and rotifers. In addition, there are various macroscopic worms and insects.[263] In general, the numbers of animals vary in response to the same factors affecting the microflora, and the greatest numbers are always found in soil with high organic content. All contribute to organic decomposition and use a part of the products for food. Several protozoa probably consume bacteria, and some nematodes are parasitic on the roots of plants, causing much trouble in cultivated soils where they are present.

Of the macroscopic fauna, earthworms are most active. Their constant burrowing facilitates aeration and drainage and their use of fresh or partially decomposed organic matter as food contributes to decomposition. Since mineral matter is also ingested in feeding, the earthworm moves quantities of soil about, and this tends to mix mineral and organic materials. In cultivated soils this has no great significance, but for natural soils the advantages are obvious. Earthworms are found in the best soils and best sites but rarely in poor soils. It would appear, then, that they serve to make good soils better but that poor soils derive little from them.

A very high proportion of all insects spend part of their lives in the soil. Their larvae tunnel through the soil and, thereby, contribute to organic decomposition and distribution.

Larger Animals.—The principal effect of larger animals upon plants results from grazing or other feeding habits. Carnivorous animals affect communities only indirectly by keeping down the population of herbivores and thus maintaining a balance in food relationships. In spite of this, the feeding by herbivores may sometimes be excessive enough to cause serious disturbance or even destruction of community structure.

Under natural conditions, grazing was undoubtedly greatest when buffalo ranged throughout our grasslands. Locally, as around water holes, their feeding and trampling sometimes destroyed

FIG. 94.   Distinct browse line on stand of ironwood resulting from deer feeding on low branches. Note the uninterrupted view under stand, and absence of shrubs and tree seedlings. Such damage commonly results when deer population is high, and especially when winter supply of food is inadequate. —U. S. Forest Service.

most of the vegetation but otherwise probably did little damage since they were constantly on the move and distributed themselves where grazing was best. Moderate grazing by cattle does not change the essential nature of a grassland community. A succession of dry years in the time of the buffalo could have resulted in local conditions similar to those in overgrazed pasture areas today.

Deer and moose similarly have little effect on the plant communities, where they browse, unless there is an overpopulation. Then, especially as a result of winter browsing, the complete destruction of young woody plants sometimes occurs.

Prairie dogs may consume all the forage for some distance about their villages. The total consumption of food by such relatively small animals is sufficient to reduce considerably the value of a range for larger herbivores. The same may be said for jack rabbits, but their feeding is less localized.

The feeding of cottontail rabbits ordinarily affects natural vegetation but little. However, if a peak in their fluctuating population comes at the time of a bad winter with much snow, they can do serious damage to seedlings and even to larger trees from which they eat the bark. Because of selective feeding, snowshoe rabbits may change the course of forest succession.[68]

FIG. 95.   Injuries to seedlings and saplings resulting from feeding by rodents and larger animals may strongly influence the development of stands and the nature of future vegetation. (1) Young ponderosa pine girdled by porcupine. (2) Scotch pine browsed by deer the year after planting. All needles and buds eaten. (3) A pine seedling eaten back by rabbits in three successive winters. Such seedlings can never make normal trees.—*U. S. Forest Service.*

Rodents that eat bark by preference may cause considerable damage, especially if their feeding is selective as to species. Porcupines are in this category, and beavers are even more destructive because their activities are concentrated around their dams. Here they cut down and strip the bark from the trees they most prefer nearest their ponds and then gradually extend their operations to surrounding slopes. Their dams, too, affect conditions locally, for they maintain ponds that sometimes flood large areas, modify drainage, and even affect the water table. This may sometimes be desirable, sometimes not.

Man.—The effects of man upon vegetation are fundamentally similar to those of lower animals. The greater the concentration of population, the greater the modification of natural communities by use and destruction. Whereas man was once essentially a dependent in community structure, he is now more and more becoming the dominant organism everywhere. By cultivation, he has eliminated natural vegetation from vast areas. Logging, even with-

FIG. 96. Center of a burned swamp in Maryland that once supported mature cypress-gum forest. Intense fire destroyed the forest and burned deep into the peaty soil, which had accumulated through the years. Rebuilding soil in the depressions, now filled with water, will require centuries and numerous generations of plants.—*Photo by* **G. F. Beaven.**

out subsequent cultivation, has changed the forests, and stands equaling the original virgin forests will probably never occupy most logged areas again. Cities, highways, airfields, and similar products of man's living mean serious disturbance of natural vegetation. Drainage and irrigation projects, canals, road fills, and dams result in soil moisture changes that promote the development of quite different communities. Many similar disturbances can be noted as a result of animal activities but always on a more localized scale and consequently with less permanent effects.

Fire is not peculiar to man's activities and, undoubtedly, occurred here and there in North America before the white man came. However, the conditions provided by lumbering operations, and the constant use of fire, often with too little concern for its effects, have made it an important factor associated with man's presence. Local small fires occur almost everywhere occasionally, and the destruction of vegetation followed by gradual replacement is characteristic. Under the right conditions, fire may be so common as to become a major factor controlling the vegetation of a region. This is true of much of the coastal plain of the south-

FIG. 97.   What fire can do to a mountain forest. Such fires are usually followed by erosion, and it requires years for the re-establishment of forest vegetation. Coconino National Forest, Ariz.—*U. S. Forest Service.*

eastern United States.[105] Prolonged dry periods and little attempt to control fire in these flatlands result in most areas burning almost every year. Only fire-resistant species predominate and only a limited degree of vegetational development is possible before fire occurs again and sets back that development. As a result, grassy savannahs with longleaf pine are characteristic instead of the potentially possible hardwood forests. In parts of California, fires have resulted in an increase of the fire-resistant chaparral and a proportionate decrease of forest. Similar illustrations may be found in many parts of the world.

The immediate economic loss from an intense forest fire is

paralleled by other less obvious losses. Such fires in the temperate zones may destroy practically all the humus accumulated through the years and necessitate the slow rebuilding of the soil before forest can occupy the area again. Leaching and erosion, which follow such fires, may delay revegetation for years. Thus the productivity of the soil may be indefinitely impaired.

FIG. 98. A subalpine flat denuded by intense fire that killed all trees and burned off organic material down to mineral soil. The fire occurred many years before picture was taken and it is obvious that it will be many more years before the soil is sufficiently rebuilt to support forest.—*U. S. Forest Service.*

It is of interest that light, controlled burning has been found beneficial for certain purposes. On some grazing land, certain undesirable species may be kept down or eliminated to the advantage of more palatable plants. More vigorous growth of certain forage types is sometimes obtained after light burning in the proper season, probably because of the nutrients released and made available. It would appear that under some circumstances fire is being used as a beneficial tool.[117]

Man, like lower animals, transports seeds and fruits, but to far greater distances and with resulting changes in vegetation of a

FIG. 99.   An introduced weed, tumble mustard *(Sisymbrium altissimum)*, dominant over the entire extent of a sagebrush burn, one year after the fire. Washoe County, Nev.—*Photo by W. D. Billings.*

more drastic nature. It is hard to believe that 60 percent or more of our weeds are not native but introduced species that have come from all parts of the world.[176] Some were brought in as ornamentals and almost immediately escaped and spread from gardens. Others came in accidentally with seeds of desirable plants. Many introductions have been useful and extremely valuable. Most of our cultivated plants have been improved by crossing with strains of foreign varieties at some time, or they were themselves originally introduced. In recent years, such introductions are not made haphazardly.

Unfortunate experiences with unconsidered or accidental introductions can be listed for all parts of the world. The water hyacinth, introduced from South America, has spread throughout the lowland waterways of our southern states where it chokes canals, impedes drainage and navigation, and destroys wildlife. A similar problem has resulted with the introduction of Elodea in the low countries of Europe. Animals may cause similar difficulties, as the spread of the introduced English sparrow and the starling in the United States. The muskrat has become a pest in central

Europe, and rabbits, introduced into Australia, increased to enormous numbers in only a few years.

Natural communities are made up of groups of species adapted to living together. The numbers and sizes of individuals are de- termined by the entire complex of environmental factors. If a species is eliminated, others of the community may increase and take its place, or there may then be opportunity for an incidental species to become a part of the community. Usually, if a species is introduced, it does not reproduce and gradually dies out. Occa- sionally, an introduced species has the necessary characteristics to compete successfully and to reproduce regularly. Then adjust- ments must be made within the community and a new balance among its members must be established. Such a species might even become a dominant, and then the adjustments would result in a new community. The prickly pear *(Opuntia inermis)*, introduced in Australia, became a dominant and made useless more than thirty million acres in Queensland alone.

FIG. 100.   Massed water hyacinth covering the water in Louisiana swamp- land. The dusting by airplane is part of an experimental eradication program. —*Courtesy of Department of Wildlife and Fisheries, Louisiana.*

When man has tampered with the balance among the species of a community by eliminations or introductions, he has not always considered the possible effects upon the community as a whole. If large carnivores are destroyed, herbivores increase, and, if their reproductive capacity is great, they may soon become so abundant that their grazing destroys the community or changes it radically. If a predator is introduced whose prey is some native species that is a pest, the predators may eliminate the pest and then become pests themselves.[10]

Only a few examples are necessary to illustrate these points. The Indian mongoose was introduced into Haiti, Jamaica, and other West Indian islands to rid them of rats and snakes. This the mongoose did most effectively, but its numbers increased, and, with its natural prey disappearing, it turned to robbing birds' nests of eggs and young. Now it may even be a problem in the raising of poultry. The gypsy moth was accidentally introduced into Massachusetts when it escaped from cultures being reared to test its silk-producing ability. It is now a serious pest of fruit and shade trees in most of the eastern United States although much money and effort have been expended to control it. On the other hand, introductions of about sixty foreign predators or parasites of the gypsy moth have resulted in the establishment of a dozen or more that are aiding in its partial control. The destruction of coyotes in some western states has resulted in such marked increase of rabbits that their winter feeding on tree seedlings modifies vegetational development (see Fig. 95).

On game reserves where predators have been eliminated and no hunting is permitted, the population of herbivores, such as deer, usually increases rapidly. When the number of deer exceeds the natural carrying capacity of the region, a shortage of food results during unfavorable seasons. Then, especially in winter, many animals die unless they are fed by man. As a result of supplementary feeding, the population is still larger the next season, and the problem is not solved. Controlled hunting is now permitted on several such reserves where the population capacity has been determined. The effects on the vegetation of such overcrowding are very conspicuous. All young woody plants protruding above snow are eaten off, and the lower limbs of young trees, even conifers, are "pruned" to the height the animals can reach, standing on their hind legs. Obviously, community structure and development in such areas is completely out of balance.

Disturbance of natural communities should not be undertaken without a reasonable appreciation of the end results. Management or manipulation of the balance among species of a community may

FIG. 101. Drained swampland in the Everglades of Florida. Many acres of these muck soils are producing winter truck crops in quantities, now that problems of drainage, tillage, and fertilizing have been worked out.—*U. S. Soil Conservation Service.*

frequently be possible but should offer the best prospects of success when the ecology of the individuals and the community is well understood.

Man's unconcern for natural resources built up through the years has led to economic losses and a reduction of those resources, which only time can replace. Soil erosion, quite unnecessary if cropping is properly handled, had reached a shameful point before we began to do anything about it. Only recently have we attempted to correct overworking of poor soils, mismanagement of others, overgrazing, and other destructive practices. Contour plowing, strip cropping, terracing, and similar procedures check runoff, hold water, and permit the rebuilding of rundown soils. On wild lands and some submarginal cultivated lands, the re-establishment of natural vegetation is being encouraged where it should never have been removed. Application of ecological principles in such reclamation has generally paid good dividends.

Not only has man disturbed or destroyed natural vegetation, but he has also modified the environment, sometimes to his advantage. By irrigation or drainage, the soil moisture has been so modified that great acreages have been brought under his control. Enormous dams hold water in artificial lakes. When this water is properly supplied to the surrounding soils, it transforms worthless desert to highly productive agricultural land. Elsewhere drainage systems put into lowlands have changed swampy, untillable soil to some of the best truck and farming acreages. Not all drainage projects have been profitable, however, especially those of muck lands. Not all are equally productive, and cost of maintaining drainage of some mucks is out of proportion to the crop yields. Many such projects have been abandoned—to the joy of sportsmen and conservationists, who objected to the extensive destruction of homes and feeding grounds of all kinds of wildlife associated with these swamps.

GENERAL REFERENCES

R. M. ANDERSON. Effect of the Introduction of Exotic Animal Forms.
J. M. COULTER, C. R. BARNES and H. C. COWLES. *A Textbook of Botany.*
   (Vol. III: Ecology. pp. 1-471.)
H. C. HANSON. Fire in Land Use and Management.
W. A. McCUBBIN. Preventing Plant Disease Introduction.
S. A. WAKSMAN. *Principles of Soil Microbiology.*

Part 4 · Community Dynamics

CHAPTER IX

PLANT SUCCESSION

HISTORICAL BACKGROUND

When a cultivated field is permitted to lie fallow, it produces a crop of annual weeds the first year, numerous perennials the second year, and a community of perennials thereafter. In forest areas, the perennial herbs are soon superseded by woody plants, which become dominant. After any disturbance of natural vegetation—such as cultivation, lumbering, or fire—a similar sequence of communities occurs with several changes in the dominant vegetation through the years.

Such relatively rapid vegetational changes are familiar to most people today and must have been observed hundreds of years ago. It was not until the seventeenth century, however, that any systematic study of such changes was made, and those studies dealt primarily with the development of peat bogs. Bog studies were continued in the eighteenth century, and, in addition, some attempt was made to apply the principles to burned and disturbed upland areas. It was then that the term, *succession*, was first applied to the vegetational changes involved. During the nineteenth century, succession was considered rather frequently but invariably as incidental to other problems. Several writers hinted at the importance of succession in all habitats, but it was not until 1885 that a regional study of vegetation in Finland was made in which succession was recognized as fundamental to all community development.

Between 1890 and 1905, the modern concepts of succession were clarified through the efforts of several writers. Two, whose influence has been as great as any, were Americans. In the first comprehensive application of successional principles in the United

211

States, Dr. Henry C. Cowles (1899) described the development of vegetation on the sand dunes of Lake Michigan. Later (1901) he described the vegetation of Chicago and vicinity, as it is related to physiography, in so logical a fashion that a pattern for studies of community dynamics was established. His papers also served to stimulate similar investigations by others. Beginning at about the same time, the publications of Dr. F. E. Clements, then working in Nebraska, included much that served to shape our present concepts of succession. The culmination of his ideas appeared in his exhaustive treatment of the entire subject of plant succession,[56] which remains a basic source of reference today.

THE CONCEPT

Plant communities are never completely stable. They are characterized by constant change,[73] sometimes radical and abrupt, sometimes so slow as to be scarcely discernible over a period of years. These changes are not haphazard, for within a climatic area, they are predictable for a given community in a particular habitat. This means, of course, that similar habitats within a climatic area support a sequence of dominants that tend to succeed each other in the same order. Contrasting habitats do not support the same sequence of communities. As a result, any region with several types of habitats will have an equal number of possible successional trends.

CAUSES

A detailed consideration of the relationships of organisms to their environment should make it clear that major changes in the composition of a community can only follow changes in the environment. The specific, immediate cause of a particular change of species may not always be obvious because of the interrelationship of controlling factors. Two general types of habitat change may cause differences in the community. Development of the community causes parallel developmental changes of the environment, and physiographic changes can likewise modify the environment materially.

Developmental changes of the environment result from reactions upon the habitat by the organisms living there. To illustrate : Accumulation of litter affects runoff, soil temperature, and the formation of humus; this, in turn, contributes to soil development, modifies water relations, available nutrients, pH, and aeration, and affects soil organisms. Thus every organism in a community may have some reaction upon the habitat. By these reactions, the habitat becomes changed and consequently is less favorable to the organisms responsible for the changes, while, at the same time, it

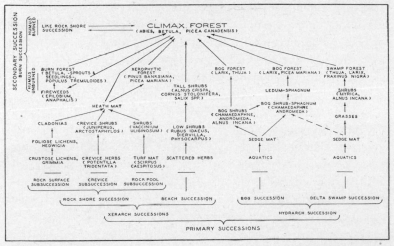

FIG. 102. A diagram of the trends of succession for the principal habitats on Isle Royale, Lake Superior. This is one of the early complete condensations of a successional story for an entire region. On this pattern, similar diagrams have been worked out for many sections of the country. Note that the system shows at a glance the kinds of habitats in which succession originates, the interrelationship of trends, and the major dominants in each of the stages of succession. Study of the diagram should help to clarify concepts of succession and climax. It must be remembered that not all trends progress with equal speed.—*After Cooper.*[70]

has become more favorable for species that could exist there previously only with difficulty. Under the changed conditions, new species are able to compete successfully with the established species and often even to replace them.

The habitat may also be modified by forces quite apart from the effects of organisms. A flood plain or swamp may become better drained as a stream cuts more deeply into its channel. Silting in of a lake or pond raises the level of mineral soil. Chemical changes in the soil may result from leaching or accumulation of salts. Such modifications of the habitat also produce vegetational changes.

These two types of causes of succession are commonly in operation at the same time, and their effects cannot always be readily separated. Since they both result in vegetational change, it seems unnecessary to distinguish between their effects in a general consideration of plant succession.

KINDS OF SUCCESSION

Primary succession is initiated on a bare area where no vegetation has grown before. It may be observed on glacial moraine exposed by recession of the ice, a new island, an area of extreme erosion, newly deposited volcanic ash or rock, or any similar habitat newly exposed to colonization. Such habitats are apt to be unsuitable to the growth of most plants, and, consequently, the pioneers that do establish themselves must have adaptations permitting survival under extreme conditions. Moisture relationships usually control their ability to invade the new area. If the habitat is extremely dry, it is described as xeric; if wet, hydric; and if intermediate, mesic. The successional trends are similarly referred to as being xerarch, hydrarch or mesarch succession.

Whatever the condition of the initial habitat, reaction of vegetation tends to make it more favorable to plants and always results in improved moisture conditions. Thus xeric habitats become moister and hydric ones become drier as succession progresses. Because of the diversity of habitats upon which succession may begin, there are an almost equal number of possible pioneer communities. Within a climatic area, however, the variety of communities decreases as succession progresses because the trend is toward mesophytism from both hydric and xeric habitats. Thus unrelated habitats may eventually support similar vegetation and may even undergo identical late stages of succession.

Secondary succession results when a normal succession is disrupted by fire, cultivation, lumbering, wind throw, or any similar disturbance that destroys the principal species of an established community. To what extent the development of vegetation on the secondary area resembles primary succession is determined by the degree of disturbance. Although the first communities that develop may not be typical of primary succession, the later stages again are similar. When disturbance is extreme, as after severe fire,

FIG. 103. An illustration of relatively rapid secondary succession. The fire that destroyed this Oregon forest (above) did not appreciably affect the soil organic matter and was not followed by erosion. As a result, Douglas fir soon became established and, when fourteen years old, formed a closed stand 10 to 15 feet tall (below).—*U. S. Forest Service*.

many of the effects of previous vegetation upon the habitat are eliminated, resulting in a slow vegetational development. After wind throw or lumbering, many of the products of community reaction remain and succession is rapid. If seedlings and young trees are not destroyed, progress of succession tends to exceed that of the original trend.

Most of the settled parts of North America have little evidence of primary succession today, and even unsettled areas have largely been disturbed by grazing or lumbering. Thus primary succession must often be interpreted in terms of small and often poor exam-

FIG. 104. Hydrarch succession as illustrated by girdles of vegetation around a shallow lake in northern Minnesota. In what remains of open water are submerged and floating-leaved aquatics, the pioneer angiosperms. A marginal, floating sedge mat is gradually filling the lake with peat and advancing over the water. On the mat are a few bog shrubs, behind which is a girdle of tamarack forming a closed stand. The oldest part of the bog is marked by the spires of black spruce, which succeed the tamarack. On the upland, behind the spruce, is a mixed white pine–hardwood forest. Eventually, the entire depression will be a peat-filled bog supporting a forest of black spruce.

ples of what once occurred. Studies of secondary succession may, however, have the greatest practical value because we are involved with secondary successions in any problem of applied ecology; yet their interpretation may be partially dependent upon an understanding of primary successions.

Representative Successions.—Because water and bare rock represent the extremes in types of habitats upon which succession is initiated, the growth form of early stages of each is remarkably similar everywhere and even genera and some species are often duplicated regardless of the region. It is, therefore, possible to present a general description of such successions, which can be applied almost anywhere and which will illustrate what we have just discussed.

FIG. 105. Hydrarch succession illustrated by swamp vegetation. The zone of cattails occupies the partially flooded, muddy margins. When soil builds up or drainage improves, bog shrubs (buttonbush, alder, willow) appear as in the middle background. On wet, but drained soil a swamp forest of mixed hardwoods develops as in background.—*Photo by H. L. Blomquist.*

Hydrarch succession progresses in response to better moisture conditions in combination with improved aeration. Initiated in a lake, pond, or stream margin where water movement is not too great, the pioneer vascular plants are submerged aquatics with thin, dissected, or linear leaves. Their depth of growth is limited,

FIG. 106 (A). Xerarch succession as illustrated by vegetational development on granitic rock in the Piedmont of the southeastern states. Early stage (upper) of mat formation initiated by the pioneer moss *(Grimmia laevigata)* upon which a lichen *(Cladonia leporina)* is well established. As mat thickens (lower), herbs come in, with eventual *Andropogon* spp. dominance.[186]

on the one hand, by light penetration of the water and, on the other, by a zone of floating-leaved species. These latter (water lilies, etc.) exclude submerged species by shading but cannot move into the zone of submerged forms until the bottom is built up or the water level falls. In still shallower water, emergent species predominate. These have their roots and rhizomes in the mud and extend upward into the air (rushes, reeds, cattails, sedges). The close growth in this zone serves to hold sediment, and the bulk results in substantial accumulation of partially decomposed organic matter. When filling is sufficient, shrubs can survive on the built-up soil. Finally, the soil will be firm enough and sufficiently raised above the water table to support lowland trees, which may eventually give way to a community similar to that of uplands.

This entire sequence can sometimes be seen as a more or less

FIG. 106 (B).   Shrub stage of rock succession, mostly *Rhus copallina* here. Note fringe of *Andropogon*, smaller herbs, and finally mosses at periphery (upper). Tree stage (lower) on an old mat, forming an island on bare rock. Oak-hickory forest in background is growing on shallow soil overlying rocks.[186]

continuous series of zones girdling a lake that is gradually filling in. Borings of the soil under any zone will show the partially decomposed remains, in vertical sequence, of each of the previous stages of succession that contributed to the development of that zone.

Xerarch succession on rock follows a definite pattern, whose progress is controlled by the rate at which soil forms and accumulates. Pioneers on rock surfaces are either lichens or mosses capable of growing during the brief periods when water is available to them and lying more or less dormant through the usually longer periods of drought. The pioneer lichens are crustose and foliose types, which usually contribute little to succession since they are not mat-forming.[186] However, they do probably cause corrosion of the rock surface and thus provide some anchorage for other species. Pioneer mosses, on the other hand, are in tufts or clumps, which catch dust and mineral matter from wind and water. This material, combined with the remains of mosses, forms a gradually thickening mat with a periphery of young plants that spreads over bare rock (and the pioneer lichens) and with a central area that may become thick enough to support fruticose lichens (Cladonia especially), larger mosses such as Polytrichum, or often species of Selaginella. Such bushy plants catch and hold still more mineral material, and their death adds much organic soil to the mat.

When soil has built up sufficiently to provide the necessary anchorage and water-retaining ability, seed plants appear on the mats. A number of hardy, annual herbs, often weeds of field and garden, appear first and are followed by biennials and perennials, of which grasses are most abundant. Later a shrub stage becomes dominant, which usually includes some species of sumac *(Rhus)* and several ericaceous shrubs. By this time, the mats may be several inches or a foot thick and then trees make their appearance.

Just as a series of girdles of vegetation usually surrounds a lake and indicates the sequence of succession from open water to solid ground, so the progress of succession on rock may be seen as a series of girdles of vegetation from the periphery to the center of an old mat. Pioneers are at the outer margin of the mat, and each successive stage of dominance is nearer the center where, on the thickest soil, trees may be present.

FIG. 107. Herb stages in secondary succession on abandoned upland fields in the Piedmont of the southeast. (1) Horseweed dominance on a field abandoned one year. (2) Aster dominance indicating two years of abandonment. (3) Broom sedge (*Andropogon*) dominance in a field abandoned five years, and young pine well established.

The early stages of these two successional trends are apt to be extremely slow, but later stages speed up considerably as reaction

FIG. 108.   Forest stages of old-field succession (continuing Fig. 107). (1) Fully stocked 15-year loblolly pine, which has eliminated all old-field herbs and under which hardwood seedlings may be found, (2) 26-year pine, under which saplings of gum, red maple, and dogwood are noticeable, (3) 50-year pine stand in which hardwoods, including oak and hickory, have formed an understory, (4) oak-hickory climax forest, of the type that could develop on an old field after 200 years or more.[183]—*Photo (1) by C. F. Korstian.*

of the vegetation becomes more effective. The final changes, after tree dominance, are again very slow. Changes of currents or drainage in the lake and wind throw or fire on the rock may disrupt either of the trends and result in secondary succession. The result of succession in both habitats is, however, a gradual change in the direction of habitat conditions that are relatively mesic for the climate of the region and a community adapted to such conditions.

RATE OF SUCCESSION

If succession is to be recognized as universal and occurring in all habitats, it becomes necessary to ignore time to some extent. A mesic habitat in a given climate will obviously produce a forest much more quickly than a xeric one, especially if the initial habitat is bare rock. Yet the potential ultimate communities of the two sites are the same, for all successions in a climatic area progress toward communities of mesophytes. Two habitats of apparently similar characteristics might support the same successional sequence, but progress of the successions might be at different rates because of the type of soil and the difference in its response to reaction. Or, if seed sources were not equally available to both sites, one might develop more rapidly than another. This could result from an oversupply of seed, producing overstocking of certain species and consequent delay in development of the next stage because of competition; on the other hand, poor seed sources or a series of poor seed years might materially delay the initiation of a community that otherwise could have started. This should make it clear that the rate of succession is extremely variable. Pioneer stages of primary succession are commonly very slow because they can progress only with soil development. An extreme example is probably that of succession on bare rock, which must wait not only upon soil development but also upon the disintegration of the rock for soil formation. In contrast, the pioneer stages of secondary succession, especially on abandoned fields, are remarkably rapid, for often the dominants change every year for several years.

STABILIZATION AND CLIMAX

All successional trends lead toward relative mesophytism within a climatic area. This explains why related successions parallel each other in their mature or late stages. Eventually, all successsional trends lead to a single community, which is composed of the most mesophytic vegetation that the climate can support and whose moisture relations are average, or intermediate, for the region as a whole. This community, determined by the climate, terminates succession and is called the climax community or *climax* for that climatic area. It is capable of reproducing itself, and, since it represents the last stage of succession, it cannot be replaced by other communities so long as the climate remains the same. It is, therefore, a stable community in which the individuals that become overmature and die are replaced by their own progeny, leaving the character of the community unchanged.

Uniformity and Variation of Climax.—Since climax is determined by climate, the distribution and range of a particular climax should be an indication of a region in which effective climatic factors are equivalent. Climax is a product of all the interacting factors of climate and is, therefore, a better expression of the biological effectiveness of climate than man can obtain by physical measurements, which he must interpret. This is well illustrated by the similarity of prairie vegetation over an area with an extremely wide range of several factors, particularly of temperature from north to south.

On this basis, it might be assumed that a climax would be uniform throughout its extent. This is true only in part. Certain variations are to be expected, which are related to the great extent of climax regions and the history of different parts of these regions. The extent of deciduous forest climax results in transitions to both coniferous forest and grassland. These transitions are not abrupt, and the composition of the climax community is affected for some distance. The deciduous forest likewise illustrates how the time element may be involved in variation. Most of its northern extent lies on glacial soils and topography and has occupied the area only in relatively recent times. Unglaciated areas to the south supported deciduous forest throughout the period of glaciation and still do today. Thus there are differences in age of vegetation, topography, and soils, all of which contribute to variation in the deciduous climax.[47]

The obvious uniformity of vegetation in a climax region is in the life form of the dominants, which is definitely a product of climate. Thus the major climax regions are easily recognized: grassland, desert, and semidesert with shrubs predominating; and forest climaxes that are distinguishable as coniferous, deciduous, or broad-leaved evergreen if tropical. In addition to life form there is uniformity of genera among the dominants of a climax. Variations of the dominant species, as well as dependent ones, are a product of the environmental variations discussed above.

The major climaxes are distinguishable on the basis of physiognomy or life form of the dominants alone. Such climaxes are termed *formations*.[56] Floristic variation within a formation is usually sufficient to produce two or more recognizably distinct climax communities, which, following Clements, would be called *associations*. Although distinct, the associations of a formation are at the same time bound together by one or more species present in all associations and by the constant presence of some dominant genera throughout. Thus the associations of a formation are quite obviously similar and related.

Just as associations are recognizable subdivisions of formations, there are distinguishable variations within associations. These geographical variants that make up the association are called *faciations*.[60] They are recognizable by differences in the abundance or relationships of the dominants. Faciations may be further subdivided into local variations, called *lociations*. Further subdivision is, of course, possible and often desirable. The various systems of classification and the terminologies that have been used make for more detail and controversy than can be presented here.

Because, unfortunately, the term, association, is constantly used in more than one sense, it deserves further mention. The systems of classifying communities, as supported by the various schools of thought, almost invariably include the term. Although not always in agreement among themselves, European ecologists consistently consider associations as basic units of classification that can be grouped into categories of successively higher rank. Thus lociations, as mentioned above, might be given associational rank in such a system. The use of the term here is in an absolutely contrasting sense in that it makes it a community of the highest rank, inclusive of, and divisible into, numerous lesser categories. It has been suggested that, to avoid conflict, the use of the term in this sense be indicated by referring to climax associations or major associations, but this has not been generally accepted as yet. An attempt was made to standardize the use of the term at a recent International Botanical Congress, but, even so, the rulings have not been completely accepted. For a summary of some of the diverse points of view and some applications of the term, reference should be made to Conard's[67] discussion of plant associations and its appended bibliography.

Types of Climax.—In a climatic area, all succession is in the direction of a community that can maintain itself permanently, and there is only one such community for the region as a whole. However, succession is often halted temporarily in almost any stage of its progress, and sometimes is halted almost permanently in late stages. Diseases, fire, insects, or man may produce conditions that prevent completion of succession and hold it indefinitely at some stage preceding the climax. Edaphic or physiographic conditions may be such that succession cannot proceed to completion. Although such communities may appear to be as stable and permanent as climax, they cannot be considered as such because they are not controlled by climate.

This is the monoclimax hypothesis. In contrast is the polyclimax view, which recognizes edaphic, physiographic, and pyric climaxes within a climatic area. The conflict between the two views lies in the interpretation of the concept of climax. Actually, the same communities are recognized by both but under different terminology. Since the basic concept of climax implies one ultimate community controlled by climate, the monoclimax view is consistent with the meaning of the term. When used in conjunction with a few precise terms,[60] which are discussed below, it is adequate for explaining all climax variations.

Subclimax.—When, in any succession, a stage immediately preceding the climax is long-persisting, for any reason, it can be called *subclimax*. It may be the result simply of extremely slow development to climax, or of any disturbance, such as fire, that holds succession almost indefinitely in its subfinal stage. In the eastern United State, most pine forests are subclimax to hardwood climax because of the relatively slow elimination of pine in the progression toward hardwood dominance. In the coastal plain, subclimax pine forests are maintained indefinitely by the constantly recurring fires to which the pines are resistant and which keep down hardwoods.

Disclimax.—When disturbance is such that true climax becomes modified or largely replaced by new species, the result is an apparent climax, called *disclimax.* The disturbance is usually produced by man or his animals and the introduction of species that, under the existing conditions, become the dominants over wide areas. The prickly pear cactus thus has formed a disclimax over wide areas in Australia. A grass, *Bromus tectorum,* forms a disclimax in much of the Great Basin where, because it burns readily, it facilitates fires, which reduce dominance of desert shrubs and increase the area of grass. The short grasses of the Great Plains were long considered as climax but now are generally considered as disclimax resulting from grazing and drought, which have practically eleminated the midgrass climax. The ravages of chestnut blight illustrate how disclimax may result from disease. Oak-chestnut climax is today an oak disclimax.

Postclimax and Preclimax.—A climatic area is normally bordered, on the one hand, by one that is drier and warmer and, on the other, by one that is moister and cooler. The contiguous climates are, therefore, either less favorable or more favorable to plant growth. As a result, each has its own climax, distinct in species and, often, in growth form. On a large scale, this is apparent in latitudinal zonation from the tropics to the arctic. Often it is noticeable in the climaxes along a line from oceanic or maritime climate to the interior of a continent. It is most conspicuous on mountains where altitude produces a zonation of climates and climaxes. Each of the climatic areas in such a sequence has a bordering climate with a more favorable water balance, usually on the north, toward the coast, or at higher altitudes; while the climate to the south, toward the interior, or at lower altitudes, usually is less favorable.

For any particular climax the contiguous climax produced by a more favorable climate, usually cooler and/or moister, is termed *postclimax,* and the one produced by less favorable conditions, usually drier and/or hotter, is termed *preclimax.* To illustrate on a broad basis, deciduous forest climax has grassland as preclimax and northern conifer forest as postclimax. At the same time, deciduous forest holds a postclimax relationship to grassland that has desert as preclimax. The use of the concept is not restricted to formations as illustrated above since it is just as applicable to associations, even within the same formation. For example, within the deciduous forest formation oak-hickory is preclimax and hemlock-hardwood is postclimax to the beech-maple association. Likewise, oak-hickory is preclimax and beech-maple (or hemlock-hardwood) is postclimax to the oak-chestnut association.

Should the present phase of relatively stable climates be interrupted, the climate of any given area would undoubtedly tend to become more like that of one of its contiguous areas and a migration or shift of climax would result. Such a shift occurred during the glacial period when the northern coniferous forest moved southward, and the northern extent of the deciduous forest was proportionately constricted. When the climate ameliorated, the ice receded, and again, the ranges of the climaxes were readjusted. When such shifts occur, remnants of the previous dominants are left behind in locally favorable habitats where they may maintain themselves indefinitely as relics of a previous climax. These relics are either preclimax or postclimax depending upon their relationship to contiguous climaxes and the direction of the climatic shift. The habitats in which they survive must have edaphic or physiographic characteristics that differ so markedly from the average for the region that conditions for growth are similar to those of a contiguous climatic area. Deep valleys or canyons with steep bluffs and contrasting exposures, poorly drained flood plains, bogs, ridges of rock or gravel, areas of deep sand or other peculiar soil conditions are specific examples.

Where there have been shifts of climax, it is apparent that preclimax and postclimax communities should occupy such habitats. Not all preclimax and postclimax communities, however, need be relics. Within the general range of a climax, there are bound to be local habitats such as those mentioned above that will continue indefinitely to be somewhat more favorable or less favorable, wetter or drier, than the conditions controlled by climate in the region as a whole. As a result, when vegetational development proceeds to a condition of stability on such a site, it will have characteristics of the contiguous more or less favorable climate. Such localized stable communities are likewise postclimax or preclimax for the region. In or approaching transition zones, such areas are particularly noticeable, and here, especially, application of the concept greatly simplifies interpretation of climax.

Since communities such as these exist to some extent in every climatic area, they must be recognized. As mentioned earlier, not all ecologists agree as to their interpretation. Some, with the polyclimax view, describe them variously as edaphic or physiographic climaxes. This is open to the general criticism that, by definition, there can be but one climax for a climatic region. Use of preclimax and postclimax is a necessary part of the monoclimax view but is consistent with the meaning of climax. At the same time, it shows relationships with contiguous and past climaxes.

METHODS OF STUDYING COMMUNITY DYNAMICS

Determination of Climax Formations.—The major climax regions (formations) are fairly obvious, and their number and approximate limits have been accepted for some time. Each has its distinctive physiognomy or life form that makes for clear demarcation. An additional number of criteria corroborating the apparent unity based upon physiognomy have been applied.

Tests of climax that have been used in fixing formations[60] are briefly summarized below. Both static and developmental criteria must be met.

Static Criteria
1. Life form must be uniform throughout.
2. All associations must include one or more of the same or closely related species as dominants or subdominants.

Developmental Criteria
3. Late stages of succession must be essentially identical for a climax; and distinct from those of another climax.
4. Postclimax should show relationships to contiguous climax or subclimax.
5. Historical records as to composition and structure must conform to the modern picture.
   a. Recent historical—old records and land surveys.
   b. Historical development reconstructed from pollen statistics.
   c. Geological record, physical history, and fossils.

Recognition of Local Climax.—The variations of a formation (associations) are not always immediately obvious, particularly in areas of transition from one association to another. Because of disturbance by man, the climax vegetation once present in virgin stands over wide areas has practically disappeared. We now, therefore, must rely upon small samples of climax vegetation, often disturbed; or, when even these are lacking, we must determine the climax on the basis of studies of succession. There may, therefore, be different interpretations, and errors are possible. To illustrate : It was generally believed for years that short grasses constituted the climax of the plains. Added evidence and reinterpretation indicated to many ecologists that mid-grasses are climax and short grasses are disclimax maintained by modern grazing under the conditions of periodic drought.

A climax association must, of course, conform to the criteria that delimit the formation of which it is a member. To check these criteria, it becomes necessary to know the successional trends of the vicinity in detail, to know the composition and structure of the postulated climax and subfinal stages of succession, and to distinguish preclimax and postclimax communities and habitats. Thus it becomes necessary to know something of related associations as well as the one involved. Finally, the history of the region, both recent and geological, is desirable for proper interpretation of observations.

The climax must be a community capable of maintaining itself indefinitely under existing climatic conditions. It must be the final community in all successional trends in the region except those isolated instances of edaphic or physiographic variation producing preclimax or postclimax by compensating for climate. It must recur throughout the area under average conditions, or the evidence from succession must indicate its potential presence.

General Procedure in Local Study.—The desirability of familiarity with the area as a whole has been emphasized. Observation and note-taking should proceed at the same time that literature is searched to learn the historical aspects of the area and the relationships of its flora to that of surrounding climaxes. With continued observation, certain ideas will develop as to probable and possible successional relationships and the relative position of dif-

FIG. 109. A phytographic comparison of the overstory species found in the two oak-hickory climax variants of the North Carolina Piedmont.[183] Values for the white oak type are indicated by solid lines, for the post oak type by broken lines. D—percent of total tree density, F—frequency percent, SC—percent of four size classes (overstory, understory, transgressives, seedlings) in which the species was found. Zero is the center, 100 percent the periphery of the circle. Only quantitative data can give information such as illustrated by these phytographs.

ferent habitats. Such methods alone have produced some excellent interpretations of vegetational dynamics. General conclusions may be as good as any obtained otherwise. However, there are reasons why supporting data are most desirable.

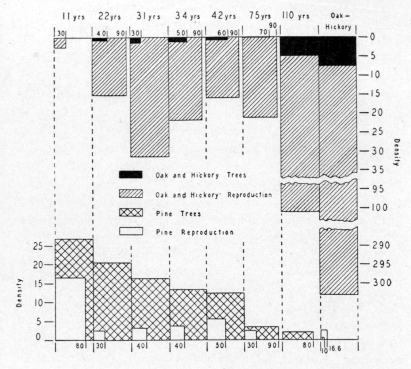

FIG. 110.   Relationships of trees and reproduction of pine and oak-hickory in old-field succession in North Carolina as shown by their density and frequency in successive ages of pine dominance leading to oak-hickory climax. Frequency is indicated by width of columns, density by height. Such phytosociological representations clarify relationships that might otherwise go unrecognized.

It is often possible for honest observation to be wrong, and only quantitative and qualitative data will demonstrate the discrepancies. Again, such data may bring to light pertinent information that could not be realized by observation alone. When questions of "why," "when," or "how" come up, they can be most satisfactorily answered with absolute data.

These things were soon realized by some early students of succession, and quadrat methods were introduced as a part of their procedure. Early methods of sampling, however, were rarely adephysiological responses all were tried. The most successfully applicable value he found[156] was one that combined a physiological temperature index, precipitation, and evaporation. Actually this was a refinement of the precipitation : evaporation ratio proposed earlier,[255] but it is scarcely more useful. These and other studies serve to emphasize the complexity of plant-environmental rela-

FIG. 111. General ranges of the principal vegetation types of North America.—*By permission from Transeau, et al (1940)*[257] *Harper and Brothers, publishers.*

tionships and the impracticality of expressing them as a function of a single variable. This becomes even more obvious when influences such as length of day, winter temperatures, and the season of precipitation are considered.

CLIMAX REGIONS OF NORTH AMERICA

The vegetation maps available for North America[230, 236, 268] serve to emphasize by their similarities that the major vegetation types are fairly obvious, but their differences in detail indicate disagree-

FIG. 112.   Alpine tundra in the Colorado Rockies.—*U. S. Forest Service.*

ment on the interpretations of climax relationships, especially within formations. An understanding of the bases for different interpretations can best be obtained by study of the many papers dealing with local investigations of vegetation. There are, however, several of a more comprehensive nature,[230, 231, 118] which give more detail than can be presented here.

The concept of climax formations and associations was discussed earlier (Chap. 9). Classification of North American vegetation on this basis is altogether logical, particularly if the point of view is a dynamic one. The system shows modern successional and climatic relationships but is based as well upon past history of the climaxes. Although growth form is the apparent major basis of classification, dynamic factors are given equal consideration.

Below are listed the major climax formations of North America.

These, together with their associations, are discussed in the section that follows. The formations restricted to the mountains of the west occur in altitudinal zones whose relationships should be clearly understood. Consequently, discussion of these zonal formations is centered about each of the principal mountain ranges rather than considering each zone separately, throughout its extent.

Climax Formations of North America

Tundra
    Tundra Formation
Forest
  Coniferous
    Boreal Forest Formation
    Subalpine Forest Formation
    Montane Forest Formation
    Pacific Coastal Forest Formation
  Deciduous
    Deciduous Forest Formation
Woodland
    Woodland Formation
Scrub
    Broad-Sclerophyll Formation
    Sagebrush Formation
    Desert Scrub Formation
Grassland
    Grassland Formation
Tropical Formations

Tundra Formation.—Tundra lies between the northern limit of trees and the area of perpetual ice and snow in the far north, or above timber line in high mountains. In North America, it forms a broad band completely across the continent, and it also occupies the narrow low coastal area around most of the periphery of Greenland. It occurs on mountains as far south as Mexico if their altitude is sufficient to produce a timber line. Thus it is limited in its northern or upward extent by ice and bounded on the southern or lower margin by boreal or subalpine conifer forest.

Vegetation is low, dwarfed, and often matlike, and includes a high proportion of grasses and sedges. Even the woody plants, including willows and birches, are prostrate. The herbs are mostly perennial and of a rosette type, producing relatively large flowers, often with conspicuous colors. Mosses and lichens may grow anywhere and in favorable habitats form a thick carpet with the low herbs. The number of species is small compared with floras of temperate climates, and, even within the tundra, the number decreases northward. Most of the genera and numerous species are to be found throughout the Northern Hemisphere wherever tundra occurs.

The uniformity of the flora is undoubtedly related to the peculiarities of environment. The growing season is short and its temperatures are relatively low. The depth to which soil thaws in summer is of great importance. Light is continuous throughout the growing season in the arctic, and is intense and high in ultraviolet rays in alpine habitats. Precipitation is largely in the form of snow and varies greatly. Drying summer winds, which are characteristic, produce high rates of evaporation and transpiration. As a result, water is often a critical factor, especially inland away from moist coasts. Local marked differences in vegetation are commonly related to minor variations in topography and the differences they produce in drainage and retention of snow. The poor, haphazard drainage associated with new topography is apparent everywhere.

Arctic Tundra.—Although the flora of the tundra is fairly well known, its communities and their successional relationships have not been sufficiently studied.[204] In contrast with temperate vegetation, many species may occur in any type of habitat, and several that appear to be climax may also be pioneers in the newest of habitats. Even climax is not agreed upon, possibly because observations have been made at widely separated points. Interpreted in terms of Greenland vegetation, Cassiope heath appears to be climax, and a Sedge-Dryas dominated community, of equal extent but on drier sites, is preclimax.[185] Two subclimaxes are frequent. Any habitat with sufficient moisture, whether it be pond margin, seepage area, or boggy ground, eventually is covered with a thick moss mat supporting several herbs of which cotton grass *(Eriophorum* spp.) is most conspicuous. Xerarch succession on rock exposures eventually results in a lichen-moss mat, which may continue almost indefinitely.

Important climax dominants are *Cassiope tetragona*, one or more species of Vaccinium, *Arctostaphylos alpina*, *Empetrum nigrum*, *Andromeda polifolia*, *Ledum palustre*, *Rhododendron lapponicum*, and species of Betula and Salix. These and other species occur in varying combinations and degrees of importance.

Practically all habitats support some of the many species of Carex, of which the commonest include *Carex capillaris*, *C. nardina*, and *C. rupestris*. The preclimax sedge community invariably includes *Elyna bellardi* in abundance. Some grow in mats, some are in clumps, but all are dwarfed. The same can be said for the grasses, which, although relatively abundant and widespread, are restricted to a few genera, of which Festuca and Poa are especially well represented. Many of the conspicuous herbs previously mentioned are included in the numerous species of one of the following genera : Saxifraga, Potentilla, Ranunculus, Draba, Cerastium, Silene, Lychnis, Stellaria, Castilleja, and Pedicularis. Conspicuous and widespread species typical of tundra are *Oxyria digyna*, *Papaver* spp., *Dryas octopetala*, and *Epilobium latifolium*.

Alpine Tundra.—Mountains high enough to have a timber line support tundra, whose upward extent is limited by the snow line. In the east, as a consequence, tundra is found only on a few high peaks in New England. Farther south, the Appalachians are not of sufficient height to support tundra. That on Mt. Washington is representative of the type and is essentially similar to the not far distant arctic vegetation.

Alpine tundra in the western mountains mostly lies far to the south of the arctic and is consequently found at high altitudes only. In the Canadian mountains, it is found as low as 6,000 feet, but southward its altitudes grow progressively higher. In the Rocky Mountains of Colorado, it is well developed between 11,000 and 14,000 feet. In the Sierra Nevada, where many peaks are higher, the snow line is lower, and thus, tundra lies mostly between 10,500 and 13,000 feet.

When climate changed and terminated the glacial period, vegetation similar to modern tundra must have followed the ice as it receded northward. This left only these high peaks and ridges where tundra could survive as relicts. The relict vegetation obviously belongs to the Tundra Formation because of the growth form and the duplication of characteristic genera as well as many species. The greater importance of grasses and the presence of numerous endemics in the western mountains suggest that these Alpine tundras might be classed as associations of the Tundra Formation.

Boreal Forest Formation.—This great forest, often called "taiga" in its northern extent, spans the continent in a broad band to the south of the tundra. Along the Atlantic coast it extends from Newfoundland on the north to the New England states on the south. Westward, the southern boundary touches the Great Lakes region, trends northwestward across Saskatchewan and along the Rocky Mountains, and then to the Pacific coast in Alaska. The band is, therefore, narrowed abruptly in the far west although it extends much farther to the north there than it does over much of the continent.

Climate is scarcely less severe than that of the tundra. The short growing season from June through August is cool, and winters are very cold. Precipitation is moderate, averaging perhaps twenty inches, except on the east coast where it may be forty inches. The precipitation : evaporation ratio is, however, favorable because of the low temperatures. The topography is almost entirely that produced by glaciation. Lakes are scattered everywhere, and many of them have filled to form extensive bogs or muskegs. The mineral soils are either thin and residual, overlying the rock masses exposed by glaciation or, along the southern boundary, deep moraine and outwash. All are immature and often poorly drained. Subsoils, in the bogs especially, may not be frost-free even in midsummer.

Climax.—The climax forest of white spruce and balsam fir is best developed in and about the St. Lawrence river valley where the trees reach maximum size and grow in close stands under a variety of conditions. Here, and over much of the range, *Picea glauca* and *Abies balsamea* form dense stands under whose canopy there are relatively few dependent or secondary species. Paper birch *(Betula papyrifera)* is a constant associate although it is successional after fire or disturbance and often occurs as subclimax in pure stands. Characteristic tall shrubs are *Viburnum alnifolium* and *V. cassinoides*. Typical lesser plants on the shady forest floor are *Aster acuminatus, Dryopteris dilatata, Oxalis montana, Clintonia borealis, Cornus canadensis, Maianthemum canadense, Aralia nudicaulis, Coptis trifolia,* and *Chiogenes hispidula*.

With increasing distance from the St. Lawrence center, both westward and northward, the number of species declines. Balsam

FIG. 113.   Interior of boreal white spruce–balsam fir forest as it appears in northern Michigan.—*U. S. Forest Service.*

fir is completely absent along the northern boundary and in most of the western range of the type. Beyond the range of fir, the subclimax species, otherwise found in bogs or on burned areas, often appear with white spruce as climax. Along the northern transition tamarack *(Larix laricina)* may take an essentially climax position as does the black spruce *(Picea mariana)*, especially on high rocky ground. Both are bog species farther south. To the west, paper birch and jack pine *(Pinus banksiana)* have climax characteristics although both are definitely subclimax nearer the center.

Successions.—Primary succession occurs mainly on bare rock or in lakes.[70] The former is initiated by xerophytic mosses and lichens, which, after mat formation, lead to a heath mat stage. In the western part of the range, this is followed by the xerophytic jack pine, or black spruce to form a subclimax, but eastward white spruce–balsam fir may come in directly. Jack pine also occupies extensive areas of sand plains and gravelly soils.

FIG. 114.   Typical stand of jack pine *(Pinus banksiana)* on sand or gravel soils in northern Michigan.—*U. S. Forest Service.*

Bog succession is everywhere apparent in the many lakes that are filling up. The usual submerged and floating-leaved aquatics are commonly followed by sedges and grasses, which may form a floating mat upon which a bog-shrub stage develops. This may include *Chamaedaphne calyculata, Andromeda glaucophila, Alnus incana, Ledum groenlandicum,* and *Vaccinium* spp. Larch is the commonest tree to come in after shrubs, followed by black spruce or, in less acid bogs, sometimes *Thuja occidentalis.* Any of these species may maintain their dominance for long periods, but they can be superseded by climax.

Secondary succession is usually caused by fire. If the burn is so severe that all humus is consumed, leaving bare rock, primary succession may be repeated. If a dry peat bog burns, it usually fills with water again, and succession is reinstated at the aquatic stage. More often a burn results in pure stands of paper birch, which eventually give way to climax. Wind throw and lumbering of climax stands may also result in birch or aspen dominance but sometimes are followed directly by climax species.

FIG. 115.   Aspen stand *(Populus tremuloides)* at forty-five years of age in northern Minnesota. Its successional nature is clearly shown by the well-developed understory of spruce and fir.—*U. S. Forest Service.*

Transitions.—The northern border is abrupt, but the line is irregular depending upon topography. Forest extends far into the tundra in sheltered valleys, and tundra appears on the high ridges well within the forest area. Timber line seems to be advancing in Alaska, retreating in eastern Canada, and remaining more or less stable in the interior. The southern transition is to deciduous forest in the east and to grassland in the west. From New England to Minnesota, the transition is marked by pure stands of white pine *(Pinus strobus)*, a subclimax of long duration. In the lake states red pine *(P. resinosa)* and jack pine may also occupy similar positions on less favorable sites. Scattered individuals of white pine especially tend to persist well into the climax. Through much of the eastern transition, spruce, fir, and hardwoods may grow in mixture or in alternating stands. The transition to grassland in the Middle West is marked by aspen *(Populus tremuloides)*[175] in a band some fifty miles wide. In spite of fluctuations produced by fire, grazing, and drought, the trees persist and, in some instances, seem to have advanced into the grassland. In the west, along the Rockies, the subalpine *Abies lasiocarpa* is associated with *Picea*

FIG. 116.   Interior of red spruce–Fraser fir forest in the southern Appalachians. Compare with Fig. 113.—*U. S. Forest Service.*

glauca, and northward in Alaska there is a merging with the northwestern coastal forest.

Appalachian Extension.—On the higher mountains of the Appalachian system, the northern conifer forest extends as far south as the Great Smoky Mountains of North Carolina. The growth form and associated species are in every way similar to the main body of the formation, but, from New Brunswick southward into New England, red spruce *(Picea rubens)* tends increasingly to replace white spruce. Still farther south, Fraser fir *(Abies fraseri)* takes the place of balsam fir so that the dominants in the southern Appalachians are ecologically equivalent to those elsewhere in the formation but are taxonomically distinct. It seems reasonable to consider the Appalachian extension as a distinct association whose limits are marked by *Picea rubens.* A northern and southern faciation are suggested by the presence of *Abies balsamea* and *Betula papyrifera* in the north but the substitution for them in the south of *Abies fraseri* and *Betula lutea*.

The compensating effect of latitude is apparent in the altitudinal limits of the association, which increase southward. In the northern range of red spruce, it may be found anywhere, as is true of

FIG. 117.   Mixed hardwood forest in Indiana. Large trees are white oaks.— *U. S. Forest Service.*

fir. Southward, the approximate lower limit of spruce-fir forest on Mt. Katahdin is 500 feet; in the White Mountains, about 2,500 feet; in the Adirondack Mountains, 3,000 feet; in the Catskills, 3,500 feet; and in the Great Smoky Mountains, almost 5,000 feet.

Deciduous Forest Formation.—This formation occupies all of the eastern United States except southern Florida. Its northern transition to conifer forest extends into Canada along a line from northern Minnesota to Maine. On the west, forest gives way to grassland as precipitation : evaporation ratios become less favorable. The irregular line of transition runs northward from eastern Texas with thirty-five inches of precipitation, to central Minnesota where precipitation falls to twenty-five inches.

The great extent of the deciduous forest includes soils and topography of diverse nature and origin. The northern portion was

FIG. 118.   Sugar maples (160-200 years old) in beech-maple forest association, Pennsylvania.—*U. S. Forest Service.*

glaciated. There are mountains in the east. The great valleys of the Mississippi and Ohio Rivers are included as are the Piedmont Plateau and coastal plain of the Atlantic and Gulf coasts. Any and all kinds of topography as well as soil types are, therefore, represented.

Climate is temperate with distinct summer and winter, and all parts are subject to frost, one of the few environmental factors that applies throughout. Precipitation varies from sixty inches in the southern mountains to less than thirty inches northwestward, but it is everywhere fairly well distributed throughout the year. The ratio to evaporation is most favorable in the north, the east, and in the mountains and becomes decreasingly favorable approaching the transition to prairie.

The southern Appalachians represent the oldest exposed land surface in the region. Here the deciduous forest is more complex than in any other part. Practically all of the species found elsewhere in the deciduous forest are represented with several extra

FIG. 119.   Sugar maple–basswood forest, illustrating the climax for much of southern Wisconsin and Minnesota.—*U. S. Forest Service.*

species. Numerous endemics occur as associates. Most of the trees also attain their greatest size here. Away from the mountains, the number of species declines, and habitat requirements become of increasing importance. It is believed that a forest similar to the present one has existed here since Tertiary time. Such evidence is taken to mean that the southern Appalachians are a center of origin for much of the widespread deciduous forest. The distribution and nature of the several associations of the formation give additional supporting evidence. In general, with increasing distance from the center, the associations are made up of fewer species and yet all are bound together or interrelated by several species that range throughout.

Mixed Mesophytic Forest Association.—Throughout the Appalachian and Cumberland plateaus, the numerous species of this climax grow in varying combination. *Fagus grandifolia, Aesculus octandra, Magnolia acuminata, Tilia* spp., *Liriodendron tulipifera, Acer saccharum, Quercus alba,* and *Tsuga canadensis* are the most abundant trees, but there are twenty or twenty-five other species, any of which may have climax status. The differing sensitivity of

FIG. 120.   Seventy-year-old jack pine with a strong understory of balsam, indicating the trend that succession may take in the Lake States region.— *U. S. Forest Service.*

the species to minor variations in environment result in their occurrence in all kinds of combinations, which may be referred to as association-segregates.[32] The best indicators of the association are large trees of basswood *(Tilia heterophylla)* or buckeye *(Aesculus octandra).*

The association prevails in the Cumberland and southern Allegheny mountains and in the adjacent Cumberland and Allegheny plateaus.[33] Away from this center, there is a progressively increasing tendency toward restriction to the most favorable habitats. To the south, the association is seldom found except in the moist coves of the high Appalachians. To the west, southwest, and east it is found only in ravines and deep valleys. To the northwest, it is represented in southern Ohio by a mixed hardwood forest of far fewer species.

Beech-Maple Association.—The northward extension of the mixed mesophytic forest shows an increasing importance of beech

FIG. 121. Virgin white pine *(Pinus strobus)* forest in Connecticut, of the type that once occurred over wide areas in the northeast.—*U. S. Forest Service.*

(Fagus grandifolia) and sugar maple *(Acer saccharum)*. North of the boundary of Wisconsin glaciation, they are the climax species over an area west of the Alleghenies from New York to Ohio and up into Wisconsin.[31] Virgin forest in Michigan showed beech predominating over maple, and associates included red maple *(A. rubrum)*, elm *(Ulmus americana)*, red oak *(Quercus borealis* var. *maxima)* and black cherry *(Prunus serotina)*.[44] The original forests of southwest Michigan, as reconstructed from land survey records, were beech-maple on good sites and oak-hickory on coarse soils with poor moisture conditions.[139] This conforms with present conditions and can be interpreted as climax and preclimax.

Maple-Basswood Association.—The natural range of beech does not extend to the northwest limits of the deciduous formation. Beech is replaced in the climax by basswood *(Tilia americana)*, beginning in Wisconsin and continuing into Minnesota.[95] Otherwise the community is changed very little.

Hemlock-Hardwoods Association.—Between the northern coniferous forest and the deciduous forest lies a transitional association

FIG. 122.   Virgin hemlock *(Tsuga canadensis)* as it once occurred in the hemlock-hardwoods association of the northeast and in mountain coves southward.—*U. S. Forest Service.*

of which hemlock *(Tsuga canadensis)* is an important and constant member, together with beech and sugar maple, and, in lesser numbers, yellow birch *(Betula lutea)*, white pine, basswood, elm, white ash *(Fraxinus americana)*, red oak, and other species. The association, which extends from northwestern Minnesota through the Lake States to Nova Scotia, has been given various names by authorities with different points of view. It is the area throughout which occurred the magnificent pine forests of the recent past—

now mostly decimated by fire and lumbering. Where pine was dominant, *Pinus strobus* tended to occur on sites with more favorable moisture conditions than the sand plains and ridges occupied by *P. resinosa*. By some[268] these pure stands of pine are considered to be climax, but many more ecologists agree that the pines are successional species occupying inferior sites for long periods as

FIG. 123. The oak-chestnut forest that once occupied the lower slopes of much of the Appalachian system.—*U. S. Forest Service.*

subclimax. That white pine especially carries over into the hardwood climax[180] is undoubtedly true. Its long life and relatively low numbers suggest that these trees in the climax should be regarded as relics even though they can maintain their numbers by reproduction under openings appearing in the hardwood canopy.[161]

Postclimax forests of the northern conifers—tamarack, black spruce, white cedar *(Thuja occidentalis)*—occupy the many bogs throughout the area. The extensive areas denuded by lumbering and fire are today largely occupied by second-growth forests of aspen or pine.

Oak-Chestnut Association.—As the mixed mesophytic forest becomes restricted to special habitats to the east and southeast of its center, the slopes and uplands are occupied by what was, until recently, oak-chestnut forest. The almost complete elimination of chestnut *(Castanea dentata)* by blight has affected practically all of the original forest that extended along the mountains from southern New England to Georgia. Chestnut oak *(Quercus montana)* and scarlet oak *(Q. coccinea)* are important species today. Tulip poplar, red and white oaks, and some hickory are common

FIG. 124.   Savannah-like transition from deciduous forest to grassland. Bur oak predominates in these scrubby clumps of trees on the Anoka sand plain northwest of Minneapolis. Note blowout in sand dune in process of restabilization by *Hudsonia.—Photo by W. S. Cooper.*

associates. None of this association remains in its original state today, for the remnants untouched by extensive lumbering operations have been modified by the ravages of chestnut blight.

Pitch pine *(Pinus rigida)* is the important successional species throughout the range, but shortleaf and Virginia pine *(P. echinata, P. virginiana)* are increasingly noteworthy southward.

In its southern extent, the association is restricted to the mountains, occupying most of the favorable slopes. Northward it is found on progressively lower sites, occurring as far east as Long Island.[66] Through the foothills of the mountains, it grades into the oak-hickory climax of the bordering Piedmont Plateau.

Oak-Hickory Association.—In all directions from the deciduous forest center, except northward along the mountains, precipitation decreases and becomes less effective. This results in dominance by the drought-resistant oak-hickory association, which consequently occurs as a fringe around all the margin of the formation except toward the north. Oak-hickory climax ranges through much of the Piedmont Plateau and the Atlantic and Gulf states coastal plain in an arc that widens westward to eastern Texas. North from eastern Oklahoma it may become savannah-like where it grades into prairie, but it is more or less continuous to western Minnesota.

FIG. 125. Typical longleaf pine savannah (Georgia) as maintained by almost annual burning. Note that the only apparent ground cover is wire grass *(Aristida)*, which is an important factor in facilitating fire.—*U. S. Forest Service.*

Northwest of the Appalachian center, in unglaciated parts of Ohio and Indiana, oak and hickory occur in combination with numerous other species, forming a mixed mesophytic forest climax, which suggests, by its similarity, that the mixed mesophytic association may still be expanding its range. Throughout the association, various combinations of oak-hickory may occur as preclimax. Postclimax communities of mixed forest may be found within the oak-hickory area on sites, such as old flood plains, where moisture may be exceptionally favorable.[183] Beech, sugar maple, willow oak *(Quercus phellos)*, overcup oak *(Q. lyrata)*, swamp chestnut oak *(Q. prinus)*, and shagbark hickories are indicator species.

The dominants of oak-hickory forest are not the same through-out its extensive range, but several species occur consistently. *Quercus alba, Q. borealis maxima, Q. velutina, Q. stellata, Q. marilandica, Carya cordiformis, C. ovata, C. alba,* and *C. laciniosa* are species that may be found in the climax anywhere. Other oaks and hickories with more restricted ranges may be in association

FIG. 126.   Slash pine savannah after protection from fire for only a few years. With continued protection, the pine will soon form a closed stand with shrubs and hardwoods forming an understory.—*U. S. Forest Service.*

and produce local variations. Shingle oak *(Q. imbricaria)*, not so important in the east, should be added for the western forest from Arkansas and eastern Oklahoma[37] northward.[4] Bur oak *(Q. macrocarpa)* is the characteristic tree of the sometimes extensive sa-vannah-like transition from forest to grassland, as well as along the rivers in the prairie, from Texas to Minnesota. Constant sub-ordinate species are sourwood *(Oxydendrum arboreum)*, dog-wood *(Cornus florida)*, black gum *(Nyssa sylvatica)*, and sweet gum *(Liquidambar styraciflua)*.

Because of the amount of abandoned land throughout the east-ern and southern range of the association, old field succession is particularly noticeable, and subclimax pine stands are conspicuous (see Figs. 108 and 110). Virginia pine *(Pinus virginiana)* predominates in the northern Piedmont, but southward and westward shortleaf *(P. echinata)* and loblolly pine *(P. taeda)*, usually in pure stands, precede the climax in secondary succession on uplands. Successional trees in lowlands are sweet gum, tulip poplar *(Lirio-*

FIG. 127.   Scrubby, open oak forest (mostly *Q. catesbaei* and *Q. cinerea)* of the southeastern sandhills areas. The open stand and expanses of bare white sand are typical.—*Photo by H. L. Blomquist.*

dendron tulipifera), sycamore *(Platanus occidentalis)*, river birch *(Betula nigra)*, red maple, elms *(Ulmus* spp.), ash *(Fraxinus* spp.) and hackberry *(Celtis* spp.).

Fire and Swamp Subclimaxes of the Coastal Plain.—The coastal plain, once covered by the sea, extends from New Jersey down into Florida and along the Gulf to Texas as a low-lying, relatively level area, mostly overlayed with sandy soil. Drainage is poor, resulting in much swampy ground, but any raised area between streams is apt to be very dry for a part of each year. The height of the water table during the wet seasons and the amount of fire in dry seasons are fundamental factors in determining the nature of the vegetation.

From the pitch pine barrens of New Jersey through loblolly pine and longleaf and slash pine in the more southern states, fire maintains pine dominance, usually in open stands, called savannahs, with the highly combustible wire grass *(Aristida stricta)*, for ground cover. These stands owe their origin and maintenance to their resistance to fire.[53a] If protected from fire, they would unquestionably be replaced by oak-hickory dominated forest.[269] No extensive areas exist where fire has been excluded for more than a

FIG. 128.   Interior of a Florida hammock.

relatively few years. The successional evidence is clear enough, however, and pine in the coastal plain must therefore be classed as a fire-maintained subclimax within the oak-hickory association.

A possible preclimax is the scrub oak-hickory forest found on sand dunes near the coast and inland. Turkey oak *(Quercus catesbaei)*, margarete oak *(Q. margaretta)*, blue jack *(Q. cinerea)* and black jack oak *(Q. marilandica)* are dominants. Wire grass may be present, but often the sand is bare, glaring white in the sun, except for a few characteristic herbs. These include *Euphorbia ipecacuanhae, Jatropha stimulosa, Stipulicida setacea, Polygonella polygama* and *Selaginella acanthonota*.[272]

Undrained, shallow depressions in savannahs form upland bogs or pocosins, sometimes acres in extent, in which evergreen shrubs predominate. *Ilex glabra, Myrica cerifera, Cyrilla racemiflora,*

Fig. 129. Southern white cedar bog *(Chamaecyparis thyoides)* in New Jersey.—*U. S. Forest Service.*

Persea borbonia, P. pubescens, Magnolia virginiana, and *Gordonia lasianthus* are representative of the numerous tall shrubs or small trees. With them are usually a large number of ericaceous shrubs of smaller size. All are commonly overgrown with lianas, of which *Smilax laurifolia* is most abundant. The presence of *Pinus rigida serotina* in the bogs explains its name of pocosin pine. Sphagnum is the usual ground cover.

It is at the margins of pocosins and in wet savannahs in North Carolina that the venus fly trap *(Dionaea muscipula)* is found, sometimes in great abundance but never continuously over an extensive area. With it several other insectivorous plants may occur. Species of Sarracenia, Drosera, and Pinguicula are common.

The hammocks of Florida, in contrast with pocosins, are mesic habitats raised somewhat above surrounding wetter areas. Over much of Florida their dominants suggest postclimax to oak-hickory, but toward the southern tip of the state, the species are more and more subtropical.

Any shallow depression in the flatland of the lower coastal plain fills with water. Permanent standing water results in open

FIG. 130.   Maritime live oak forest *(Quercus virginiana)* on Smith's Island, N. C. Once characteristic of the banks and islands of the south Atlantic and Gulf Coast, much of it has been destroyed because of neglect. Note the dunes at right, which were once forested.—*Photo by C. F. Korstian.*

marshes,[198] sometimes miles in extent, dominated by rushes and grasses. If flooding is not continuous, subclimax swamp forests develop. Bald cypress *(Taxodium distichum)*, which dominates where water normally stands most of the year, occupies stream and lake margins or entire lakes to the exclusion of other trees. Gum swamps are usually flooded only seasonally. *Nyssa biflora* and *Nyssa aquatica* are the important species,[114] with ash *(Fraxinus profunda, F. caroliniana)*, bald cypress, and red maple as associates. The less the flooding, the greater the number of pocosin species that may be present.[16]

Still another forest of undrained areas is formed by *Chamaecyparis thyoides*, which occurs on peat bogs where it apparently becomes established only after fire occurs when the water table is high. Although the stands have subclimax characteristics, there is evidence that they may be succeeded by species characteristic of pocosins.[38] These valuable trees have been cut so systematically that they remain only as small sample stands or in relatively inaccessible places.[145]

Perhaps the most extensive bog and swamp forests still remaining in virgin condition are to be found in parts of the Dismal Swamp in Virginia and in the Okefenokee Swamp in Georgia.

The plant communities of the banks[155] and islands[197] along the coast, as well as a narrow fringe of the coast itself, are distinctive enough to merit more discussion than can be given them here. The effects of salt spray on vegetation were considered earlier. (p.102.) Live oak *(Quercus virginiana)* is the most important tree of the forested areas, and the associated shrubs include *Myrica cerifera, Ilex vomitoria, Batodendron arboreum*, and several others, mostly evergreens.[199, 271] Thus, this maritime climax forest is an evergreen variant of the oak-hickory association.

Rocky Mountain Forest Complex.—Changes of environmental factors with altitude and the resulting zonation of vegetation on mountains have been discussed earlier (see Fig. 66 and related text). The great height of the Rocky Mountains provides conditions for a discontinuous alpine zone on the peaks, a subalpine zone, a montane zone, and a zone of woodland forest, which grades into the surrounding desert or grassland. These zones are recognizable by their distinctive climax vegetation over an area extending latitudinally from northern Alberta to the southern end of the Sierra Madre of northern Mexico and from the Black Hills of South Dakota on the east to the eastern foothills of the Sierra Nevada and the eastern slopes of the Cascades on the west.

Climaxes with so great an areal extent would be expected to vary somewhat in different parts of their ranges, especially as to associated species. The zones are not always continuous, nor are they always all present. Near the northern limits of the area, the lower zones run out and the upper zones are found at relatively low altitudes. Southward all zones are, of course, found at successively higher altitudes. Because the prevailing winds are from the west and carry with them oceanic climatic influences, the entire eastern slope of the Rocky Mountain system has different growing conditions from those of the west slope and, accordingly, differences in vegetation. Within the system, the individual ranges likewise have similar east-west slope differences. North and south exposures produce marked irregularities in zonation. Narrow valleys permit the dominants of one zone to extend downward into a lower zone, and high dry ridges allow upward, fingerlike projections of dominants into continuous higher zones. Cold air drainage locally causes marked disruption of the zonal pattern.

The factors operative in producing and controlling vegetation and its zonation in the Rockies have been studied in a number of localities just as there have been many local studies of the vegetation. An unusually complete review and synthesis of all these investigations is available[85] with an extensive bibliography. What follows is largely an adaptation from this report.

Vegetation Zones.—The zonal climaxes may be grouped as follows :

> Alpine Zone
>   Tundra Climax (discussed earlier—p. 239-240)
> Subalpine Zone
>   Engelmann spruce—Alpine fir climax
> Montane Zone
>   Douglas fir climax
>   Ponderosa pine climax
> Foothills (Woodland) Zone
>   Piñon-Juniper climax
>   Oak–Mountain mahogany climax

Each of these types of vegetation extends over an altitudinal range of about two thousand feet, where fully developed, and is a true climax. The foothill zones narrow down and disappear entirely in the north where the upper zones are found at progressively lower altitudes.

Near the upper and lower limits of a zone, the characteristic species are more and more restricted to special habitats. Upward, the climax species do best on south-facing slopes, which are warmer and drier than the general climate. Thus, in its upper transition area, each association shows its preclimax relationship to the climax of the next higher zone. At its lower limits, the association tends to be restricted to moist and cool sites and extends into the next lower zone only in such habitats. It, therefore, holds a postclimax relationship to the climax below. Subalpine and alpine zones tend to be drier and colder than the zones below, and, consequently, preclimax and postclimax relationships may be reversed above the montane zone.

FIG. 131.   Virgin Engelmann spruce *(Picea engelmanni)*, with some alpine fir *(Abies lasiocarpa)* of the subalpine zone in Colorado.—*U.S. Forest Service.*

Subalpine Spruce-Fir Climax.—From timber line downward for about two thousand feet, the climax forest is made up largely of Engelmann spruce *(Picea engelmannii)* and alpine fir *(Abies lasiocarpa)*, which grow in dense stands. The spruce is the larger and more abundant tree. In Arizona, New Mexico, and southward, *Abies lasiocarpa* var. *arizonica* is as important as *A. lasiocarpa*. In Montana and northern Idaho, mountain hemlock *(Tsuga mertensiana)* is often found in the zone, and still farther north, approaching the merging with northern conifer forest, *Picea glauca* and *A. lasiocarpa* may grow in association.

Subordinate species vary far more than do the dominants. On the relatively dry eastern slope of the central Rockies, ground cover is sparse and made up largely of dwarf Vacciniums, while the moister west slope has an abundance of bryophytes and herbs. Northward, the bryophytes increase until they practically cover the ground, and the vascular plants, both herbs and shrubs, also increase.

The most conspicuous succession in the subalpine zone follows fire and may result in subclimax stands of lodgepole pine *(Pinus*

FIG. 132.   Dense aspen stand *(Populus tremuloides)* that came in after fire in the subalpine zone in New Mexico. Spruce reproduction underneath.— *U. S. Forest Service.*

contorta var. *murrayana)*, aspen *(Populus tremuloides)*, or Douglas fir *(Pseudotsuga taxifolia)*. Progression to climax is extremely slow. Lodgepole pine is absent in the southern Rockies, but elsewhere aspen is favored over the pine on moist sites, and after light fires it has an advantage, probably because of its ability to regenerate from sprouts. Near timber line, burned areas are revegetated directly by climax.

The transition from subalpine forest to alpine tundra is usually gradual with a thinning out of trees, which here commonly have the dwarfed and distorted form known as *Krummholz*. Characteristic of timber line are several trees that cannot survive in the tundra above and cannot compete with climax species below, where they are only found on dry and windswept ridges. Foxtail

FIG. 133.   Foxtail pine *(Pinus aristata) Krummholz* at timber line of the subalpine zone in Colorado.—*U. S. Forest Service.*

pine *(Pinus aristata)* occupies this position in the southern Rockies, limber pine *(P. flexilis)* in the central Rockies, whitebark pine *(P. albicaulis)*, and alpine larch *(Larix lyallii)* in the northern Rockies, except in the far north where lodgepole pine occurs at timber line.

Douglas Fir Climax.—Below the subalpine zone, Douglas fir *(Pseudotsuga taxifolia)* is the climax dominant, growing in such dense stands that subordinate species are negligible. As in the subalpine zone, climax associates differ in the north and south. In the central and southern Rockies, white fir *(Abies concolor)* and blue spruce *(Picea pungens)* are found in relatively small numbers and mostly on moist sites. In the north, grand fir *(Abies grandis)* is an associate west of the continental divide and principally on west slopes. East of the divide, *Picea glauca* of the northern conifer

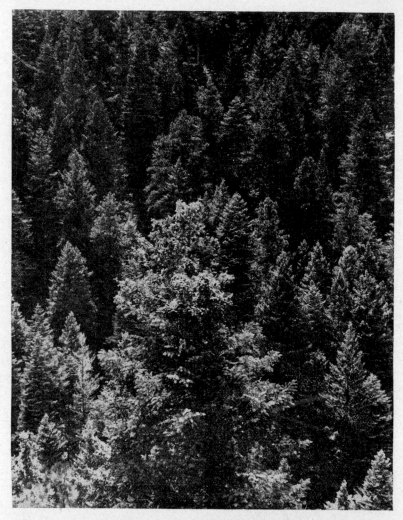

FIG. 134.   Montane zone climax forest of Douglas fir *(Pseudotsuga taxifolia)* and white fir *(Abies concolor)* in Colorado.—*U. S. Forest Service.*

forest shares dominance with Douglas fir and extends southward through the montane zone as far as the Black Hills.

Dry, exposed ridges in both the montane and subalpine zones support open stands of pine, including several species characteristic of timber line. *Pinus strobiformis* is important in the south. *P. aristata* occurs in northern Arizona and southern Utah and Colorado, while *P. flexilis* is more common northward to where *P. albicaulis* takes over in the northern Rockies.

Fire in the Douglas fir climax results in the establishment of lodgepole pine or aspen stands, which bear the same relationships here as in the subalpine zone.

Ponderosa Pine Climax.—Below the Douglas fir is a belt in which *Pinus ponderosa* or a close relative forms a relatively open climax forest that becomes savannah-like with decreasing altitude. The widely spaced trees form little shade so that the ground cover is made up of grasses, among which numerous species of *Festuca*, *Agropyron*, *Poa*, and *Muhlenbergia* are important. Between the zone of Douglas fir and the drier, lower altitudes with pure stands of ponderosa pine is a fairly broad transition where the two trees may share dominance.

Although the climax is termed ponderosa pine, the species is dominant only in the northern Rockies to the west of the continental divide. Elsewhere it is replaced by or in association with closely related varieties whose ecological characteristics are similar. *Pinus ponderosa* var. *scopulorum* is the important tree on the east slope in the north and throughout the zone southward. In the

FIG. 135.   Subclimax stand of lodgepole pine in Montana.—*U. S. Forest Service.*

southern Rockies, the substitutes are *P. ponderosa* var. *arizonica*, *P. leiophylla*, and *P. contorta* var. *latifolia*.

The only exceptions to ponderosa pine dominance are found along streams and drainage lines where narrow-leaved cottonwood

FIG. 136. Climax forest of ponderosa pine *(Pinus ponderosa)* in typical open stand. Montane zone, Arizona.—*U. S. Forest Service.*

(Populus angustifolia), the commonest tree, forms postclimax stands with *P. acuminata* and *P. sargentii* in association. Aspen *(P. tremuloides)*, in glades, and box elder may also occur frequently on these moist sites. Although fires are common, in dry summers,

favored by the grasses of the forest floor, they are rarely severe enough to kill the fire-resistant older trees. That pine seedlings are destroyed is indicated by the even-aged groups of saplings, each of which can be related to a series of summers that were free of fire. Severe fires in the upper part of the ponderosa pine zone may be followed by stands of lodgepole pine. Lumbering and over-grazing often result in the development of a dense scrub made up of species from the oak–mountain mahogany zone.

FIG. 137.   Characteristic open stand of piñon-juniper, and the transition from sagebrush desert.—*U. S. Forest Service.*

Piñon-Juniper Climax.—This open forest of widely spaced, small trees (ten to thirty feet) forms the lowest coniferous zone in the Rockies and, on many of the low ranges of the Great Basin, represents the only zone present. It is, therefore, typical of the inter-mountain region as well as forming a distinct zone in the southern Rockies. Although it is fairly constant in appearance and charac-teristics over its wide range and extensive acreage, several species with restricted ranges are involved. The junipers include *Juniperus scopulorum, J. monosperma, J. utahensis, J. occidentalis, J. pachy-phloea, J. mexicana,* and others, and the piñons, or nut pines, are varieties of *Pinus cembroides (edulis, monophylla, parryana).*

The type extends from northern Mexico along the west slope of the Rockies to the Snake River in Idaho, beyond which it con-tinues into southern Alberta with piñon replaced by limber pine. Along the east slope, its northern limit is in Colorado although it is represented northward through Wyoming by *Juniperus scop-*

ulorum, often with sagebrush in association. Piñon-juniper is completely lacking in Sierran zonation, which goes directly from *Artemisia* and *Purshia* to *Pinus ponderosa*. However, almost without exception, it occurs on every westernmost range and mountain of the Great Basin, often lying just across a valley from the base of the Sierra.

FIG. 138.   An example of the scrub oak–mountain mahogany zone in the foothills near Colorado Springs, Colo. *Quercus gambellii* predominates here with *Cercocarpus parvifolius* and *Rosa arkansas* as associates. Although the scrub is sometimes taller, its open, irregular distribution is typical.—*Photo by R. B. Livingston.*

The openings between trees support a grass cover *(Bouteloua, Stipa, Agropyron, Poa)* and numerous other herbs, together with a few shrubs *(Ceanothus, Cercocarpus, Purshia, Cowania, Artemisia, Opuntia)* characteristic of the next lower zone. Overgrazing or fire may result in the temporary dominance of these shrubs.

Oak–Mountain Mahogany Climax.—The transition from the conifer forest of the lower slopes to the treeless plains and plateaus may be marked by a zone of broad-leaved scrub. The zone is widest and best developed in the southern Rockies, narrows and becomes discontinuous in the central Rockies, and fades out entirely farther north. The components of the community vary, but oaks *(Quercus gambellii, Q. gunnisoni, Q. undulata, Q. fendleri, Q. emoryi,* and others) are the largest (up to thirty-five feet) and most conspicuous dominants in the south. North of the latitude of Denver, Colorado, the oaks are spottily represented, and mountain mahogany *(Cercocarpus parvifolius, C. ledifolius,* etc.) is dominant. Other important associates include *Rhus triloba, Purshia tridentata, Fallugia paradoxa, Amelanchier* spp., and *Symphoricarpos* spp., any of which may assume local dominance. The vegetation does not form a continuous cover but occurs in dense clumps, or even as individual plants, separated by areas of grassland or desert vegetation.

The Black Hills.—Although they are now isolated, the Black Hills are geologically and ecologically related to the Rockies. They deserve especial mention because of their mixture of eastern, western, and northern species. Because the altitude is only a little over seven thousand feet, the montane zone is chiefly represented. There is no Douglas fir present. Instead, *Picea glauca,* which extends southward from Canada along the east slope of the Rockies as an associate of Douglas fir, here is the only dominant on the high slopes at the southern limit of its range. Paper birch from the northern conifer forest is also present. Ponderosa pine dominates most of the lower slopes, which include most of the area, and lodgepole and limber pine in small numbers are additional representatives from the Rockies. Species from the eastern deciduous forest are ash, hackberry, elm, birch, and bur oak, of which only the last attains any size. The scrubby appearance of the community, as well as its distribution along the lower margin of the conifer forest, suggests the oak-mahogany zone of the Rockies.[85]

Sierra Nevada Forest Complex.—The area here considered includes the southern portion of the Cascade Mountains and the Sierra Nevada, which together extend from Oregon southward along the eastern boundary of California as the innermost ranges of the coastal mountain system. The long west slope of the Sierra rises gradually to altitudes of 14,000 feet and more, but the east slope drops abruptly to the floor of the Great Basin, which lies at about 4,000 feet. At the base of the west slope, there are only ten to fifteen inches of rainfall and a long, unbroken, dry summer season. Upward precipitation increases, temperatures decrease, the dry summer season shortens, and a larger proportion of precipitation falls as snow.

FIG. 139. Interior of the red fir *(Abies magnifica)* forest that occupies most of the subalpine zone of the Sierra Nevada.

Because the general north-south axis of the range lies across the path of the prevailing westerly winds, climatic conditions for the region as a whole are influenced by them and east slopes are much drier than west slopes. Winter precipitation makes up 80-85 percent of the total, and at high elevations, most of the moisture falls as snow (thirty-five to seventy feet in the subalpine zone). The greatest total precipitation occurs in the middle slopes, between 5,000 and 7,000 feet, which support the luxuriant mixed coniferous forest of the montane zone. The subalpine zone coincides with the altitudes of greatest snowfall, where precipitation equals about forty to fifty inches a year.

FIG. 140. Lodgepole pine at 8,800 feet in the subalpine zone, Carson Range of the Sierra Nevada.—*Photo by courtesy of the Agricultural Extension Service, Univ. of Nevada.*

Subalpine Zone.—This zone extends through an altitudinal range of little more than 1,000 feet, its limits, varying with latitude, being between 6,500 and 9,500 feet. The climate may be described as cool, winter-wet, summer-dry, with a short growing season.

Red fir *(Abies magnifica)* is the important climax species, growing in dense stands and making up 80-90 percent of the forest.[189] Of the associated species, none is an important component of the climax. Although western white pine *(Pinus monticola)* is constantly present in small numbers, it is only a minor constituent. Lodgepole pine *(Pinus contorta)* is often present, especially in wet meadows, but its role is primarily successional. Mountain hemlock *(Tsuga mertensiana)* and white fir *(Abies concolor)* occur in an extremely irregular fashion. Of the shrubs, which are few, *Ribes viscosissimum* and *Symphoricarpos rotundifolius* are the most

FIG. 141.   Virgin forest in the Sierran montane zone of California, in this instance made up of sugar pine *(Pinus lambertiana)*, ponderosa pine *(P. ponderosa)*, and white fir *(Abies concolor)*.—U. S. Forest Service.

abundant and most constantly represented. The herb flora is also sparse. Constant species are *Chrysopsis breweri, Pedicularis semibarbata, Gayophytum ramosissimum, Pirola picta* and *Monardella odoratissima*. The yellow-green lichen *(Evernia vulpina)* is conspicuously present on the trees throughout the zone.

Although the altitudes in the Sierra are often greater than those of the Rockies, conditions are severe and timber line is lower, varying from about 7,000 feet in the north to some 10,000 feet in southern California. The characteristic trees are *Pinus albicaulis,*

P. flexilis, and *P. balfouriana.*[241] On exposed, bare, rocky slopes, *Juniperus occidentalis* is common at timber line and, especially on the west slope, at much lower altitudes.

The upper margin of the red fir forest does not commonly extend to timber line but, instead, grades into a relatively narrow

FIG. 142.   Giant redwoods *(Sequoia gigantea)* of the Calaveras grove, Sequoia, Calif.—*U. S. Forest Service.*

zone of *Pinus contorta–Tsuga mertensiana* dominance. Although
P. contorta is successional to *Abies magnifica* at lower altitudes, it,
with hemlock, has climax characteristics in this zone. This would
suggest three faciations for the subalpine zone, namely, white bark
pine or timber line faciation, lodgepole pine–hemlock through the
upper part of the zone, and red fir, which, from the lower margin
upward, occupies the major part of the zone.

Montane Zone.—The altitudinal range of this zone lies between
about 2,000-6,000 feet in the Cascades, 4,000-7,000 feet in the central Sierra, and 5,000-8,000 feet or more in the south. Five or six
principal species have climax characteristics and may appear in
any combination at any altitude. However, the upper and lower
parts of the zone tend to have consistent vegetational differences.[69, 144] White fir *(Abies concolor)* is usually the important
dominant in the upper part of the zone, sometimes in pure stands,
and decreases markedly at lower elevations. Lower down, incense
cedar *(Libocedrus decurrens)*, predominating on the most favorable sites, sugar pine *(P. lambertiana)*, Jeffrey pine *(P. jeffreyi)*,
ponderosa pine, and Douglas fir are the species of importance.
Douglas fir is more abundant in the north than in the south.[151]
Sugar pine and Jeffrey pine are more conspicuous than ponderosa
pine at the upper altitudes, a logical arrangement since the latter
is the most drought-resistant of the major species.

Fire subclimaxes are formed by *Pinus attenuata*, *P. muricata*, and
P. radiata in different parts of the range[268] although preceded by
dense chaparral communities of species of *Arctostaphylos*, *Ceanothus*, *Rhamnus*, etc., which may last for years.

Included in the montane zone, on the western slope, are the forests of giant redwood *(Sequoia gigantea)*, at altitudes of 4,500-
6,000 feet. Once widespread, they now occur only southward
from the latitude of San Francisco in a disrupted zone. Their present best development is in the southern Sierra where they reproduce but do not spread. Sugar pine, ponderosa pine, and incense
cedar are common associates.

Foothills (Woodland) Zone.—As in the Rockies, the vegetation
of the lower slopes and foothills is made up of coniferous and
scrub associations, but they are not as sharply separated here. The
zone ranges between about 1,500 and 4,000 feet. In the upper part,

digger pine *(P. sabiniana)* and blue oak *(Q. douglasii)* are the dominants, forming typical open, or woodland, stands. The lower altitudes are characteristically covered with close-growing, evergreen scrub, or chaparral, in which *Ceanothus* spp. and *Arctostaphylos* spp. predominate. Common associates are several scrub oaks *(Q. wislizeni, Q. chrysolepis, Q. dumosa), Aesculus califor-*

FIG. 143.   Characteristic open oak woodland of the Sierran foothills. Sequoia National Forest, Calif.—*U. S. Forest Service.*

nica, Rhamnus californica, and numerous other species are represented.

East Slope.—Although the same zones are present on both the west and east slopes, many of the generalizations made above must be qualified for the east slope because of its less favorable conditions. The red fir forest occurs only in restricted areas on the east slope, such as in the Carson Range east of Lake Tahoe and locally in the northern Sierra. The subalpine zone is represented, therefore, largely by the timber-line pines and patches of lodgepole pine. The montane and foothill zones extend to high altitudes, and the vegetation is poorly developed. *Pinus jeffreyi* is the important species of the montane zone in which the open forest has little resemblance to that of the west slope. The woodland forest is practically absent. Although piñon-juniper occurs as a major zone on the next ranges across the valley, it is not found on the east slope of the Sierra except where an occasional high spur extends eastward. The scrub zone is sometimes made up of oak and mountain mahogany as in the Rockies, but is more often represented by species from the desert below (*Artemisia, Purshia, Chrysothamnus*, etc.), which, especially on areas of disturbance or fire, may be found high up in the montane zone as well as on the lower slopes.

Pacific Conifer Forest.—This area parallels the coast from northern tree limits in Alaska southward to central California. Coastal mountain ranges with varying altitudes are included throughout its length. The climate, tempered by the Pacific Ocean, is mild and without extremes. Although Alaskan winters are cold, subzero temperatures are uncommon along the coast. Southward, temperatures are progressively less severe until, in Oregon and California, frosts are rare. Precipitation is adequate to heavy (30 to 150 inches), and the humidity is always high, producing an extremely favorable P/E ratio. The southern part is winter-wet with no snow; here fog compensates for the summer drought. Northward, the summer dry season shortens until, in Alaska, there is none. Northward, too, there is an increase in the proportion of precipitation falling as snow. In the higher mountains, it may be entirely snow with falls as great as sixty to sixty-five feet a year.

The coastal forest is primarily montane in character, although ranging from sea level to altitudes of 5,000 feet. Only in the United States, as in the Cascades, and for a short distance into British Columbia does it include a subalpine forest. Here it is well developed, but the dominants are derived from the Rockies (*Abies lasiocarpa*), the Sierra (*Tsuga mertensiana*), as well as the coastal forest (*Abies amabilis, A. nobilis*). Northward, the zone becomes fragmentary or disappears entirely.

Species of the coastal forest are most fully represented in the general vicinity of Puget Sound, and the best development of the forest is indicated by the luxuriant vegetation of the Olympic Peninsula. Here the ranges of all the major species overlap and most of the trees attain their maximum size. The climax dominants

FIG. 144. Douglas fir *(Pseudotsuga)* and western arborvitae *(Thuja plicata)* in the coastal montane forest. Snoqualmie National Forest, Wash.— *U. S. Forest Service.*

are western hemlock *(Tsuga heterophylla)*, arborvitae *(Thuja plicata)*, and grand fir *(Abies grandis)*. Subordinate broad-leaved species and many herbaceous species are associated in abundance.[133] Douglas fir, which reaches its greatest size here, is the most abundant and widespread species, but it occupies drier sites, is relatively

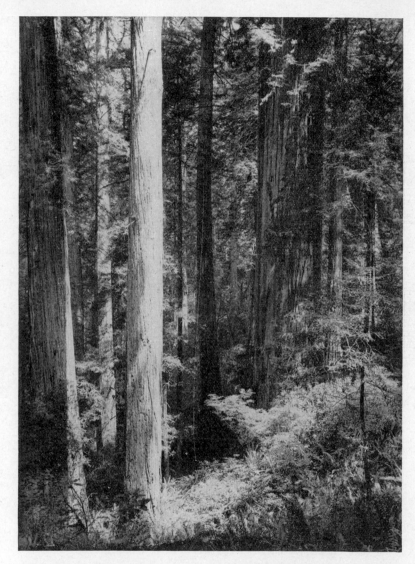

FIG. 145. Pacific coastal forest in California showing redwood *(Sequoia sempervirens)* predominating and Douglas fir in association. Conspicuous subordinate species are *Lithocarpus densiflora, Rhododendron californicum, Gaultheria shallon, Vaccinium* spp., *Polystichum* sp.—*U. S. Forest Service.*

intolerant of shade, and is the major dominant after fire. It is, therefore, subclimax in nature.[124]

To the north of the Puget Sound region, Sitka spruce *(Picea sitchensis)* becomes increasingly important as the forest becomes more closely associated with coastal conditions. Although it has subclimax characteristics near its southern limits, Sitka spruce becomes, with *Tsuga heterophylla* and *T. mertensiana*, an important climax dominant in the northern extension of the forest.[75] At its extreme limit in Alaska, the coastal and boreal forests meet and both *P. sitchensis* and *P. glauca* are found at timber line advancing into the tundra.[110]

Southward, the important species of the Puget Sound center

FIG. 146. Successional community of western white pine *(Pinus monticola)* and western larch *(Larix occidentalis)* in Idaho. Understory of *Thuja plicata* and *Tsuga heterophylla.—U. S. Forest Service.*

extend down the low coastal mountains into Oregon with Port Orford cedar *(Chamaecyparis lawsoniana)* as an added climax species and Douglas fir of relatively greater importance.[195] Along the coast, however, Sitka spruce is replaced by redwood *(Sequoia sempervirens)*, which, in pure stands, closely follows the limits of the fog belt[71] to below San Francisco and fades out southward.

If the ranges of the principal species of the Puget Sound area are mapped, they appear in the form of a peninsula extending eastward across northern Washington and southern British Columbia and expanding north and south on the west slope of the Rockies.[85] The coastal dominants extending into this area are *Tsuga heterophylla, Thuja plicata*, and *Pseudotsuga*, which occupy a zonal position between the normal Douglas fir and spruce-fir zones of the Rockies. Although the importance of hemlock and arborvitae decreases eastward and Douglas fir increases, the zone remains distinctive largely because of the species peculiar to the forests developing after fire. The two principal successional trees are western larch *(Larix occidentalis)*, which is endemic to the peninsula area, and western white pine *(Pinus monticola)*, which grows more abundantly here than anywhere else. The presence of *Abies grandis* in association with these species is another indication of coastal affinity.

Daubenmire[85] points out that this eastward overflow of coastal species marks an area in which steady winds blow inland from the coast, following a well-developed storm track, and thereby extend the coastal climate far inland. This theory is supported by the superior development of the coastal species in the peninsula on westward slopes at intermediate altitudes and their occurrence in the Rockies only in the storm path and west of the continental divide.

Broad-Sclerophyll Formation.—As the name indicates, major species in both associations of this formation have thick, hard, evergreen leaves. One climax is dominated by trees and termed *broad-sclerophyll forest*. The other is a shrub climax called *chaparral*. Both reach their best development on the coastal ranges of southern California, but their ranges extend from southern Oregon southward through the coast mountains, as well as through the Sierra Nevada foothills, into Lower California. Several of the species are found on the east slopes of the Sierra, and some appear in the desert woodland zone on the lower slopes of the Rocky Mountains.

The climate of the sclerophyll region is mild-temperate to subtropical with long, dry summers and heavy winter rainfall. Total precipitation is not less than ten or more than thirty inches, and, of this amount, no more than 20 percent falls in summer. In this area, desert vegetation appears where precipitation is less than ten inches, and, if it is over thirty inches, conifer forest is dominant.[72]

The two climaxes may be found in alternating patches in almost any part of their more or less coinciding ranges. However, chaparral occupies the greatest area and is climax in the south where it

FIG. 147. Broad sclerophyll forest *(Quercus agrifolia, Arbutus,* etc.) on north-facing slope (foreground and right). Chaparral on south-facing slope (left). Santa Lucia Mountains, Calif.—*Photo by W. S. Cooper.*

grades into desert, and sclerophyll forest is climax in the north and at the margin of montane conifer forest where its variations may be a part of the woodland zone. Where found together, the two communities bear no successional relationship to each other. The forest consistently appears on north slopes and the better sites, chaparral on south slopes and drier sites. The forest is postclimax in the south, and chaparral is preclimax in the north.

Sclerophyll Forest.—The important evergreen forest trees are *Quercus agrifolia, Q. chrysolepis, Q. wislizeni, Lithocarpus densiflora, Umbellularia californica, Arbutus menziesii, Castanopsis chrysophylla,* and *Myrica californica.* Several deciduous trees are almost as characteristic, as are a number of shrub and herb associates. The dominants may occur in various combinations related to altitude and exposure.

Chaparral.—This community extends its dominance over a wide area and a diversity of habitats, and its composition is proportionately diverse. It includes at least forty species of evergreen shrubs with varying degrees of dominance and importance, which may occur in many combinations but which invariably form low, dense

FIG. 148. Chaparral in the Santa Lucia Mountains, Calif. Smooth cover at top, mostly *Adenostoma*. Light-colored shrubs in shallow ravine at left, *Arctostaphylos glauca*. Grades into broad-sclerophyll forest in deep ravine at right.—*Photo by W. S. Cooper.*

thickets. The most important and constant species is chamiso (*Adenostoma fasciculatum*). The numerous species of manzanita (*Arctostaphylos*) are scarcely less characteristic, and of these *A. tomentosa* is the widest ranging. Others with high constancy are *Heteromeles árbutifolia, Ceanothus cuneatus* (9 other spp.), *Quercus dumosa,* and *Cercocarpus betulaefolius.*

Fires.—The long, dry summers and the nature of sclerophyllous vegetation make frequent fires the rule. A study in the Santa Monica mountains showed that chaparral stems were mostly about twenty-five years of age, and a stand without fire for fifty years was considered old. An ordinary fire causes chaparral to sprout profusely, and then, come back to normal within ten years.[12] Fire usually favors the extension of chaparral at the expense of sclerophyll forest. Too frequent fires, however, may cause the death of chaparral and its replacement by grassland. Undoubtedly, the orig-

inal extent of sclerophyll dominance has been much reduced by
fire, since, once they are destroyed, the return of the sclerophyll
species is long delayed.

Desert Formations.—The major area of the North American
desert extends from southeastern Oregon and southern Idaho
southward through the Great Basin, including most of Nevada
and Utah except high elevations, continues southward into southern California and western Arizona, down most of the peninsula
of Lower California and, on the mainland, through Sonora as far
south as the Yaqui River. The highlands of eastern Arizona and
western New Mexico interrupt the continuity of desert, but from
south-central New Mexico, there is almost continuous desert
through eastern Chihuahua and most of Coahuila in Mexico.[238]

In spite of the great extent of this area, there are certain environmental features characteristic throughout. Precipitation is low and
erratic; temperatures of air and soil are extremely high by day and
drop abruptly at night; atmospheric humidity is usually low, and
bright sunny days are the rule. These factors serve to explain why
predominating plants are those that can survive desiccation without injury or that store water in their succulent tissues. This is not
to imply that desert vegetation is uniformly similar throughout.
Climatic differences, associated with latitude and altitude, are accompanied by differences in species and life forms. Locally, the
physical differences in topography, exposure, and soils produce
distinct vegetational variations just as in moister climates. Finally,
there are numerous undrained depressions into which the water of
winter rains flows and, upon evaporation, deposits the silts and
clays it has transported as well as salts of various kinds. The resulting mud flats (playas) in themselves constitute a special habitat
with associated species, but the nature and concentration of salts
in the soil is even more effective in controlling the communities
there.

Four desert areas are distinguishable on the basis of regional environments and, likewise, by the nature and importance of the
major dominants :[238] namely, the Great Basin, Mojave, Sonoran,
and Chihuahua deserts. In each of these areas there are communities that occur with minor variations wherever conditions are not
extreme. These may be recognized as climax. Other communities,

which seem equally permanent, are found only in special habitats. Succession, as ordinarily conceived, is almost nonexistent since reaction of the vegetation is negligible. Unless there is marked disturbance, most communities remain indefinitely unchanged and dominant in their special habitats. It seems best, therefore, to present the characteristics distinguishing the four deserts and to indicate the dominant vegetation in different habitats with less than the usual emphasis upon climax or its relationships. What follows

FIG. 149. Sagebrush desert (*Artemisia tridentata*) northwest of Reno, Nev.—*Photo by W. D. Billings.*

is adapted almost entirely from Shreve's[238] excellent summary of desert vegetation except for the distinction made here between Sagebrush and Desert Scrub Formations.

Sagebrush Formation.—Great Basin Desert.—There is physiographic, climatologic, and vegetational unity throughout all the Great Basin area north of southern Nevada and southern Utah. The wide valley floors, lying at about 4,000 feet, are interrupted by numerous ridges, often rising to more than 8,000 feet, and depressions of the playa type. The meager rainfall, four to eight inches, is heaviest in spring but may come in any season. Temperatures are not as high as farther south, and frosts are common. The combination of lower temperatures, lower evaporation rates, and better distribution of rainfall explains the use of the term, "semi-desert," for the area. Likewise distinctive is the growth form of the dominants, made up largely of shrubby chenopods and composites, which further supports the desirability of its recognition as a formation distinct from the scrub of the southern desert.

FIG. 150. Typical dry desert expanse with shadscale *(Atriplex conferti-folia)* dominance. Mineral County, Nev. Characteristic gravelly desert pavement shows here.—*Photo by W. D. Billings.*

The two major communities are simple, with few dominants in each, and often extend uninterrupted for miles. The sagebrush association is dominated by *Artemisia tridentata* (common sagebrush), which is climax in the northern portion of the Great Basin or at relatively high altitudes. The shadscale association, with shadscale *(Atriplex confertifolia)* and bud sage *(Artemisia spinescens)* as its important species, ranges through the south and at low altitudes. In its northern and eastern distribution, shadscale is found on heavy lowland soils containing some alkali, but, to the south, it is climax on gray desert soils with a shallow carbonate layer and regardless of salts. Sagebrush tends to occur on brown soil, either sandy or clayey, with the carbonate layer at a deeper level and with a minimum concentration of salts.[21]

The controlling effect of salts on community structure has been amply demonstrated for different parts of the area.[21, 98, 134] Zonal patterns around playa lakes are the same everywhere (see Fig. 86). Where flooding is periodic and salt content excessive, vegetation

FIG. 151.   Creosote bush *(Larrea divaricata)* with *Franseria dumosa* in association as is typical of much of the Mojave Desert. Numerous desert annuals can be seen.—*Photo by W. D. Billings.*

is absent or dominated by glasswort *(Salicornia* spp.) or iodine bush *(Allenrolfea occidentalis).* With somewhat less salt, shadscale and greasewood *(Sarcobatus vermiculatus)* or red sage *(Kochia vestita)* are dominant. Away from the playas on soils with a minimum of salts, sagebrush may be the major species.

Many other species occur, of course. They are mostly semi-shrubs with the same growth form. There are numerous species of *Atriplex* and *Artemisia. Chrysothamnus puberulus, Grayia spinosa, Coleogyne ramosissima, Eurotia lanata, Purshia tridentata,* and others are variously associated with the major species or sometimes assume dominance under local special conditions. Several species of *Ephedra* are characteristic.

Desert Scrub Formation.—Mojave Desert.—This, the smallest of the desert units, lies almost entirely in California below the southern end of the Sierra Nevada. Physiographic conditions are similar

FIG. 152. Joshua tree *(Yucca brevifolia)*, characteristic of the northern Mojave desert, particularly in the transition from creosote bush dominance to shadscale of the sagebrush formation.—*Courtesy Univ. of Nevada Agricultural Extension Service.*

to the Great Basin but elevations are generally lower (1,000-4,000 feet). The irregular precipitation of less than five inches is distributed over fall, winter, and spring. Summers are very hot and dry. The area includes Death Valley, with a minimum elevation of 480 feet below sea level. Its infrequent maximum rainfall is two inches, and official records show at least one period when temperatures held above 100° F. for 538 days.[192]

Conditions are not too different from those of the Great Basin although somewhat more extreme. This is borne out by the vegetation, which includes many of the same species, their distribution controlled here, too, by soil texture and salt concentration. Certain character species do stand out, however, and this justifies the vegetational distinction from the Great Basin. At the upper elevations (3,000-4,000 feet) and in the transition from sagebrush, with maximum precipitation (near five inches), Joshua tree *(Yucca brevifolia)* is conspicuous. With decreasing altitude and precipitation, creosote bush *(Larrea divaricata)*, with burro weed *(Franseria dumosa)* in association, becomes the major dominant. This community occupies 70 percent of the total area of the Mojave Desert.

Sonoran Desert.—The lowlands around the Gulf of California in Mexico and Lower California, which lie chiefly below 2,000 feet, constitute the Sonoran Desert. Much of the area is made up of dunes and sand plains. Precipitation is extremely uncertain, not exceeding two to four inches in the vicinity of the Gulf, although increasing some with altitude. Its effectiveness is counteracted by the extremely high temperatures.[237]

FIG. 153.   Sahuaro *(Carnegiea gigantea)*, the giant of the columnar cacti that characterize the uplands of the Sonoran Desert.—*U. S. Forest Service.*

The low plains are dominated by *Larrea-Franseria*, with various associates, as in the Mojave Desert. Because drainage here is not internal, margins of streambeds support a distinctive mixed com-

FIG. 154.   Mesquite *(Prosopis chilensis)*, a common ground-water indicator in the desert scrub formation.—*Courtesy Univ. of Nevada Agricultural Extension Service.*

munity including species of *Prosopis, Cercidium, Olneya, Dalea*, etc. In the higher elevations of Arizona and northern Sonora (1,000-2,000 feet), there is a great mixture of species and life forms. Although numerous species characteristic of the other deserts are present, *Cercidium microphyllum* is a dominant with numerous arborescent and columnar cacti, including *Carnegiea gigantea, Lemaireocereus schottii*, and many species of *Opuntia*. The variable topography of the peninsula of Lower California supports an equally variable flora including many species. Near the coast, there are more leaf succulents than in any of the other desert areas.

Chihuahua Desert.—Extending from southern New Mexico southeastward to western Texas and down into Mexico, much of this area is interrupted by high mountains and lies between 4,000 and 6,000 feet. Precipitation varies with altitude from three to twelve inches and falls largely in summer. Temperatures are somewhat lower than in the Sonoran Desert, and frosts are not uncommon.

Under these conditions, the communities are not as complex as those of the Sonoran Desert or as simple as those of the Great Basin, but there is much regional variation. Shrubs and semishrubs predominate with a great variety of inconspicuous stem succulents in association. Ocotillo *(Fouquieria splendens)*, which is found throughout the area, creosote bush *(Larrea tridentata)*, and mesquite *(Prosopis chilensis)* are the only three species common in the Sonoran Desert that are also important and widespread here. A number of species are conspicuous because of size or unusual form. *Yucca*, *Nolina*, and *Dasylirion* are large semisucculents. *Agave* and *Hechtia* are particularly abundant leaf succulents. Leafless, green-stemmed trees, columnar cacti, and *Dasylirion longissimum* with its six-foot, linear leaves, are examples of locally important species of striking appearance.

Grassland Formation.—Grasses are climax dominants over all the vast area extending from southern Saskatchewan and Alberta to eastern Texas, and from Indiana and the western margin of deciduous forest westward to the woodland zone of the Rockies. Separated from this major area are the Palouse region of Washington and the grasslands of the great valley of California. The formation has the greatest extent of any in North America and consequently grows under a great diversity of conditions. This is possible because of the growth form of the species, their long period of dormancy, and the fact that their moisture requirements are critical only in spring and early summer.

The eastern transition to forest is marked by an annual precipitation of thirty to forty inches from Texas to Indiana and twenty or twenty-five inches farther north. A high proportion of this precipitation falls as spring rain, but westward, as the total decreases to about ten inches near the Rockies, the proportion falling in spring and summer also decreases. Temperatures are equally variable. In the north, the growing season is cool and short, and subzero temperatures occur for long periods in winter. In the southern part of the range, frosts may be almost unknown, and extremely high summer temperatures are characteristic. Throughout the formation, late summer dry spells with high temperatures and drying winds are the rule, but, if there is sufficient moisture for the grasses during the spring growing period and summer maturation, such extremes affect them but little because of their long period of dormancy. The hot season with limited precipitation is probably of great importance in maintaining grassland climax against the advance of forest.

The increasingly severe moisture conditions from east to west are accompanied by changes in the dominant species whose combinations are distinguishable as associations of the formation. Three major regions are recognizable either by climate or vegetation, or both. Their limits, climate, and vegetation have been summarized and the important regional and local studies of grassland have been listed in a concise presentation by the late Dr. J. R. Carpenter.[52] This condensation of grassland information could well be used as the starting point for any consideration of the nature and distribution of grassland. The great number of classifications attempted for grassland communities and the disagreements as to major dominants and most important species implied by the terminology suggest the complexity of the formation. Probably, too, there is a suggestion of much more variation regionally than might at first be supposed. Of necessity, we are restricted here to a simple presentation. On this basis, the discussion will deal with only three major associations, which may be termed Tall Grass Prairie, Mixed Prairie, and Short Grass Plains. Some authorities recognize as many as seven associations,[57] and, even then, most of these can be divided into several faciations. Furthermore, a detailed discussion must recognize within each faciation the usually distinct upland, slope, and lowland variations.

Tall Grass Prairie.—Sometimes called "true prairie," this association borders the deciduous forest, receives the most rainfall, has the greatest north-south diversity and the greatest number of major dominants of the association. Bunch grasses are the conspicuous species, for many of them grow in excess of six feet tall, but sod-forming species are also dominants. Because of the generally favorable climatic and soil conditions, most of the area is cultivated and little of the original vegetation remains today.

FIG. 155. Tall grass, or true prairie, community in which *Andropogon scoparius, Bouteloua gracilis*, and *Sporobolus heterolepis* are the most important species.—*Photo by R. B. Livingston.*

The long list of major dominants includes tall grasses, such as *Stipa spartea, Andropogon furcatus*, and *Sorghastrum nutans;* medium grasses, such as *Andropogon scoparius* and *Bouteloua curtipendula;* and the short grasses, *Bouteloua gracilis* and *B. hirsuta*. The association of dominants with topography should be indicated at some point even though it is impossible to recognize it throughout our discussion. The following groupings are not uncommon for Tall Grass Prairie.

UPLANDS	SLOPES	LOWLANDS
Agropyron repens		
Bouteloua gracilis		
B. curtipendula		
Andropogon scoparius		
Poa pratensis	*Poa pratensis*	*Poa pratensis*
Sorghastrum nutans	*Sorghastrum nutans*	*Sorghastrum nutans*
	Koeleria cristata	
	Andropogon furcatus	*Andropogon furcatus*
	Stipa spartea	
		Agrostis alba
		Spartina pectinata
		Panicum virgatum

This distribution is not the same everywhere. In the north, *Koeleria* and *Stipa* appear in the uplands, and *Poa* and *Sorghastrum* do not appear at all. In the central region, *Panicum virgatum, Bulbilis dactyloides*, and *Bouteloua hirsuta* are added to the uplands and *Sporobolus heterolepis* and *S. cryptandrus* to slopes. The

FIG. 156.   Mixed grass prairie in which *Bouteloua gracilis, Stipa comata*, and *Calamovilfa longifolia* are the principal species. Colorado.—*Photo by R. B. Livingston.*

southern faciation, sometimes regarded as a separate association, is even more distinct, especially because of added species in the uplands, such as *Stipa leucotricha, Andropogon saccharoides, A. tener*, and *A. ternarius.*

There has been much discussion and study of the eastern margin of Tall Grass Prairie, its extension as a "peninsula" into Illinois and Indiana, and the isolated areas farther east, particularly in

Ohio. Because here it includes somewhat different combinations of species, some of which are dominant, the community is regarded by some as a separate association. The predominating tall grasses, as well as other basic similarities, make it reasonable to

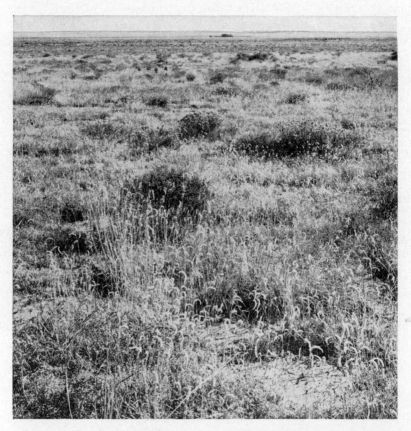

FIG. 157.   Mixed grass community in Arizona in which grama grasses predominate.—*U. S. Forest Service.*

others to consider the prairie peninsula as a faciation of Tall Grass Prairie to which it bears a postclimax relationship. The soils within the peninsula are prairie soils although the climate is now that of forest climax. The community may, therefore, be regarded as preclimax to the forest, maintained by edaphic conditions.

Mixed Grass Prairie.—Although the mixed grasses occupy an area between that of the tall grasses and short grasses and the dominants are derived from both these communities, it is generally agreed that there is sufficient unity and distinctness to justify associational rank. Important dominants throughout the area are *Bouteloua gracilis*, *B. hirsuta*, *Andropogon scoparius*, and, except in the north, *Bulbilis dactyloides*. In the north, *Koeleria cristata*, *Stipa spartea*, and *S. comata* are added dominants, which suggest the recognition of a northern faciation. Other important species included among the dominants are *Andropogon furcatus*, *Sporobolus cryptandrus*, and several species of *Stipa*.

FIG. 158.   Short grass plains pastured to sheep in Wyoming.—*Photo by W. D. Billings*.

The western limit of the association may be taken as the line where tall grasses disappear and beyond which only short grasses are dominant. Since the tall grasses require available soil moisture to a depth of twenty-four or more inches during their active growing season, the limit of mixed grass prairie is a line beyond which precipitation is insufficient to provide moisture to this depth. The eastern limit is not as sharply defined but is also determined by soil moisture, since mixed prairie is marked by prairie grasses in bunch-grass habit sharing dominance with permanently established short grasses.[3] Thus the area forms a strip from Saskatchewan through the central Dakotas, Nebraska, Kansas, and western Oklahoma into Texas. The sand hills of Nebraska are an exception, for here soil conditions are such that postclimax tall grasses predominate. During protracted dry periods, the short grasses increase at the expense of the moisture-requiring tall grasses.[267] Thus the boundaries of the association are not particularly static and are represented by a wide transition zone.

FIG. 159.   Short grass range in Colorado under average grazing and consequently in good condition.—*U. S. Forest Service.*

Short Grass Plains.—Westward from the Mixed Grass Prairie to the woodland zone of the Rockies, the xeric short grasses are dominant. On the basis of exclosure studies and other observations, the climax nature of short grasses has been questioned, and the community has been described as disclimax resulting from overgrazing an area that would otherwise support mixed prairie.[268] This interpretation is gradually gaining favor. Regardless of terminology, the short grasses are, at present, dominant over the entire area.

The most important species are *Bouteloua gracilis* and *Bulbilis dactyloides*, except north of the Dakotas, where the latter is absent. Several faciations are recognizable that result from combinations of the major dominants with *Stipa comata*, or *Agropyron smithii*, or *Aristida longiseta*.

The desert plains area extending from western Texas across northern Mexico and southern New Mexico and Arizona supports short grasses, which, although including different species, are related to short grass dominance. Several species of *Bouteloua* and *Aristida* predominate. Overgrazing has greatly increased the numbers of desert shrubs here, and these include *Larrea*, *Opuntia*, *Flourensia*, and several others of which widely spaced individuals occur everywhere.

Other Grassland Climax.—There is evidence that the great valley of California was once dominated by grasses, which, because of fire and grazing, have been eliminated except for relict areas. The latter suggest that the dominants were bunch grasses, which produced grassland similar in appearance to mixed prairie. Throughout most of the area it appears that *Stipa pulchra* was the principal species, except near the coast. Today introduced annual grasses occupy most of the remaining grassland areas, especially species of *Avena*, *Bromus*, *Festuca*, and *Hordeum*.

The rolling hills of the Palouse region, as well as most of eastern Washington and Oregon and eastward into Idaho, supported prairie grasses before being cultivated for wheat production. Although numerous species characteristic of other grassland areas are present here, the major dominants are distinctive, including *Agropyron spicatum*, *Festuca idahoensis*, and *Elymus condensatus*. Possibly much of the sagebrush dominance in this region is only the result of grazing, and certainly the dominance of the annual, *Bromus tectorum*, results from fire and grazing as it does southward in the Great Basin.

The Palouse and California grasslands, in contrast with the major areas, are products of winter, rather than spring and summer, precipitation.

Aspect Dominance.—Probably no other formation has such marked variations in appearance through the growing season. Since not all the grasses mature at once, there are times when simple observation might lead to incorrect conclusions as to their relative importance. Associated species other than grasses, often called forbs, may be seasonally so conspicuous as to obscure the grasses and, temporarily at least, to give the appearance of dominance.

Tropical Formations.—The truly tropical vegetation of North America, which occurs only in southern Mexico and Central America, probably includes as great a diversity of communities as is usually found in temperate climates. The major controlling factor in this diversity is moisture, as affected by topography, exposure, and seasonal distribution. Although numerous local studies of the vegetation of American tropics have been made, it is only recently that a comprehensive classification of the plant communities has been attempted in the light of modern concepts.[15]

A misconceived but popular idea of tropical vegetation is undoubtedly one which can best be placed in the category of rain-forest-in-its-jungle-form. But such tangled masses of vegetation are found only on areas of disturbance and "True rain forest always gives the impression of the vault of cathedral aisles."[15] It is made up of many species of tall broad-leaved, evergreen trees in several strata with the tallest sometimes rising ninety feet to the lowest branch. Undergrowth is sparse, lianas are few, and epiphytes are not abundant near the ground. Apparently, after disturbance of any kind, such forests are replaced by a tangled jungle of growth that is almost impenetrable. The rain forest is not widespread because conditions for its development are by no means everywhere available. It occurs where temperatures are fairly constantly high, precipitation is plentiful (over two hundred inches in some areas), and on good sites with proper drainage but with a continuous supply of available water.

It should be re-emphasized that not all tropical vegetation is rain forest, and to this should be added that not all broad-leaved evergreen forest is rain forest. The presence in the tropics of mountains of sufficient height to have permanent snow on their peaks insures altitudinal zonation similar to that of temperate regions. These mountains may interrupt moisture-bearing winds and so maintain desert conditions. Seasonal deciduous forests, pine forests, and even tundra are to be found on their slopes. The major variations in American tropical vegetation have been grouped into six formations, each of which may be divided into from two to nine associations.[15]

1. Rain Forest (Optimum formation)
2. Seasonal Formations
3. Dry Evergreen Formation
4. Montane Formation
5. Swamp Formation
6. Marsh or Seasonal Swamp Formation

The subtropical climate of the southern tip of Florida and the Gulf coast down into Mexico permits the growth of numerous species with tropical characteristics and affinities. The palms, the many broad-leaved evergreens, the mangroves, the many epiphytes and lianas, and the sometimes jungle-like masses of vegetation are all suggestive of tropical conditions.

GENERAL REFERENCES

E. LUCY BRAUN. The Undifferentiated Deciduous Forest Climax and the Association Segregate.

J. R. CARPENTER. The Grassland Biome.

F. E. CLEMENTS. *Plant Indicators : The Relation of Plant Communities to Processes and Practice.*

R. F. DAUBENMIRE. Vegetational Zonation in the Rocky Mountains.

J. W. HARSHBERGER. *Phytogeographic Survey of North America.*

B. E. LIVINGSTON and F. SHREVE. *The Distribution of Vegetation in the United States, As Related to Climatic Conditions.*

H. L. SHANTZ and R. ZON. The Physical Basis of Agriculture : Natural Vegetation, in *Atlas of American Agriculture.*

V. E. SHELFORD (ed.). *Naturalist's Guide to the Americas.*

F. SHREVE. A Map of the Vegetation of the United States.

J. E. WEAVER and F. E. CLEMENTS. *Plant Ecology.*

CHAPTER XI

THE DISTRIBUTION OF CLIMAX COMMUNITIES
SHIFTS OF CLIMAXES WITH TIME

The present distribution and limits of climax communities are not necessarily static, nor have they been in the past. Looked at in terms of geological time, changes of climate must be recognized that were so extreme that vegetation must likewise have changed radically. Within relatively recent geological time, glaciation of northern North America obviously must have produced such changes in climate that disruption of then existing lines of vegetational distribution were inevitable. Advance of the ice southward resulted in constriction of vegetational zones and retreat of species and growth forms as the climate changed. With the recession of the ice, there was again a northward advance of species and a readjustment of plant communities as the glaciated area was reoccupied by vegetation. Probably there were several minor advances and retreats of vegetation correlated with the shifting ice fronts and the similarly varying climate.

Within historical time, there have been major shifts of climate producing conditions that may have had serious effects on vegetation. There is evidence that early Norsemen who colonized Greenland were able to carry on a primitive sort of agriculture on lands along the southern coast. Between the twelfth and the fourteenth centuries the climate there deteriorated rapidly so that summers became shorter and colder, the soil remained frozen, and the colonists disappeared. Today, as for some time past, the receding glaciers in Greenland indicate an increasingly favorable climate. Receding glaciers in Alaska have been similarly interpreted.[76] In recent years, conifer forest has been advancing into the tundra in Alaska.[110] Periodically, prairie vegetation is invaded for some distance by forest, and although drought often eliminates such advances, they may be permanent or, at least, appear so.

That climates have changed over long periods of time cannot be questioned, and that slow change continues today in certain areas is undoubtedly true. With climatic change, vegetational change is to be expected. Some modern changes are easily recognized, as indicated above. In highly populated areas, the changes may be much less obvious because natural vegetation has been disturbed by man.

PALEO-ECOLOGY

This phase of ecology deals with the history of vegetation, especially the reconstruction of past climaxes and climates, their rise, decline, and migration over long periods of geological time. Its basic source materials are derived from paleontology and geology and must be interpreted in terms of what is known of the ecology of modern organisms.

Tracing changes in modern climax vegetation is a complex process involving the use of every kind of evidence available. P. B. Sears' [218] reconstruction of the natural vegetation of Ohio and its prehistoric development[221] illustrates how historical records and pollen statistics may contribute evidence. H. M. Raup's[203] study of New England climate and vegetation utilizes still other sources of evidence. Archaeology, zoology, botany, and geology all were drawn upon in a variety of ways before he concluded that New England had had a warmer climate within recent years—probably no more than a thousand years—and that the trend has since been to the cooler and moister, with parallel vegetational changes.

Knowing that climates have changed, one may be equally certain that vegetation has varied accordingly. Major alterations in vegetation may likewise be assumed to indicate modification of climate. In some instances, however, such shifts have been interpreted as purely successional in nature, a point not to be ignored since succession has gone on in the past as it does today. Change within historical time, if still in progress, may be observed, or may become apparent from detailed quantitative and qualitative studies of transition areas.[39] A less reliable source of information is the historical literature not always dependable, unfortunately, because of the limited knowledge of the early writers. It is, nevertheless, a source from which much of value can be learned,[36, 203] particularly when the information is drawn from several sources and is correlated with other kinds of evidence.

The difficulties of reconstructing the vegetational picture during early historical time are as nothing compared with those involved in determining prehistoric climaxes.[50] Fossils, variously preserved, are the chief source of our knowledge of ancient floras, many of which have disappeared completely. Considering that different species and even parts of the same plant are unequally preserved, it is surprising that we know as much of these old

FIG. 160.   Interglacial forest relicts on beach below high tide, Glacier Bay, Alaska. These hemlock stumps, probably several thousand years old, represent forest that lived before the last major advance of ice, which buried them under glacial debris (above beach). Tide action has again exposed the stumps. —*Photo by W. S. Cooper.*[75]

floras as we do. Certainly we know that there have been extreme climatic changes on various parts of the earth and that with them have come modifications in vegetation, which sometimes eliminated entire floras.

More recent vegetational history has been given greater attention because of its direct relationships to our modern flora and, possibly, because it offers greater probability of solution. Postglacial climate and vegetation have been studied more intensively, therefore, than those of preglacial time. Plant remains, buried and preserved between layers of glacial drift, have yielded much information on the amount of time involved, the climate, and the vegetation. These deposits, often preserved in a natural state as wood, leaves, fruits, or seeds, have been uncovered by erosion, excavation, and even in driving wells at considerable depth. Such findings have been fortuitous largely, since the deposits do not occur generally and, when stumbled upon, must be brought to the attention of those interested if they are to be of any scientific

FIG. 161.   Well-preserved Pleistocene plant remains found in silt or peat layers buried under 10 to 12 feet of undisturbed moraine in Minneapolis, Minn. (1) *Calliergon giganteum*, (2) *Neocalliergon integrifolium*, (3) *Picea* sp., wood structure almost perfect, (4) *Picea* sp., wood structure distorted by pressure, (5) cone of *Picea glauca*, (6) cone of *Picea mariana*, (7) cone of *Larix laricina.—From Cooper and Foot.*[77]

value. As a result, the information they have yielded is fragmentary and discontinuous both in time and space.

A more promising approach to the problem began with the study of the nature and composition of the strata of plant remains and other sediments that have accumulated in lakes and ponds as peat or related material.[82] These strata may give almost continuous records back to glacial time, and, since deposits are distributed over wide areas, their study makes possible the correlation of findings, particularly regarding climate, in one place with those in another. Obviously such studies can not be entirely satisfactory since they indicate vegetation only within the bogs themselves, or at their immediate margins, and bog vegetation is not of the climax type.

POLLEN ANALYSIS

When, in 1916, von Post presented the results of his studies of pollen preserved in Swedish peat deposits, an entirely new approach to the reconstruction of prehistoric vegetation was begun.[97]

FIG. 162.   A type of sampler frequently used for pollen studies of peat and marl deposits. It consists of a jacketed plunger that completely closes the sharpened end of the jacket. After it is pushed down to sampling depth, using the four-foot extension rods, it is drawn upward a few inches. This partly withdraws and locks the plunger in the upper part of the jacket. Then, when forced downward, the jacket cuts a ten-inch sample core.— *Courtesy of Eberbach and Sons Company.*

Wind-borne pollen is deposited everywhere and much of that which falls in a lake is preserved in its sediments because of the low rate of oxidation. Since the pollen of most dominant trees is wind-borne, the pollen deposited at any one time should include that of the important tree species in the general vicinity and the numbers of grains of a species should be indicative of the relative importance of that species in the surrounding forest at the time. Because pollen grains of a species are constant in size and form, genera, and sometimes species, can be identified positively. Conse-

FIG. 163.   An example of a common form of pollen diagram, which also illustrates what we know of the vegetational history of the northeastern United States although derived from one place (Upper Linsley Pond, North Branford, Conn.) Zone A indicates a spruce-fir forest; the high values for pine are attributed to over-representation resulting from its light weight and its abundant production. In the northeast, a secondary maximum for spruce (A-2) is not uncommon in this period and is thought to represent a local readvance of retreating ice. Zone B, a warm dry period, shows a pine maximum and the beginning of warmth-loving, deciduous trees. Then followed deciduous dominance over a long period, in which hemlock-oak were first important (C-1), then oak-hickory (C-2), and, with cooler moister conditions (C-3), an increase of chestnut, followed by a reappearance of spruce in some localities.—*From Deevey.*[80]

quently, if samples of lake deposits are taken from the bottom upward to the present surface of the sediment, the pollen content of successive strata should indicate the nature of the forest, as to genera and their relative abundance, throughout the period of accumulation.

Sediments on lake bottoms as well as peat deposits have been studied. Samples must be taken with care to prevent contamination, and several types of augers have been devised for the purpose. With these, cores can be cut that, placed end to end, form a continuous column of material for the entire depth of the deposit. Borings are made in summer under most conditions, but, since it is desirable to have them from the deepest part of the depression, it is often advantageous to make them in winter from the frozen surface.

Identification and counting of the pollen grains must be done under a microscope. This necessitates treatment of the samples with one of the several methods recommended[48] to eliminate foreign material and to concentrate the grains. Identification is facilitated by reference to illustrations[274] and by comparison with a series of grains taken from modern plants. What constitutes an

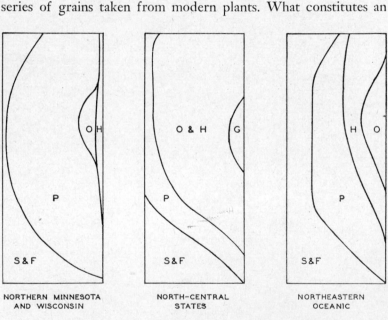

NORTHERN MINNESOTA
AND WISCONSIN

NORTH-CENTRAL
STATES

NORTHEASTERN
OCEANIC

FIG. 164. Schematic pollen profiles that show the general picture of what is known of vegetational history for the eastern United States. F—fir, G—grassland complex, H—hardwoods except oak, O—oak, P—pine, S—spruce. Depth shown vertically, percentages horizontally. Although there are differences relatable to continental and maritime climates, there is regional similarity in the indications of a middle warm, drier period, and the suggestion of subsequent cooler, moister conditions leading into the present, as well as the shift toward early proportions of species in the upper portions of the diagrams. Succession may be a factor in these latter shifts.—*After Sears.*[219]

adequate sample in the count of grains is not agreed upon by all investigators but fewer than 150-250 grains are rarely counted.

When the proportions for genera are known for each stratum, they are represented in a standardized form, known as a pollen diagram, in which pollen spectra—the relative importance of each genus in a stratum—are plotted on horizontal lines, one spectrum above another to show the progressive changes for genera, which are shown on vertical lines. A pollen diagram is no more than a means of visualizing the pollen spectrum of a section—a vertical series of samples from the bottom to the surface of a deposit. Changes in the spectra from the bottom upward are, of course, to be correlated with time.

The shortcomings and pitfalls of pollen analysis as a method of determining past vegetation and climate are appreciated by all who have used it.[48, 97] There are sources of error in methods, in records, which may be incomplete, and in identifications which may not always be correct, and interpretations may be based upon inadequate data. Because of its simpler flora and greater amount of study, the pollen spectrum for Europe is better established and

FIG. 165. A composite of ten pollen profiles from the Puget Sound region, which is indicative of postglacial climate and vegetation in the northwest although not typical of all areas as to species. The volcanic ash level, present in all northwestern profiles, is considered to be of common age. Such composite profiles, because they eliminate the sharp fluctuations from level to level found in individual profiles, give a better picture of the trend of postglacial vegetation.—*From Hansen.*[115]

accepted than in North America. Most of our studies have been made in areas where bogs are common and within a reasonable range of accessibility of an individual or his students : the northwest, the north-central states, and the northeast. There is still much to be done within the glacial area to complete the picture.

It is somewhat surprising that investigators are in as close agreement as they are. Most generally accepted is a postglacial climatic series beginning with increasing warmth, followed by a period of maximum warmth and drought, followed by a period of decreasing warmth, the present.[224] This is applicable to both Europe and America. Some students would subdivide these three major periods, claiming that greater refinement is possible. Others contend that their data contain no evidence of a warm dry period in North America.

More studies are certainly necessary in North America before agreement can be reached as to all phases of the basic normal pollen spectrum and its meaning in terms of climate. Several scattered studies have been made of deposits beyond the limits of glaciation, and these offer real possibilities. Likewise, there must be more efforts to correlate all sources of contributing evidence,[89, 203] a truly paleo-ecological approach : floristic, vegetational, zoological, geological, archeological, as well as evidence from pollen analysis.

DENDROCHRONOLOGY

Another bioclimatic approach to past history was originated by an astronomer. Dr. A. E. Douglass, when he began studies of annual growth rings of trees in an attempt to correlate their differences with climatic variations, presumably related to solar activity. Cross-dating, or matching the growth patterns year by year, for modern trees in Arizona was first accomplished in 1904, but its significance was not fully appreciated until several years later.[91] Then a chronology was established from modern times back to A.D. 1400 by matching ring records of modern trees to the exterior ring records of earlier trees and so on with trees that grew still earlier. When these records were matched with rings in beams taken from ancient pueblos, the records became complete back to A.D. 1299, then to A.D. 700 and, more recently, successively to A.D. 643, A.D. 500, and finally to A.D. 11. Recent finds suggest that the chronology will be carried even further back.[119] Some of the record was completed and some of the cross-matching was made possible by fragments of wood from ancient pueblos and some even with charcoal, which was better preserved than wood. It should be noted that an even longer chronology has been worked out for the giant redwoods, which is complete for 3,000 years.

When the pueblo dendrochronology was completed, it was a major contribution to archaeology since some thirty prehistoric ruins were immediately given absolute dates, and later hundreds more were dated. This usefulness of the method was immediately apparent to archaeologists, who accepted it and adapted it to their purposes. At the same time, their findings in archaeology have contributed to the establishment of dendrochronology as a means of studying past climate.

Recent ring studies in moist cool regions indicate that no better climate than the arid Southwest could have been selected for the initial investigations. In extremely dry regions, growth and size of rings are closely related to annual precipitation and the correlation is not complicated by light or temperature effects. It is now known that in the north, or at high altitudes, tree growth is most responsive to temperature and that in temperate regions with adequate rainfall, both temperature and moisture factors are reflected in the rings.[90]

This does not mean that tree-ring studies are successful only in arid regions but rather that their interpretation may be more dif-

FIG. 166. A diagram illustrating how the bridge method is used to extend knowledge of dated rings, an important part of the building of complete and continuous chronologies. The usual desirable overlap is fifty years.—*After Glock.*[107]

ficult elsewhere. That cross-dating and correlation with climatic variation is possible in moist-temperate climates was demonstrated by Douglass' studies in Europe and several parts of the United States. In the Mississippi drainage area, the deviation from the normal annual precipitation has been shown to affect ring growth more than total precipitation, but the relationship is modified by temperature and wind as they influence evaporation.[119] Ring growth in New England has been shown, in a chronology from hemlock, to have close correlation with climate as indicated by exceptional and poor crop years.[164]

Since tree-ring analysis was originally begun with the hope that it would show solar-terrestrial relationships, it was natural that, with the establishment of long, dated chronologies, the data should be studied for cyclic characteristics. Permanent periods, or those of fixed length, showed no correlation; therefore, this idea was discarded for one of cycle complexes in which any obvious or significant recurrence of variation in data was considered to be cyclic. On this basis, definite relationships were demonstrable between sunspot activity in the past and terrestrial climate as recorded in certain long-time chronologies of tree rings. An eleven- (ten to twelve) year cycle is especially pronounced throughout the old records and continues to be borne out, in a general way, for modern conditions. During periods of sunspot maximum, drought is characteristic, and sunspot minimum is associated with excessive precipitation. Application of the method to climatic prediction may be possible as more long-time meteorological records are analyzed and as more tree records of great length are worked out to show the nature of prehistoric climates on many parts of the earth.

THE RELICT METHOD

As for several other phases of dynamic ecology, we are indebted to Dr. F. E. Clements for recognizing the potentialities of the relict method, for demonstrating its usefulness, and for a clear and complete exposition of the entire subject. The brief discussion that follows can hardly avoid being a condensation of his ideas.[58]

"In the ecological sense, a *relict* is a community or fragment of one that has survived some important change, often to become in appearance an integral part of the existing vegetation." The concept may be applied to individuals or a species, but is more often used for communities. It may be used to describe delayed or lagging stages of succession, but it has far greater usefulness in connection with climax vegetation.

The usefulness of relicts lies in their indicator value of past conditions of habitat and vegetation as well as of the causes underlying changes that have occurred elsewhere in the area. A relict

Fig. 167. Relict (postclimax) black spruce forest in a Minnesota bog.— *U. S. Forest Service.*

community having remained relatively unchanged because of peculiar local conditions is an actual sample of, or shows strong similarities to, previous vegetation. At the same time, the peculiarities of the relict habitat are indicative of environmental conditions previously characteristic of the area as a whole and may, therefore, be suggestive of why vegetation changed generally there.

Relict communities occur where local edaphic, topographic, or biotic factors differ sufficiently to compensate for the effects of environmental conditions obtaining generally. Thus altitude, exposure, or soil may provide locally unusual moisture conditions. Ridges, streams, and lakes may constitute barriers to fire. Peculiarities of drainage may result in swamps, bogs, and low flood plains. Any such condition may be effective in maintaining relict communities, which, in terms of climate, could not be anticipated. They are the relicts indicative of shifts of climax and climate over long periods.

FIG. 168. Effect of grazing on mixed prairie in central Colorado. Short grass, to left of fence, is typical over much of the region but, where cattle are excluded, to right, mixed prairie develops.—*Photo by R. B. Livingston.*

A quite different kind of relict is one that is maintained by man, purposely or otherwise, after he has destroyed or modified the picture of climax generally. Overgrazing, cultivation, and lumbering have destroyed or modified climax over extensive areas to such a degree that its recognition and interpretation, even though its destruction was within historic time, are dependent upon remnants of the former vegetation. Such relicts may be found in fence rows, along railroad right-of-ways, in old cemeteries, and in any areas long undisturbed and may yield much information about the past. The deliberately protected areas, such as game and wildlife preserves, natural areas, Indian reservations, and national parks, offer still more possibilities because of their extent, frequently included virgin areas, and relative permanence.

FIG. 169. Postclimax community of ponderosa pine occurring as an isolated island in sagebrush desert wherever the special local soil conditions exist in Nevada. Often disjunct from nearest ponderosa pine forest of the Sierra by fifty miles or more.—*Photo by W. D. Billings*.[22]

Relicts related to climatic change are most abundant in the transitions from one climax to another but may likewise be found well within the general range of a climax, provided the local conditions are present that maintain the necessary compensating factors. Usually the local conditions are a result of topography, which, through its effects on precipitation, drainage, temperature, and air movements, permits the relict to survive. The resulting relict communities are the postclimaxes and preclimaxes previously discussed in detail. With an understanding of the concept of postclimax and preclimax, their presence greatly simplifies the interpretation of shifts of climate and climax in the past. The present condition of the relict, if free from disturbance, may furnish strong evidence of the present degree of climatic stability. Judgment of such evidence must, of necessity, be tempered by what is known of climatic cycles. In parts of the West, precipitation may be several times as great during a period of sunspot minimum as that during sunspot maximum. The condition of vegetation, particularly in relict communities, must be interpreted accordingly.

GENERAL REFERENCES

S. A. CAIN. Pollen Analysis as a Paleo-Ecological Research Method.
S. A. CAIN. *Foundations of Plant Geography.*
F. E. CLEMENTS. The Relict Method in Dynamic Ecology.
A. P. DACHNOWSKI. Peat Deposits and Their Evidence of Climatic Change.
G. ERDTMAN. *An Introduction to Pollen Analysis.*
W. S. GLOCK. *Principles and Methods of Tree-Ring Analysis.*
P. B. SEARS. Climatic Interpretation of Postglacial Pollen Deposits in North America.

Part 5 · Practical Considerations

CHAPTER XII

APPLIED ECOLOGY

Man is rapidly becoming the earth's dominant organism. To an increasing extent, natural communities survive because he tolerates them, are modified to suit his purposes or fancy, or are destroyed, sometimes through his carelessness, but usually so that land may be used for agriculture, industry, or other activities. His dominance is of a different order from that characteristic of communities in nature, for, with his knowledge and technology, his activities are often so extreme and so rapid that their effects are like those of a series of catastrophic natural events. Thus he may not only destroy or modify natural communities, but he may also frequently modify the environment to a great extent. Suggestive of a different form of environmental modification are the recent experiments with rain-making by the use of dry ice. All this is necessary from our modern point of view and will continue, perhaps at an accelerated rate, as populations increase and the earth is more completely occupied and used.

Natural communities and their environments, particularly the soil, are natural resources. When they are destroyed or modified, they may reappear only after a long period of time or, with extreme disturbance, this may even be impossible. It becomes increasingly apparent that future generations may require these natural resources and likewise that man has been most wasteful of them, especially in modern times. A problem today, which will become greater in the future, is that of how to use such natural resources to the fullest extent without jeopardizing their continued availability for future needs. The problem is fundamentally ecological. Its solution depends upon the comprehension and application of ecological principles.

Since man is becoming the dominant organism and also is gifted with thought processes, his dominance should be such that he turns natural laws to his advantage or, at least, does not permit them to work against him. It is in this connection that applied ecology becomes useful. The characteristics and distribution of natural communities, the nature of the environment, and the interrelationships of organisms and environment are subject to natural laws, which the ecologist seeks to recognize and verify. The more completely the pattern of these interrelated processes is understood, the greater the probability that man will remain a permanent dominant, assuming that he restricts his activities to the limits of these laws. Only if biological laws are recognized in full can we hope to rebuild the natural resources we have destroyed, or even maintain those still available to us.

If we knew the ecology of all natural vegetation and that of all crop plants, strong recommendations for land use could be made in terms of its greatest contribution to society. Not only could agricultural, forestry, and grazing lands be positively recognized, but the details of management for maximum continuous production could be recommended with certainty. Quite obviously, ecological knowledge has not accumulated to this extent. The ecology of natural vegetation is still inadequately known, and the ecology of cultivated plants has not been sufficiently studied. If the ecologist is to contribute successfully to the direction of man's activities as a dominant, there is still much that must be learned. On the other hand, even though knowledge is incomplete, ecology has much to contribute that has not been fully utilized in applied fields. What is known should be applied when man destroys or modifies natural communities. Much progress has been made in the use of ecological principles in several fields, but their potential application is still great.

FORESTRY

The early history of lumbering in North America indicates, on the part of lumbermen, a complete disregard for forests as a natural resource and little concern for the future. Foresters have long been conscious of this improvident attitude although until recently they were usually unable to change the lumberman's methods or point of view. Through the years, forestry has become a respected profession as the necessity for scientific management has become apparent. An important part of a forester's training is forest ecology, or *silvics*, in which he learns the scientific background upon which silvicultural practices are based.

A generally accepted definition of silviculture states that it is that branch of forestry dealing with the establishment, development, care, and reproduction of stands of timber.[254] More often than not, the silviculturist aims to control the establishment and development of forests so that they will be made up predominately of economically desirable species or so that merchantable timber will be produced in a minimum of time. Or, he may be interested in results not directly related to the production of lumber. Cultural operations may point to erosion control, watershed protection, dune stabilization, game encouragement, or recreational purposes,[244] or, if in the West, to a better balance between timber production, watershed control, and use of the forest for range purposes. If his methods are scientific, they will be based upon reasons derived from silvics. Consequently, the more completely forest ecology is understood, the more successful should be its application in silviculture.

Since the practice of silviculture almost invariably involves attempts to control forest communities and their development, a knowledge of successional trends and the climax of the region is all important. Knowing the principles of succession, it should be obvious that the simplest form of management would be one that least modifies the natural development of vegetation. To maintain a successional community indefinitely requires considerable effort, if it can be done at all, but the nearer the desired forest type is to the climax, the easier it should be to maintain it. These may seem to be obvious generalizations, but they have not been, and are not, fully appreciated or applied.

In the past, artificial forest types have been attempted under a great variety of conditions. Species have been planted outside the limits of their natural ranges, even including several introduced from other continents. Often such trees are grown in pure stands or, if not, then in combination with native species to make quite unnatural communities. Even more common have been the attempts to grow species on sites to which they are not naturally adapted. The situation in New England is illustrative. Here the original forest has long been gone, and reforestation and silvicultural programs have been in progress for some time. Introductions include Scotch pine, European larch, and Norway spruce from Europe, and white spruce from the northern conifer forest. Red pine and white pine have been grown at the fringe of their range in pure stands on rich, heavy soils instead of the sandy soils on which they naturally occur.

The production of artificial forest types in New England can, as a whole, be described as unsuccessful. S. H. Spurr and C. A. Cline,[245] pleading for the application of ecological principles, say that older trees are often of poor form, and growth is likely to decline sharply in later years. Very few artificial stands have been profitably brought to maturity. Furthermore, these types are especially susceptible to damage—from insects and other animals, from disease, and from the elements. Norway spruce is severely attacked by the white pine weevil; exotic larch plantations may be severely damaged by the porcupine and squirrel; red pine, south of its natural range, is particularly susceptible to Tympanis canker and to attacks by the European pine-shoot moth; crookedness of Scotch pine has been attributed to frost damage; weevils do more damage to white pine on heavy than on light soils. These authors admit that eventually, if sufficient knowledge is acquired, artificial types may be grown successfully. For the present, they cannot be recommended for New England because of previous lack of success, the risk involved, and the high cost of production. Probably similar generalizations can be made for most of the forest regions of North America but with less evidence because there has not been as much experimenting elsewhere. Although forest species have been successfully introduced into new areas, as, for example, the eucalyptus into California, the results in New England are suggestive that such experimenting might be of dubious value and certainly would not yield the necessary information except at great cost over a long period of years.

If only natural forest communities are to be the objective, there are two general types to be considered. Silviculture is usually given consideration only after the old forests have been destroyed and, not uncommonly, after much of the land has been used for agriculture and subsequently abandoned. Under these conditions,

FIG. 170. Eight-year-old plantations of pine on the same soil type (Duke Forest, Piedmont of N. C.) to compare growth of northern species, (1) red pine, and (2) white pine, with that of native loblolly pine (3). The pictures speak for themselves.—*Photos by W. R. Boggess.*

the abandoned land supports various early stages of secondary succession, and cutover land is in late successional or subclimax forest. The problem then becomes one of cultural practices designed (1) to maintain the temporary forests of successional nature or (2) to permit stands to develop to climax or near-climax conditions.

The relatively short-lived successional communities often include as dominants the most valuable trees (e.g., pine where hardwoods are climax) and, because of their rapid growth, the most desirable commercial species growing in the region. But, because of their successional position, when these species are removed, they are replaced by other species, representing later stages of succession, whose seedlings were there and released by the cutting. The problem of maintaining dominance of such temporary species has been given much study, but it is by no means solved. Without expensive cultural operations, usually including planting and periodic weeding, these temporary types cannot be maintained indefinitely. Even though the productiveness of a desired species in a stand may be extended by various types of cutting and treatment, its replacement is inevitable. Almost invariably, the succeeding stand tends to be nearer the climax than its predecessor and will include a higher proportion of economically less desirable species. Where successional species are fire resistant, there is the possibility of using controlled burning to hold back succession and maintain dominance of the temporary type. Under these conditions a temporary type could be cut selectively and provide a continuous yield. The merits of the method have been argued and are being tested for the longleaf pine forests of the coastal plain of the southeast.

The alternative would be to allow all forest land to develop toward the climax or at least to near-climax conditions. Once established, such forest would require a minimum of silvicultural attention. Continuous production would be assured, and with judicious selection of species for cutting, undoubtedly the proportions of desirable and undesirable species could be controlled. Additionally, permitting natural development of stands should result in a distribution of species in the habitats to which they are best adapted. Different conditions of soil, exposure, and moisture would support stands of different composition, but presumably these species would be making their best growth although a minimum of management would be involved. This is not to imply that silviculture is unnecessary. For example, artificial planting is frequently economically justifiable since it assures uniform stocking and even-aged stands and may speed stand development by several years. If there are few seed sources of desirable species, succession may be so long delayed, by shrub stages perhaps, that planting becomes a necessity.

Silviculture is usually desirable and sometimes a necessity, but it should be emphasized that its practices, to be most effective, should be governed by ecological knowledge. The less cultural practices tend to modify the natural trends of succession, and the more nearly the desired forest is to the climax of the region, the less the effort and expense there will be in developing and maintaining it. Here is an economic reason for learning the nature of virgin forest wherever it still remains and for determining all that is possible of its variations with habitat. Similarly, successional trends must be known in detail for every major soil type and situation if cultural practices are to be adjusted accordingly. Secondary successions are of major importance these days, and they can be worked out for any region. Climax forest in virgin condition is rapidly disappearing and usually only remnants remain for study. Their characteristics should be recorded at every opportunity. When possible, representative portions of these virgin forests should be saved intact for future study.

RANGE MANAGEMENT[248]

The objective of range management is to produce the highest possible forage yield while the condition of the range is maintained or actually improved. To this end, the methods of ecology have been used to such an extent that range management is largely applied ecology, and just as silvics is the basis of silviculture, so is range ecology the basis of range management.

Range ecology has, on the one hand, concerned itself with the purely ecological concepts of regional climaxes with grazing value and the patterns of succession for each. On the other hand, there has been the practical consideration of the quality and type of

FIG. 171. Illustrations of blue grama–oak savannah range that tell their own story of good and poor range management. (Above) "One of the finest demonstrations of range and livestock management in the southwest." (Below) Range depleted by overuse and poor management. Note differences in condition of cattle, amount of forage, ground cover, and erosion.—*U. S. Forest Service.*

forage provided by each of the communities and of how they may be controlled or modified to advantage. Only suggestions of the nature of the research on these problems can be given here, but they should indicate the degree to which ecology is contributing to the solution of range problems.

FIG. 172. To permit grazing to continue until range is entirely depleted and gullying has reached such extremes is obvious mismanagement, but it happens all too frequently. Note absence of gullies under protection of oak tree.—U. S. Forest Service.

The seasonal variations of major species have been studied in terms of grazing value. Competitive relationships of grasses and forbs (associated herbs) have been investigated as well as their relative palatability. The effects of grazing on community structure have been given much attention, particularly with regard to criteria for the recognition of excessive use and the time and conditions necessary for recovery to normal. As a result, the carrying capacity of many forage types is well known, even for different seasons of the year. With regard to range condition and carrying capacity, the effects of rodents have been studied as well as the effects of predators upon the rodents. Effects of drought have been given much attention as well as the rates with which ranges recover from drought, and, in this connection, the water requirements of important individual species have been determined. In the consideration of water, the effects of different types of cover on runoff, flooding, erosion, and water supplies have been studied in detail. In attempts to rebuild depleted and eroded ranges, there have been studies of artificial seeding and planting to speed recovery. As in forestry, numerous foreign species have been tested with some successes (e.g., crested wheat grass) in an attempt to improve conditions.

FIG. 173. Two years before, this Idaho range supported only Wyethia and sage. Seeding with timothy, smooth brome, and clover, and protection for one year produced this abundance of forage at the end of the first grazing season.—*U. S. Forest Service.*

Because grazing is a part of every question in range ecology, the exclosure method is an important technique in range research. Exclosures are especially useful for testing experimental conditions, but they, or equivalent isolated areas, are likewise necessary for determining the nature of climax and related successional communities. In experimental studies, exclosures, in combination with grazed areas around them, are one of the better means of determining the effects of conditions in progress on that range. If causes are to be investigated, they are tested separately, each with its controlled treatment, on individual plots within an exclosure. Such treatments may include clipping (for grazing), burning, trampling, seeding, etc. As indicated earlier, the installation of exclosures of sufficient size, which will keep out rodents and yet will not alter microclimate, presents numerous difficulties. Consequently comparative studies on ranges supporting different, but known, animal units are coming into use whenever possible because they do not require exclosures.

When the results of such studies are evaluated and expressed in general terms, it becomes apparent that several principles have been established that appear to be universally applicable.[59] From an ecological point of view, these principles, determined by experiment, would seem to be self-evident since they conform to ecological theory. It must be remembered, however, that these things were originally theory and now can be stated as principles supported by experimental evidence. The testing was necessary to establish them as tried bases for range management. In grasslands, no less than elsewhere, succession is operational, and all trends constantly proceed toward the climax unless they are modified by disturbance or are held in check by an unfavorable swing of climate, as during a series of dry years. Grassland is a climatic life form, which maintains itself in the absence of disturbance and which, if destroyed, reappears when the disturbance is removed. All evidence indicates that perennial grasses become dominant and eliminate annual grasses, forbs, and shrubs in the absence of grazing, fire, or similar destructive agencies. The grasses of a particular climax are adapted to its climate and usually have an advantage in terms of competition over introduced ones.

From the above, it becomes apparent that, as in forestry, practices of management which least disturb the natural balance of grassland and its environment are most desirable. Those that take into consideration the trends of succession and local climax are likely to be most successful at the same time that they require a minimum of expended effort. Although a few exotic species have proved to be easier to propagate than native ones, the introduction of foreign species for range improvement or erosion control is likely to be unsatisfactory unless those species are to be given extra care or special cultural conditions. In fact, there is evidence that seeding of native species should be done only with locally produced seeds since the species may consist of geographic physiological races.

The establishment of general principles is being followed by more and more intensive studies of local variations in communities and environments. The productivity of most range lands has been reduced by man's domestic animals coupled with seasons of unfavorable climate, and to rebuild ranges to a higher level of productivity will require an understanding of the special conditions of local areas as well as the broad principles for the region. Our public lands in the West, most of which are grazed, have been divided, for research and administration, in a fashion that suggests a natural application of the above. Several grazing *regions* are designated, which correspond to the major differences in the grassland and scrub formations. These in turn are divided into several districts, which represent local variations in dominants and environment. Application of the general principles is possible for regional administration and management, but local application must be modified in terms of detailed local studies.

AGRICULTURE

If a crop is planted and grown successfully, it follows that the methods applied, within the general region, to the particular field and for that season, were ecologically correct since cultivated crops are as subject to ecological laws as are plants growing naturally. Study of the ecology of cultivated plants has progressed rapidly in recent years. It includes crop ecology, which is applied ecology in the ordinary sense, and ecological crop geography, which considers the effects of both physiological and economic factors on production and distribution of crop plants.[143] With this addition of "social" factors to the physical and physiological ones, the already complex environment becomes still more so, and the crop ecologist must integrate his observations and conclusions with additional fields. This phase of ecology is, as a whole, beyond our consideration here, but it is appropriate to emphasize that ecological principles are becoming a part of our way of thinking. They should undoubtedly be given even greater attention in these days of a planned economy, which affects us all.

Crop Ecology.—The cultivated plant is as subject to ecological law as a native one, and, consequently, there is as much ecology to be studied in a corn, tobacco, or cotton field as there is in a forest. To be sure, largely by trial and error, the farmer has learned to grow crops so that they give a reasonable return for his labor. But, on the whole, this has been done at the expense of the soil as a natural resource. The natural fertility of most of our soils is largely depleted, erosion has ruined thousands of acres and reduced the productivity of many more, and water tables have been lowered to such an extent that crops in areas with rainfall sufficient for hardwood forest are suffering during dry spells as much as they would in grassland climate. Thanks to increased knowledge of fertilizers, the development of productive hybrid strains of various crop plants, and modern mechanized methods, our yields have steadily increased, but this cannot proceed indefinitely, especially since much of the increase in yield has resulted in further depletion of the soil.

To counteract the inevitable downward trend of productivity, soil conservation and erosion control are receiving greater attention. Increased knowledge of crop ecology is imperative so that the highest yielding species will be grown under the proper conditions of cultivation and on the right sites. If possible, yields must be maintained at high levels at the same time that soils are improved rather than being depleted. The ecology of weeds, pests, and diseases must be studied so that the depredations of these products of cultivation may be held in check effectively. These things are not being neglected by agronomists and horticulturists, but there are special contributions that can be made if the investigator has the ecological point of view.

Land Use.—It has been customary to clear all workable land for agriculture, permit plowland to revert to pasture only when it becomes unprofitable, and permit pasture in turn to revert to forest only under the same conditions. It may be desirable to reverse this procedure completely. Perhaps the soundest ecological apportionment of the landscape would be represented by a minimum of carefully selected, skillfully operated plowland with a maximum of natural vegetation. Where this natural vegetation consists of grassland, regulated pasture is an aspect of its normal development; where it consists of forest, it should be scrupulously protected against grazing, and whatever pastures are required should be handled with the same measure of skill that has been suggested

FIG. 174.   Once-fertile farm land that has been unnecessarily destroyed by surface erosion and gullying because of lack of concern (note that straight-row cultivation still prevails) and lack of understanding. Perhaps this area should have been put into forest long since. If it had been, it would still be valuable.—*U. S. Soil Conservation Service.*

for the plowland.[223]

Maintaining stands of natural vegetation provides areas for ecological comparison and diagnosis, insures that soil is being rebuilt and retained, provides organic matter, insures a regulation of moisture conditions that man cannot duplicate, and provides food and shelter for wildlife, which may be significant in reducing crop pests.

The planning of such land use should be, in so far as possible, based upon ecological principles as related to soil, topography, exposure, and drainage in terms of the climate and cultivated crops it will support. Special land-use problems arise on hilly land, which need not necessarily be unproductive. Ecological studies of hill-culture[172] are showing how some such lands may be used to grow orchards, vineyards, pasture, and other crops without depletion or erosion of the soil.* Where streams occur, it has been shown

*Much of the following discussion of applied ecology in agriculture is adapted from an unpublished report by the Committee on Applied Ecology of the Ecological Society of America, 1944.

that artificial fishponds can be a profitable investment. The eco-logical problems to be solved for such ponds include sizes and depths for different climates, drainage, amount of available water and necessary aeration, rate of silting under different conditions, fish food relations, kinds and amounts of fertilizer necessary, kinds of fish, and rate of stocking. Marshes might be retained and im-

FIG. 175. A half-acre farm pond in West Virginia of the type being wide-ly installed for food production and recreation.—*U. S. Soil Conservation Service.*

proved for muskrat production, but, again, the practical problems, largely ecological, have not been sufficiently explored. Stream margins create other land-use problems. Usually they are grazed, and, as a result, they erode. The species that would appear under protection should be known, as well as the most desirable species for checking erosion. In many sections, planted hedges and field border plantings are being recommended on the unproductive margins of fields to reduce erosion and provide cover for wildlife. The ecology of the planted species must be known as well as its effects on the crop beside it. Also the ecology of the insects, birds, and mammals of these margins must be known. Are they desirable, beneficial, or are they harmful to desirable species?

Land Management.—The operations by which land is prepared for crops, their planting, harvest, and use are known as *land man-agement.* For greatest efficiency, good land management must parallel good land use. These are arts but, today, arts requiring all

FIG. 176. This eroded stream bank in Wisconsin was graded, laid with willow poles, and planted with a few willow sprouts. Only two seasons were required to produce the growth shown in the second picture where undercutting is effectively stopped and shelter is provided for wildlife.—*U. S. Soil Conservation Service.*

FIG. 177. Waste field-margins such as the fourteen-foot strip (1) abandoned because of root competition and erosion can be made useful. (2)
Lespedeza bicolor (tall) and *L. sericea* planted in strips are holding the margin stable and producing food and cover for small game.—*U. S. Soil Conservation Service.*

the help of science possible.[226] A farm planted year after year to
wheat or cotton does not, even with fertilizer, conform to the
balances that occur in nature. Well-managed fields may seem to

approach a condition of balance as a result of rests with rotation pasture, the use of legumes, and the addition of fertilizer. Yields may be high and sustained, soil may not erode, and all appear to be at its best.

In terms of natural vegetation, however, our modern methods of land management may be questioned. Cultivation produces

FIG. 178.   A simple illustration of improper management. The amount of runoff on this slope means leaching and erosion. Certainly the rows should not have been put in up and down the hill, and perhaps, without terraces, clean cultivation should be ruled out on this field.—*U. S. Soil Conservation Service.*

conditions similar to those in early stages of succession, conditions that in nature would be temporary and soon change in the direction of climax. We must have crops, but, if climax vegetation utilizes natural conditions most effectively—and that seems reasonable—are our methods of cultivation the best we can use for obtaining our crops? Is our method of deep plowing, with destruction of soil structure, best under all conditions? Should all crops

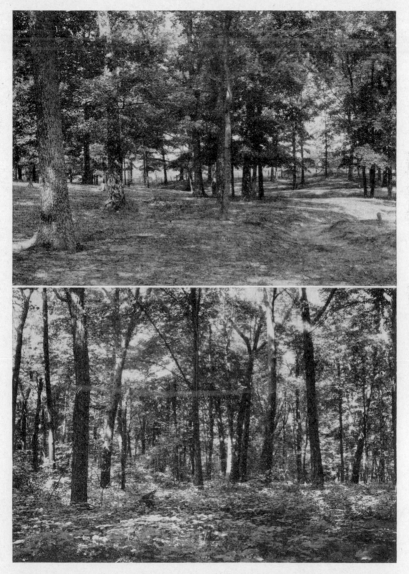

FIG. 179. Deciduous forest farm wood lots, pastured (above) and not pastured (below), which illustrate the effects of browsing and trampling on reproduction and general forest condition.—*U. S. Forest Service*.

be cultivated clean and all organic matter be turned into the soil? Might mixed crops producing a complete cover as in nature not be more desirable? Perhaps we have gone too far in producing unnatural conditions. The artificial environment of cultivation results in soil erosion, a modified soil flora and fauna, and changes in water relations. Also we have more diseases of crop plants and more insect pests than ever before.

These are ecological problems. Intelligent land use minimizes some of them. Practices like contour plowing, terracing, and strip cropping are moves in the direction of reducing them. But when the ecology of crop plants is studied further, especially in terms of natural vegetation, some of our methods of use and management may require revision.

Pasture Problems.—Above, it was suggested that the same attention to management should be given to pastures as to plowed land. This would be a reversal of the usual point of view since pastures are, more often than not, largely on the poorest land and are given little or no attention. With the steady expansion of dairying, especially into sections of the country where adequate pastures do not

FIG. 180 (1).   An Indiana field after fall plowing showing severe erosion. Picture taken when it was decided to retire field to permanent pasture with contour furrows.

FIG. 180 (2). The next year, after gully-control work, this excellent planted pasture had taken over, the soil was stabilized and the field saved for long-continued usefulness.—*Both photos by U. S. Soil Conservation Service.*

produce themselves, the need for pasture ecology increases. The necessity for seeding is now widely accepted. Many species have been tested for palatability, yield, food value, and soil-building properties. Growing pastures is still, however, largely a hit-or-miss affair that requires much more study. Regional pasture ecology has not progressed as far as range ecology. There is much yet to be learned, tested, and put into practice. The implementation of such a program will be difficult in many sections where pastures are not generally recognized as a crop to be managed like any other.

An illustration of the misconceptions regarding pasture is the common practice of including the farm wood lot in the pastured area although it provides little more than browsing, which supplements feed during off seasons. To the ecologist, it is obvious that this is at the expense of seedlings and ground cover and that it will result in stand deterioration.[160] Silviculturists have shown that properly managed wood lots can yield as great a return as any average farm acreage, but the wood lot pasture persists. A study of maple groves in Ohio[225] showed that in three years the elimination of grazing resulted in an increased yield of maple syrup, worth more than twice what the rental for pasture would have been. At the same time, the condition of the stand was noticeably improved. As more such information is accumulated[83] it is to be hoped that its application will follow.

Regional pasture studies must be continued so that both species and their culture can be recommended with confidence for climate, soils, and land management policies as they occur. To obtain such results, it would appear that ecological methods should be the most promising.

Insect Problems.—The relationship between land-management practices and insect populations is inadequately known.[116] Whether insect pests will increase or decrease with strip-cropping or particular crop rotations cannot be said with certainty. Probably more complex are the relationships of insect populations to the birds and mammals that will appear in response to such conservation practices as cover crops, hedges, and field border plantings. Whenever the acreage of a cultivated species is increased extensively in an area or a new species is introduced for special purposes such as erosion control, insects may appear with it or abruptly increase in numbers to pest proportions. Such relationships and innumerable others need more study. The possibilities for applied insect ecology in agriculture and forestry are almost unlimited.

Rodent Problems.—Especially for range lands, ecological knowledge of rodents is still inadequate. In spite of this, rodent control has been attempted in these areas for years. More should be known of the effects upon rodent populations of kinds and degree of grazing as well as what effects the various rodent-control measures have on the condition of the range. With the latter, it should be possible to say what percentage of a rodent population can be destroyed by a control measure, how long before the surviving population will return to normal, and to what extent species move in from untreated areas. Complicating the above problems is the usually cyclical fluctuation of most rodent populations and the obvious desirability for adjusting control to these natural fluctuations. Other suggested ecological problems are the relationship of rodents to reseeding, succession, and climax in range land, and their numbers and effects upon orchards when managed with cover crops.

Weeds.—The occurrence of weeds as a result of land use and their control by cultural practices have received far less attention than control by direct, aggressive means. Yet cultural control or control as a result of good land management is likely to be the most permanent and least costly. Certainly the weed problem has not been reduced by centuries of cultivation, mowing, and burning. Even modern "hormone" sprays are no panacea.[208] If progress is to be made, the autecology of the principal weed species must be studied in detail. If, then, the effects of various types of land use and management upon the occurrence of specific weed species is learned, there is a reasonable possibility that ecological controls could be recommended that would reduce the weed problem, under certain situations at least.

CONSERVATION

The problems of conservation are extremely diverse, including as they do such things as soil and soil water, wildlife of all kinds, and aesthetic considerations. All that we have discussed of applied ecology could be classified under the general heading of conservation. The field is so broad as to require specialists of all kinds in its management, but this, of all fields, requires training to see each problem in the light of others. Nowhere can the ecological point of view be more effectively applied.[250]

To illustrate the limited effectiveness of specialization without ecological appreciation, witness such operations as have been known to take place almost simultaneously on public lands : a road crew cutting a grade in a clay bank so as permanently to roil a trout stream that another crew is improving with dams and shelters; a silvicultural crew felling wolf trees and border shrubbery necessary for game food; a roadside cleanup crew burning all fallen oak fuel available for fireplaces that are being built by a recreation crew; a planting crew setting out pines in the only open fields available to deer and partridge; and a fire-line crew cutting and burning all hollow snags on a wildlife refuge.[153] Such conflicting activities have not been uncommon in the name of conservation. Some government agencies have spent millions for flooding marshes and improving them for wildlife while other agencies were attempting to drain marshes of questionable agricultural value. Great dams have been built for reclamation pur-

FIG. 181. The deposition of silt and sand behind a dam in this fashion defeats its purpose of water storage and reduces the efficiency as a source of hydroelectric power.—*U. S. Soil Conservation Service.*

poses, but the watersheds above them have been ignored.[227] With continued lumbering and grazing, the reservoirs are silting in so rapidly that the usefulness of the dams promises to be short-lived. To assure integration of such activities may not require a "declaration of interdependence,"[250] but certainly the recognition of the interdependence of biological phenomena is necessary. This end will certainly be served if those responsible are ecologically trained or have an ecological point of view regardless of their special interests.

Soil Conservation.—The recognition of soil conservation as a national problem is of recent origin. The Soil Conservation Service was made a permanent bureau of the U. S. Department of Agriculture in 1935 athough it originated as the Soil Erosion Service in the Department of the Interior in 1933. Since then great progress has been made in educating the public to the need for a continuous program of conservation, and soil conservation as a science has developed rapidly. The scope of the field and the problems involved have been admirably summarized in various publications.[18, 136]

Early publicity by soil conservationists was essentially a plea to save our irreplaceable land, a great deal of which was already permanently lost and much of which is in the process of being ruined. More recently, the emphasis has been upon rebuilding lands that have deteriorated. The modern philosophy considers soils, like forests, to be natural resources that are renewable and, therefore, subject to management that will give a sustained yield over an indefinite period of time.[174] Such a program is, of course, as justifiable as the original, which aimed primarily at erosion control. It indicates that the conservation program has been successful and is maturing.

Soil conservation is, therefore, more than erosion control. It also involves the retention of water, especially on slopes, and its utilization to best advantage. At the same time, it aims to maintain or increase soil fertility and productivity. Thus soil conservation is merely the practice of agriculture in the best possible way, and we have already suggested how the ecological approach to such problems is most likely to be successful.

Not all the various measures successfully introduced for erosion control and soil building are applicable everywhere but must be adjusted in terms of soil types and climate. However, certain generalizations can be made which have wide application and whose special use or desirability often must be determined by a knowledge of local ecology. Vegetative cover is the most effective means of checking erosion. This raises questions as to what cover is desirable or possible under different conditions, where it should be permanent, and when it should be of native vegetation. These problems are related to strip-cropping, gully control, cover crops, and decisions to cultivate hilly land, put it into pasture, or plant it to forest. It is now assumed that the control of erosion will pay dividends only when proper crop rotations and fertilizing practices are followed. The interrelationships must be known for every crop and region.

Much advance has been made in cultural practice. Contour plowing, in which cultivation follows lines of equal elevation, is becoming steadily more common. In many areas, strip-cropping is an additional control, in which clean-cultivated crops are planted between strips of cover crops, such as legumes, which retard runoff and hold soil. A further necessity on contoured

FIG. 182. Aerial view showing strip-cropping of terraces that follow contours. Erosion is checked, much water is retained, and what runs off is directed to a sodded runaway channel. Such elaborate operations may require co-operation of several landowners. In this instance, two farms are involved. —*U. S. Soil Conservation Service.*

slopes may be terraces, which are ridges so placed that they catch and hold water in a channel behind themselves and thus check runoff and cause water to soak in. In special instances, deep furrows are maintained (listing) in which water and snow are held and crops are planted in the bottom of these troughs. Basin listing is done on some soils with special machinery that shapes these troughs with cross dams at regular intervals further to reduce runoff. It has been shown that wind erosion can be reduced by "stubble mulching" in which subsurface tillage keeps old organic debris on the surface. Windbreaks of various kinds are known to be effective also.

All these are examples of modern practices that are proving effective under special conditions. They are not by any means new, since they have been reported in various forms far back in history. It is their application in the light of modern knowledge that marks advance. The more complete the knowledge of all factors involved—crop, soil, climate—the greater the success of their application in the future. The research programs continue, and the kinds of investigations in progress are invariably ecological in nature. Here is a list of a few of the projects being studied for a single district :[172]

1. The effect of contouring corn, soybeans, and oats on soil and water conservation
2. The effect of divergence of rows from the contour on losses of soil and water
3. Cultural practices and methods of handling crop residues in relation to soil and water conservation and crop yield
4. The effect of cover crops on the conservation of soil and water and on crop yield
5. Investigations of soil moisture content under different crops, cropping systems, and mechanical conservation practices
6. Effect of crops and organic matter treatment on the movement of water through the soil profile

Other studies include effects of cropping systems, crop rotations, handling of crop residues, and management in terms of runoff, yield, and soil properties.

Some special problems of soil conservation still requiring a great deal of study are related to drainage of water-logged land and swamps, irrigation of lands with insufficient water, clearing of toxic salts from irrigated land and other lands not previously cultivated.

Water Supply.—The conditions necessitating soil erosion control and the prevention of runoff of surface water are commonly reflected in the general water supply. In many agricultural areas with adequate rainfall, there are water problems that did not exist at the time of settlement. Where once streams and springs were abundant and flowed continuously, now they are intermittent, and summer water supplies are often low. In Ohio, the water table, as evident in well depths, is from fifteen to fifty feet lower than

FIG. 183. The type of dam and spillway being installed primarily for water conservation. When full, this reservoir extends fifteen miles upstream over an area of 10,000 acres. The flow from the dam can be controlled, thereby providing constant flow during dry periods and reducing danger of flooding with high water.—*U. S. Soil Conservation Service.*

originally. Floods appear to be more frequent and are certainly more destructive than before. On the credit side, there are now no malaria problems related to undrained swamps or typhoid epidemics resulting from improper city water supplies.[223] The adverse conditions result partially from the removal of natural vegetation for agriculture. As much water falls today as before, but more of it runs off rapidly. Thus summer drought and spring floods are partially explainable.

There are other contributing factors. Roads, so important to the farmer for transportation, likewise serve to drain off water from his fields. This has been especially bad in the mid-western states where all roads were originally laid out in an east-west, north-

FIG. 184. A power-dam lake at the edge of a town in Minnesota as it appeared in 1926 when it was extensively used for fishing and recreation. By 1936 excessive silting had left only a small channel. Watersheds above the dam were improperly handled; timber was removed, slopes were cultivated, and few precautions were taken to prevent erosion.—*U. S. Soil Conservation Service.*

south grid pattern of blocks, which disregarded topography and provided a powerful system of artificial drainage. Also great drainage projects were instituted in the earlier days of agriculture, and these, too, served to speed the removal of water.

The trend in concern over surface water proceeded from drainage projects to those dealing with flood control. Such concern is still with us, and necessarily so, because of the destructiveness of floods to both property and land, but, a new trend is now apparent in the attempts to conserve, retain, and store water so that it may be available when needed, so that water tables may be held at higher levels, and so that flood waters may be controlled. Dams and reservoirs are being constructed and watersheds are being protected.

A recent factor in the lowering of water tables is the great increase of use of water in industry and the rapid increase of air-conditioning. Much of the water used for the latter is wasted because it is not used for any other purpose. The lowering of the water table by using water for this purpose has caused much concern in large cities. Various legislation is aimed at controlling the use of this natural resource. Most large users drill their own wells, but this practice is being limited. In some cities, it is required that the water must be forced back into the earth at the levels from which it is drawn.

Our water supply is a natural resource just as are the others we have discussed. When its availability is reduced, it affects agriculture, industry, fish and game, recreation, and perhaps home use. The trend is already in the direction of its conservation. Probably it will go further. Ecological problems of many kinds will arise in connection with control of water in streams and reservoirs, and the effects upon water table levels. It is a part of all the applied ecology we have discussed.

Another facet of the problem of water supply is its pollution by industrial waste and sewage. Here again, there are innumerable problems of an ecological nature. Their solution often requires the co-operation of engineers, chemists, bacteriologists, and limnologists. As always, when such specialists are drawn together, their success is greatest when they see their own fields in relation to the whole. This is the ecological approach.

Wildlife.—Like soil, water, and forests, our wildlife constitutes a renewable natural resource, which, consequently, can be restored or maintained even while it is used, if the use is a wise one. All of these renewable resources are so intimately related that a program for the conservation of one must necessarily consider the others as well. This ecological point of view is fully appreciated by leaders in wildlife management. It is also realized that, when man becomes the dominant organism, the management of soil, water, forests, and grassland is inevitable—and wildlife, too, if it is to be preserved.

If wildlife management is to be successful, man must know the ecology of the species involved, whether they are fish, birds, or game animals. Life cycles must be known, as must breeding habits, food habits, and food chains, migration routes, preferred habitats, diseases, predators, population trends, and the carrying capacities of given habitats. Such complete information is not yet available. "In its present state, wildlife management is an effort to apply to urgent problems the ecological and biological data that are now available, always with the consciousness that existing tools, methods, and processes may have to be discarded as new and better information becomes available."[100] Ecological knowledge is still woefully incomplete for most of our wildlife, although information accumulates steadily. As it accumulates, programs of management increase in effectiveness.

The range of ecological problems related to wildlife management is tremendous. The complexity of management can perhaps be suggested by indicating some of the kinds of things that must be taken into consideration. It would seem that, if food and cover are provided for an organism, its needs should be satisfied. But, for many species, the feeding habits are inadequately known. Cover can be provided for some species but, under present conditions, frequently only in localized areas. If that is true, it is not uncommon for food problems to become complicated during the winter months when the species tends to become concentrated on these restricted areas. A population that is reasonable in summer may become excessive in winter and result in death by starvation for many individuals. Encouraging the increase of one species may be detrimental to another one; consequently, individual species must be studied in relation to others. In this connection, predation must be considered from an ecological standpoint.

Species whose numbers have declined to extremely low levels may be propagated under controlled conditions and then released, but the cost is often excessive. Others may be taken from areas of overpopulation and transported elsewhere to start a new population. Such activities have sometimes been successful but in other instances have failed because of factors that were not known or understood. The ecology of the species and of the region must be known. If it is known, there is a reasonable possibility that the species can be encouraged to increase naturally at much less expense and trouble. The problems related to overpopulations of protected species are no less complicated, the ideal being a condition in which natural propagation produces a constant population supportable by the environment and perhaps an excess sufficient to permit a reasonable take by the sportsman.

When it is realized that such problems and many more are in the process of solution for big game, birds of all kinds, fur animals, fish, and other wildlife, it should be apparent that there is much basic ecological work to be done that has possibilities of application. The mistakes that have been made in wildlife management have undoubtedly resulted more often from inadequate ecological information rather than from lack of appreciation of how such knowledge could be applied if it were available. Wildlife management is applied ecology, and it will progress as basic ecological knowledge becomes available and is integrated by wildlife ecologists.

Game refuges provide a safeguard against lack of knowledge and provide the opportunity for acquiring needed information. Particularly, they insure that scarce or disappearing species do not become extinct as some have in the past, for here they are protected and given every encouragement to increase. Usually such refuges do not result in the restoration of a vanishing population. They do, however, insure a continuous breeding stock from which restoration may be made, and they give excellent opportunity for the study of the species involved under relatively undisturbed conditions or under available conditions.[101] A few such refuges are still in near primitive condition and thus can provide much of the biological knowledge of habitat, vegetation, and wildlife that must be learned to manage other refuges and ultimately the general program of wildlife conservation. Other refuges provide the testing grounds for management procedures as knowledge accumulates.

FIG. 185. An unsightly, eroding road cut in Illinois and its stable appearance three years after planting with trees that blend with topography and native vegetation.—*U. S. Soil Conservation Service.*

LANDSCAPING

The planning and planting of vegetation for home beautification or in public parks or gardens involves aesthetic considerations but likewise should be backed by an appreciation of the ecology of the species involved. If plantings are not made in terms of the requirements of the species used, they cannot be successful. Soil

FIG. 186.   On such road-building projects erosion control must be given serious and prompt attention. These great fills have been stabilized by mechanical means and have likewise been planted. If aesthetic considerations have entered into the stabilization program, they are not yet apparent.—*U. S. Forest Service.*

texture and structure must be considered as they affect water relations. Slope and exposure modify drainage and temperature just as they do in natural environments. Tolerance of shade, light, or extremes of temperature cannot be ignored when planning artificial combinations of species. Some species must be planted in moist places, some require full sunlight, some need to be partially shaded. Competition and all the other factors affecting natural communities operate among planted species as well. The same factors that limit the ranges of natural communities operate to limit the usable materials of landscape design for different sections of the country. Landscaping is, therefore, most successful when based upon ecological principles.

Natural landscaping is a recent development resulting from man's modern engineering activities, which drastically change topography, drainage, and vegetation when he constructs modern highways, dams, and airports. Great exposures of subsoil in cuts and fills require cover and replanting not only for aesthetic reasons but also to check erosion and slumping. It is to be expected that engineers should give first consideration to the efficiency of installation and use of a project under construction, but, when this

FIG. 187. The old and the modern manner of handling a road cut. Note the gradual back slope, seeded surface, and shallow, sodded runoff channel, all designed to check erosion.—*U. S. Soil Conservation Service.*

has been the only concern, after effects on drainage and erosion have frequently created serious problems. Not only has natural beauty been destroyed unnecessarily at times, but extensive expanses of bare soil, in fills and cuts, have been left for nature to recover and stabilize. The re-establishment of natural vegetation is often impossible before erosion and slumping cause disruption of drainage, road blocks, and similar difficulties. Consequently, stabilization must be provided for through artificial means and by seeding and planting. The problem is intensified by the infertility of the subsoil, upon which few things will grow. Although the first concern should be stabilization, there should be consideration of succession and the possibility of harmonizing the developing vegetation with that of the surrounding terrain.

In addition to large cuts and fills along mountain highways, there are problems of maintaining road shoulders, ditches, and spillways. Certainly not all is known about the best species for such purposes under all conditions. Also the natural beauty destroyed by a new right-of-way need not be permanently lost. With a minimum of management it would seem that native species could be encouraged to provide cover and beauty, especially along the new express highways, which are increasing in number. It does not seem impossible that ecological knowledge applied in advance could prevent some erosion and drainage problems and save some of the destruction of natural vegetation. Certainly roadside ecology is worth considering both practically and aesthetically.

PLANT INDICATORS

Elsewhere we have emphasized that plant communities give a better indication of the nature of environment than we can obtain by measurements of individual factors. The character and make-up of vegetation is an expression of the integrated effects of all factors operating in a habitat. When the relationships involved are well known, the vegetation becomes an indicator that can be interpreted or, in some instances, read like an instrument.

The practical use of plants as indicators is nothing new, for Pliny[135] wrote of selecting soil for wheatland by the natural vegetation it supported. More recently, in the settling of North America the pioneers used the principle widely in selecting their lands for agricultural purposes. With increasing knowledge, their selections became more effective as is indicated today by lands that have been abandoned and that have remained so. In any agricultural region, an experienced farmer knows the characteristics of soils and habitats supporting local peculiarities of vegetation, or often only a single indicator species.

Such practices and beliefs are usually the result of trial and error experiences, as well they must be, until the responses of a crop plant are tested under the conditions indicated by native vegetation. The knowledge has often been acquired after costly experience. If the requirements of an introduced plant are known and the characteristics of the habitats of native species are studied, the guessing may be reduced. Selection of native species as indicators of local conditions and fitting the ecological requirements of appropriate cultivated plants to these conditions involves ecological methods and thinking. Actually this is not easily accomplished, because of our still limited knowledge of the ecology of both native and cultivated plants. It suggests the possibilities of the indicator method, however, in an applied field.

The scope of possible uses of indicators involves much of the entire field of ecology, which necessarily limits the discussion here. Clements'[57] exhaustive treatment explores most of the possibilities of their application, and many of these we have considered in other connections. Consequently, only certain practical aspects, in which they have been successfully applied or might be further expanded will be discussed. The available source material has been brought together, and a review is available on the modern status of the concept and its application.[212]

It may sometimes be difficult to recognize or select indicator species. Those with restricted distributions and those tolerating only narrow ranges of habitat conditions should be most useful. Such plants should show responses to minor habitat differences. Thus it follows that similar local conditions in different climatic areas would probably support different indicators. Also the same species might not always be indicative of the same things throughout its range. Differences in geological or cultural history might make it necessary to interpret the significance of an indicator since it need not always be the same. It is rather generally agreed that a group of species or a whole community is more reliable as an indicator than a single species and that dominants, especially of the climax,[57] or at least characteristic species[34] are more useful indicators than lesser species. Above all, application of the method cannot be successful without judgment, good sense, and interpretation in terms of each situation.

Agricultural Indicators.—That crop centers and types of agriculture are correlated with climate and climax vegetation is obvious. The agricultural areas of North America follow a pattern very similar to that of a map of natural vegetation.[229] The northeastern conifer region suggests general agriculture at the lower altitudes and latitudes where the land is level and soil is deep. In the transition from boreal to deciduous forest, white pine–red pine–jack pine forests are on sandy soils, which are, in general, undesirable for agriculture, while the northern hardwoods-hemlock forest indicates the best soils for cultivation. The range of the deciduous forest formation marks the best agricultural region of the east with the greatest diversity of crops. Away from the southern Appalachian and Ohio Valley center, as the associations become less complex and oak and hickory become relatively more important, so also does agriculture become more specialized.

On the prairie, both tall and mixed grasses indicate fertile and productive land for cereals, hay, and fodder. Likewise, the natural grass cover provides valuable grazing facilities. The short grass area indicates productive soil whose cultivated crops are limited by moisture. The most favorable sections can be dry-farmed, but otherwise irrigation is necessary for cultivation. As a result, the land is most widely used for grazing.

Vegetation indicating general land use has been given more attention in the western United States than elsewhere.[230] Subalpine vegetation indicates a growing season too short for cultivated crops, steep slopes, and poor agricultural soil. The montane zone also has a short season with cool weather but permits some cultivation if the land is not too rough. Piñon-juniper in the woodland zone indicates productive soil if irrigation is possible, but chaparral indicates inferior agricultural land under almost any circumstances.

Plant indicators of land use in the arid regions of the West are rather well known because of several intensive studies in different areas. Irrigation is necessary everywhere except on the best soils in the sagebrush areas of the northern portion of the Great Basin. Elsewhere, in addition to the need for irrigation, native species indicate other necessities or precautions.[228] The tabulation on page 354 although specifically applicable only to the Sonoran Desert region of Arizona and southeastern California, illustrates the principles involved.

Fig. 188. These productive fields and orchards in Hurricane Valley, Utah, irrigated from the big ditch at left, are bordered on all sides by sagebrush desert. Knowledge of natural vegetation and soil gained from such projects makes possible confident statements of probable success or failure when others are to be established.—*U. S. Forest Service.*

These generalizations indicate how natural vegetation may be useful in determining regional land use. It is the details of local conditions as indicated by native species that need more study. If the equivalent cultivated and native species were known for different soils, sites, and exposures, it would be possible to state with confidence which fields should be cultivated and which should be put to pasture or wood lot, as well as which crops should be grown in a particular field. The more complete such knowledge is, the more effectively land can be used, and the more certainly land values can be fixed for sale and taxation.

TABLE 11—Potentialities of Lands for Crop Production as Indicated by the Principal Plant Communities of the Southwestern Desert (after Sampson[212]).

Vegetation	Predominant species	Probable success under irrigation
Creosote bush....	*Larrea divaricata*.......	Successful where native cover is luxuriant; of doubtful success on lands of rock outcrop or with rock layers or hardpan
Desert sage......	*Atriplex polycarpa*......	Successful where native cover is luxuriant; of low value on hardpan soil
Mesquite and chamiso.......	*Prosopis glandulosa* *Atriplex canescens*.....	Partly successful; special crops on level tracts
Chamiso.........	*Atriplex canescens*......	Successful
Mesquite thicket.	*Prosopis glandulosa*.....	Successful; salts leached out
Seep weed.......	*Dondia intermedia*......	Not successful; much abandoned farm land on this cover. Successful when salts leached out
Saltbush and arrowweed.....	*Atriplex lentiformis* *Pluchea sericea*.........	Successful when drained
Pickleweed......	*Allenrolfea occidentalis*..	Successful when drained and leached
Saltgrass........	*Distichlis stricta*........	Successful when drained and leached
Yucca-cactus....	*Yucca mohavensis* *Ferocactus acanthodes* *Opuntia bigelovii*	Partly successful; land usually too steep or soil too rocky
Giant cactus-paloverde	*Carnegiea gigantea* *Cercidium torreyanum*..	Successful when drained

Land evaluation on an ecological basis has been made use of at various times, and a simple illustration will serve to indicate the possibilities. Not long ago the construction of dams for water control in the upper Mississippi River necessitated legal action to fix the value of much lowland that would be flooded when the project was completed. One of the basic questions involved the establishment of criteria for determining which acreages were cultivatable and which were not. It was possible to show by means of the natural vegetation, regardless of whether the land had or had not been cultivated, which areas were only rarely flooded and, therefore, desirable agriculturally, which flooded frequently, and which were always too wet for cultivation. Once this was worked out it could be applied generally throughout the area. The information was used effectively for establishing equitable land values in several court proceedings.

Range and Pasture Indicators.—The use of plants as indicators is basic to range management.[248] A knowledge of the important indicator plants and the application of their meaning to handling of grazing land has become fundamental to successful management. Plant indicators are used to judge the condition of the range and particularly to recognize signs of deterioration or improve-

FIG. 189. Death of shrubs and a browse line in a pasture as indicators of too heavy grazing by cattle.—*U. S. Forest Service.*

ment under certain usages. They are used to determine the kind, degree, and time of grazing, and for determining the grazing capacity of a range. When the plants present are considered in conjunction with soil conditions and the climax, the previous use of the range can be interpreted and its potential usefulness under proper management can be predicted.

FIG. 190.   Winter range *(Atriplex nuttallii)* in Colorado, so badly over-grazed that there is practically no vegetation left and gullying is serious on all the slopes. Such depletion is obvious to anyone, but recognition of the onset of these conditions should be possible for those who know the indicators.—*U. S. Forest Service.*

Misuse of range lands is obvious in late stages, but it is difficult to recognize when it first begins and should be corrected. Among the indicators that must be watched for are thinning of cover and a lowered vitality of the principal species, replacement of good forage plants by inferior ones, close grazing of species that ordinarily would not be preferred, and, with this, accelerated erosion.[249] It is also highly desirable that the slow successional changes in species composition resulting from grazing under a certain system be recognized. Usually if these are in the direction of climax, they are advantageous. If they show an increase of forbs or of unpalatable species, management practices must be corrected before the trend becomes serious.

In each grazing region, the significant indicators must be known and interpreted. Often selected species can be used and checked upon to simplify evaluations. Likewise, restricted areas, selected on the basis of experience, may be used for observation as representative of the general conditions on a range as a whole.

Range management is obviously applied ecology in which indicators play an important part. The more completely the ecology of the species and communities is known under grazing conditions, the more readily their responses can be interpreted and the more effective management practices can be.

Forest Site Indicators.—In forestry, as in agriculture, the indicator significance of one group of plants must be interpreted and applied to an entirely different group of plants. Since forest indicators are commonly herbs or shrubs, there is often some difficulty in translating their meaning to apply to trees. In the broadest sense, forest indicators are site indicators, but rarely do they suggest more than a portion of the several factors that contribute to site. Physical or chemical characteristics of soil, moisture relationships, aeration, or erosion may be indicated by some species. With these and others the probable development of a particular stand can be interpreted. Still others may indicate the past history of vegetation on the site or the probable successional trend to be anticipated in the future.

It is fundamental to indicator interpretation that the successional trends of a region be thoroughly understood for every type of habitat. Only when an indicator is considered in relation to the stage of succession concerned can its meaning be at all clear.

The use of subordinate or dependent species as indicators of site quality has been attempted under various conditions since Cajander[51] set up such a system for classifying forest types in Finland. This system assumes that, since communities of similar structure occupy similar sites, it is possible to judge a site and the nature of the dominants from the ground cover alone. Thus recognition of the herbs, mosses, and lichens on the forest floor with an estimate of their relative proportions might suffice for evaluation of the stand and the quality of the site on which it grows.

Perhaps the most comprehensive attempt to apply the method in North America was made in the Adirondack Mountain area.[121] Elsewhere smaller areas with fewer communities have been studied. Although special phases of the method have proved useful in certain situations, the method as a whole has found limited application. Although herbs undoubtedly affect the dominants by modifying soil structure and water relations, and likewise through competition with seedlings of dominant species, there are arguments against the validity of information based on herbs alone, particularly since they derive water and nutrients from different soil horizons than do the dominant trees. It is, therefore, suggested that all the lesser woody vegetation should also be included. There is evidence that the same herbaceous species predominate on more than one soil type, and, therefore, their significance is questioned. Often the indicator types are of limited extent, and several may be present within a single stand. Interpretation, then, becomes difficult in terms of management. Undoubtedly, the foresters' not uncommon lack of familiarity with lesser vegetation and frequent inclination to ignore it entirely have been factors in limiting the testing and application of the method in American forests.

Because the subordinate vegetation changes after lumbering or fire and because height of trees, the commonest criterion of site, cannot then be known, it is desirable that some relatively simple means of evaluation of site be available that can be applied at any time. T. S. Coile[65] has approached this problem through physical measurement of the soil, as others have attempted before, and, after extensive investigation, has found that the site index can be accurately determined if only the depth of the A horizon and the soil type are known. Using the xylene equivalent (determined like moisture equivalent) of the B horizon (known for the soil type) and the depth of the A horizon, a positive statement of site quality can be made whether the land is in forest, cultivated, or abandoned and regardless of slope or exposure. This would seem to be the most promising approach to recognition of site quality. Once these two factors are known for the soils of an area, they can be recorded like a soils map, which then becomes a map of site index to be interpreted for management purposes.

Innumerable indicators, other than site indicators, are used in forestry. Relicts are particularly useful, and successional indicators are applied regularly. Special instances have been suggested elsewhere. It is appropriate to emphasize that indicator applications are invariably successful when the ecology of the region and the species is known.

HUMAN ECOLOGY

Perhaps this final section seems out of place in a textbook intended as an introduction to plant ecology. Undoubtedly, its subject should not be looked upon as an application of ecology in the sense of the preceding paragraphs of this chapter. The intent is to emphasize that *all* organisms are related to their environments and, consequently, to each other and that, therefore, they will be best undestood when studied from an ecological point of view.

Considering the youthfulness of the science of ecology, it has contributed much to our understanding of plants and animals at the same time that its methods have won approval and even adoption in other fields to the benefit of all. Although we still have plant ecologists and animal ecologists, and probably will continue to have such specialists, there has been a steady increase in the appreciation of interrelationships among plants and animals.[61]

Furthermore, there is a growing realization that man is likewise subject to ecological laws. This is completely reasonable since man, like other organisms, is basically dependent upon his environment and is likewise a factor in that environment. With man's increasing dominance, it is desirable that these relationships be better understood. How better can one approach that understanding than through studies of the structure of the communities in which man dominates, their origins and successional development, and the controlling factors involved. This is human ecology.

This is not a new idea, but it has not been widely recognized or accepted. There is much evidence that it is gaining recognition. There is an increasing appreciation of the concepts and values of ecology among the public in general as evidenced by the not uncommon use of the term in popular magazines and even occasionally in newspapers. This represents one phase of progress. The other is indicated by the use of the term and ecological methods by scholars and investigators in fields ordinarily not thought of as ecological. Anthropologists have undoubtedly led the way in adapting ecological methods to their problems and have, consequently, influenced others to try similar applications in different fields. Although the social ecology of animals has been given much attention,[6] there have been only a few advocates of ecological methods in the analysis of man's social behavior.[2] However, human ecology is gaining increasing recognition among sociologists under the pioneering influence of a few of their number[177, 178] who have thought in terms of social ecology for many years. As a part of the interpretation of man's activities and responses, it follows that certain phases of psychological action must likewise be given consideration in human ecology. Also, if human communities are to be studied as a whole, economics, too, becomes susceptible to ecological interpretation. These things make it apparent that human ecology is a comprehensive subject but one with promise of substantial returns for its study.

Some ideas of human ecology as expressed by a sociologist[177] seem particularly pertinent here. The scope of human ecology is so great that it must have a synoptic view of plant, animal, and human communities since all are interrelated and governed by the same principles involved in competition, symbiosis, succession, balance, and optimal population. Approached in this fashion, the laws, processes, and structure of human population are seen to be subservient to the more comprehensive laws of ecology since the latter are the determiners of regional economic and social types. When the arrangement and spatial adaptations of populations are considered, such ecological processes as aggregation, mobility, specialization, distance, and succession are excellent bases of evaluation. They permit the establishment of ecological indices for the measurement of types and trends of social mobility, distance, dominance, and change.

Finally, let us return to a phase of the discussion that has been touched upon earlier in several connections. No science can be completely justified for itself alone since science is supported by society. It is hoped that, in this last chapter, enough practical aspects of ecology have been suggested to show its wide applicability. Furthermore, the aim has been to show that its application is necessary if man is to continue to enjoy the full benefits of his environment upon which he is dependent, in which he is a factor, and over which he is a dominant. We have suggested that people with a wide variety of interests have concerned themselves with the general subject of human ecology. Among plant ecologists, Dr. Paul B. Sears is outstanding for his efforts in behalf of applied ecology and, particularly, human ecology. As a conclusion to this section it is, therefore, entirely proper that we quote one of his chapter headings from "Life and Environment,"[220] which reads, "The social function of ecology is to provide a scientific basis whereby man may shape the environment and his relations to it, as he expresses himself in and through his culture patterns."

GENERAL REFERENCES

C. C. ADAMS. General Ecology and Human Ecology.

H. H. BENNETT. *Soil Conservation.*

F. E. CLEMENTS. *Plant Indicators: The Relation of Plant Communities to Processes and Practice.*

I. N. GABRIELSON. *Wildlife Conservation.*

E. H. GRAHAM. *Natural Principles of Land Use.*

C. E. KELLOGG. *The Soils That Support Us.*

K. H. W. KLAGES. *Ecological Crop Geography.*

P. B. SEARS. *Life and Environment.*

H. L. SHANTZ. *Natural Vegetation as an Indicator of the Capabilities of Land for Crop Production in the Great Plains Area.*

L. A. STODDART and A. D. SMITH. *Range Management.*

J. W. TOUMEY and C. F. KORSTIAN. *Foundations of Silviculture upon an Ecological Basis.*

References Cited

1. AAMODT, O. S. War among plants. *Turf Culture*, **2**: 240-244, 1942.
2. ADAMS, C. C. General ecology and human ecology. *Ecology*, **16**: 316-335, 1935.
3. AIKMAN, J. M. Native vegetation of the shelterbelt region. In *Possibilities of shelterbelt planting in the plains region* (pp. 155-174). Washington, D. C., Govt. Printing Office 1935.
4. ——, and SMELSER, A. W. The structure and environment of forest communities in central Iowa. *Ecology*, **19**: 141-150, 1938.
5. ALLARD, H. A. Length of day in relation to the natural and artificial distribution of plants. *Ecology*, **13**: 221-234, 1932.
6. ALLEE, W. C. *Animal Aggregations. A Study in General Sociology*. Chicago: Univ. of Chicago Press, 1931. 431 pp.
7. ANDERSON, D. B. Relative humidity or vapor pressure deficit. *Ecology*, **17**: 277-282, 1936.
8. ANDERSON, L. E. The distribution of *Tortula pagorum* in North America. *Bryol.*, **46**: 47-66, 1943.
9. ANDERSON, P. J., and RANKIN, W. H. Endothia canker of chestnut. *Cornell Univ. Agr. Exp. Stat. Bull.* 347: 530-618, 1914.
10. ANDERSON, R. M. Effect of the introduction of exotic animal forms. *Proc. 5th Pacific Sci. Congr.*, Vol. 1: 769-778, 1933.
11. BALL, JOHN. Climatological diagrams. *Cairo Sci. Jour.*, **4**: no. 50 n.v., 1910.
12. BAUER, H. L. Moisture relations in the chaparral of the Santa Monica mountains, California. *Ecol. Monog.*, **6**: 409-454, 1936.
13. ——. The statistical analysis of chaparral and other plant communities by means of transect samples. *Ecology*, **24**: 45-60, 1943.
14. BAVER, L. D. *Soil Physics*. New York: John Wiley & Sons, Inc., 1940. 370 pp.
15. BEARD, J. S. Climax vegetation in tropical America. *Ecology*, **25**: 127-158, 1944.

16. BEAVEN, G. F., and OOSTING, H. J. Pocomoke Swamp: A study of a cypress swamp on the eastern shore of Maryland. *Bull. Torr. Bot. Cl.*, **66**: 367-389, 1939.
17. BEDFORD, THE DUKE OF, and PICKERING, S. U. Effect of one crop upon another. *Jour. Agric. Sci.*, **6**: 136-151, 1914.
18. BENNETT, H. H. *Soil Conservation*. New York: McGraw-Hill Book Co., 1939. 993 pp.
19. BERNARD, M. Precipitation. In *Physics of the Earth IX: Hydrology*, pp. 32-55. New York: McGraw-Hill Book Co., 1942.
20. BILLINGS, W. D. The structure and development of old field shortleaf pine stands and certain associated physical properties of the soil. *Ecol. Monog.*, **8**: 437-499, 1938.
21. ——. The plant associations of the Carson Desert Region, Western Nevada. *Butler Univ. Bot. Stud.*, **7**: 89-123, 1945.
22. ——. Vegetation and plant growth as affected by chemically altered rocks in the western Great Basin. *Ecology*, **31**: 62-74, 1950.
23. ——, and DREW, W. B. Bark factors affecting the distribution of corticolous bryophytic communities. *Am. Midl. Nat.*, **20**: 302-330, 1938.
24. BLUMENSTOCK, D. I., and THORNTHWAITE, C. W. Climate and the world pattern. In *Climate and Man*, pp. 98-127. (*See* No. 260.)
24a. BÖCHER, T. W. 1933. Phytogeographical studies of the Greenland flora. *Meddel. om Grønland* 104 (3): 1-56.
25. BOOTH, W. E. Tripod method of making chart quadrats. *Ecology*, **24**: 262, 1943.
26. BOUYOUCOS, G. J. Making mechanical analyses of soils in fifteen minutes. *Soil Sci.*, **25**: 473-480, 1928.
27. ——. The hydrometer method for making a very detailed mechanical analysis of soils. *Soil Sci.*, **26**: 233-238, 1928.
28. ——. Directions for making mechanical analyses of soils by the hydrometer method. *Soil Sci.*, **42**: 225-230, 1936.

29. BOUYOUCOS, G. J., and MICK, A. H. An electrical resistance method for the continuous measurement of soil moisture under field conditions. *Mich. Agr. Exp. Stat. Tech. Bull.* 172, 1940. 38 pp.

30. BOYNTON, D., and REUTHER, W. A way of sampling soil gases in dense subsoils and some of its advantages and limitations. *Proc. Soil Sci. Soc. Amer.* **3**: 37-42, 1938.

31. BRAUN, E. LUCY. Physiographic ecology of the Cincinnati region. *Ohio State Univ. Bull.* 20: no. **34**: 116-211, 1916.

32. ———. The undifferentiated deciduous forest climax and the association segregate. *Ecology*, **16**: 514-519, 1935.

33. ———. The differentiation of the deciduous forest of the eastern United States. *Ohio Jour. Sci.*, **41**: 235-241, 1941.

34. BRAUN-BLANQUET, J. *Plant Sociology: the Study of Plant Communities.* (Trans., rev., and ed. by G. D. Fuller and H. S. Conard.) New York: McGraw-Hill Book Co., 1932. 439 pp.

35. BRIGGS, L. J., and SHANTZ, H. L. The wilting coefficient for different plants and its indirect determination. *U. S. Dept. Agr., Bureau of Plant Industry Bull.* 230, 1912.

36. BROMLEY, S. W. The original forest types of southern New England. *Ecol. Monog.*, **5**: 61-89, 1935.

37. BRUNER, W. E. The vegetation of Oklahoma. *Ecol. Monog.*, **1**: 99-188, 1931.

38. BUELL, M. F., and CAIN, R. L. The successional role of southern white cedar, *Chamaecyparis thyoides*, in southeastern North Carolina. *Ecology*, **24**: 85-93, 1943.

39. ———, and GORDON, W. E. Hardwood-conifer forest contact zone in Itasca Park, Minn. *Am. Midl. Nat.*, **34**: 433-439, 1945.

40. BURKHOLDER, P. The role of light in the life of plants. *Bot. Rev.*, **2**: 1-52, 97-172, 1936.

41. BYRAM, G. M., and JEMISON, G. M. Solar radiation and forest fuel moisture. *Jour. Agr. Res.*, **67**: 149-176, 1943.

42. CAIN, S. A. Concerning certain phytosociological concepts. *Ecol. Monog.*, **2**: 475-505, 1932.

43. ———. Studies on virgin hardwood forest: II. A comparison of quadrat sizes in a quantitative phytosociological study of Nash's Woods, Posey County, Indiana. *Am. Midl. Nat.*, **15** 529-566, 1934.

44. ———. Studies of virgin hardwood forest: III. Warren's Woods, a beech-maple climax forest in Berrien County, Mich. *Ecology*, **16**: 500-513, 1935.

45. ———. The composition and structure of an oak woods, Cold Spring Harbor, Long Island, with special attention to sampling methods. *Am. Midl. Nat.*, **17**: 725-740, 1936.

46. ———. The species-area curve. *Am. Midl. Nat.*, **19**: 573-581, 1938.

47. ———. The climax and its complexities. *Am. Midl. Nat.*, **21**: 146-181, 1939.

48. ———. Pollen analysis as a paleo-ecological research method. *Bot. Rev.*, **5**: 627-654, 1939.

49. ———. Sample-plot technique applied to alpine vegetation in Wyoming. *Am. Jour. Bot.*, **30**: 240-247, 1943.

50. ———. *Foundations of Plant Geography.* New York: Harper & Brothers, 1944. 556 pp.

51. CAJANDER, A. K. Theory of forest types. *Acta Forestalia Fennica*, **29**: 1-108, 1926.

52. CARPENTER, J. R. The grassland biome. *Ecol. Monog.*, **10**: 617-684, 1940.

53. CHANDLER, R. F., JR. Cation exchange properties of certain forest soils in the Adirondack section. *Jour. Agr. Res.*, **59**: 491-505, 1939.

53a. CHAPMAN, H. H. Is the longleaf type a climax? *Ecology*, **13**: 328-334, 1932.

54. CHURCH, J. E. Snow and snow surveying. In *Physics of the Earth IX: Hydrology*, pp. 83-148. New York: McGraw-Hill Book Co., 1942.

55. CLAPHAM, A. R. The form of the observational unit in quantitative ecology. *Jour. Ecol.*, **20**: 192-197, 1932.

56. CLEMENTS, F. E. *Plant Succession: An Analysis of the Development of Vegetation.* Carnegie Inst. Wash. Publ. 242, 1916. 512 pp.

57. ———. *Plant Indicators: The Relation of Plant Communities to Processes and Practice.* Carnegie Inst. Wash. Pub. 290, 1920. 388 pp.

58. ———. The relict method in dynamic ecology. *Jour. Ecol.*, **22**: 39-68, 1934.

59. ———. Experimental ecology in the public service. *Ecology*, **16**: 342-363, 1935.

60. ———. Nature and structure of the climax. *Jour. Ecol.*, **24**: 252-284, 1936.

61. ———, and SHELFORD, V. E. *Bioecology.* New York: John Wiley & Sons, Inc., 1939. 425 pp.

62. CLINTON, G. P., and McCORMICK, F. A. Dutch elm disease, *Graphium ulnii. Conn. Agr. Exp. Stat. Bull.* 389: 301-752, 1936.

63. COILE, T. S. Soil samplers. *Soil Sci.*, **42**: 139-142, 1936.
64. ——. Some physical properties of the B. horizons of Piedmont soils. *Soil Sci.*, **54**: 101-103, 1942.
65. ——. Relation of soil characteristics to site index of loblolly and shortleaf pine in the lower Piedmont region of North Carolina. *Duke Univ. School of Forestry Bull.* 13, 1948. 78 pp.
66. CONARD, H. S. The plant associations of Central Long Island. *Am. Midl. Nat.*, **16**: 433-516, 1935.
67. ——. Plant associations on land. *Am. Midl. Nat.*, **21**: 1-27, 1939.
68. COOK, D. B, and ROBESON, S. B. Varying hare and forest succession. *Ecology*, **26**: 406-410, 1945.
69. COOPER, A. W. Sugar pine and western yellow pine in California. *U. S. Dept. Agr.*, *Forest Service Bull.* 690, 1906.
70. COOPER, W. S. The climax forest of Isle Royale, Lake Superior, and its development. *Bot. Gaz.*, **55**: 1-44, 115-140, 189-235, 1913.
71. ——. Redwoods, rainfall and fog. *Plant World*, **20**: 179-189, 1917.
72. ——. *The Broad-Sclerophyll Vegetation of California.* Carnegie Inst. Wash. Publ. 319, 1922. 124 pp.
73. ——. The fundamentals of vegetational change. *Ecology*, **7**: 391-413, 1926.
74. ——. Seventeen years of successional change upon Isle Royale, Lake Superior. *Ecology*, **9**: 1-5, 1928.
75. ——. A third expedition to Glacier Bay, Alaska. *Ecology*, **12**: 61-96, 1931.
76. ——. The problem of Glacier Bay, Alaska; a study of glacier variations. *Geogr. Rev.*, **27**: 37-62, 1937.
77. ——, and FOOT, HELEN. Reconstruction of a late Pleistocene biotic community in Minneapolis, Minnesota. *Ecology*, **13**: 63-73, 1932.
78. COULTER, J. M., BARNES, C. R., and COWLES, H. C. *A Textbook of Botany.* Vol. III. Ecology (revised by Fuller, G. D.), 1-499, New York: American Book Co., 1931.
79. COWLES, H. C. The ecological relations of the vegetation on the sand dunes of Lake Michigan. *Bot. Gaz.*, **27**: 95-117, 167-202, 281-308, 361-391, 1899.
80. ——. The physiographic ecology of Chicago and vicinity. *Bot. Gaz.*, **31**: 73-108, 145-181, 1901.
81. COX, H. J. Thermal belts and fruit growing in North Carolina. *Mo. Weath. Rev.* Suppl. 19, 1923.
82. DACHNOWSKI, A. P. Peat deposits and their evidence of climatic change. *Bot. Gaz.*, **72**: 57-89, 1921.

83. DAMBACH, C. A. A ten-year ecological study of adjoining grazed and ungrazed woodlands in northeastern Ohio. *Ecol. Monog.*, **14**: 255-270, 1944.
84. DAUBENMIRE, R. F. Exclosure technique in ecology. *Ecology*, **21**: 514-515, 1940.
85. ——. Vegetational zonation in the Rocky Mountains. *Bot. Rev.*, **9**: 325-393, 1943.
86. ——. Temperature gradients near the soil surface with reference to techniques of measurement in forest ecology. *Jour. Forest.*, **41**: 601-603, 1943.
87. DAVIS, R. O. E., and BENNETT, H. H. Grouping of soils on the basis of mechanical analysis. *U. S. Dept. Agr. Circ.* 419, 1927. 14 pp.
88. DECANDOLLE, A. L. *Géographie Botanique Raisonée.* Paris: 1855. 1365 pp.
89. DEEVEY, E. S. Pollen analysis and history. *Am. Scientist.* **32**: 39-53, 1944.
90. DILLER, OLIVER D. The relation of temperature and precipitation to the growth of beech in northern Indiana. *Ecology*, **16**: 72-81, 1935.
91. DOUGLASS, A. E. *Climatic Cycles and Tree Growth. A study of the annual rings of trees in relation to climate and solar activity.* Carnegie Inst. Wash. Publ. 289: 1-127, 1919.
92. ——. Vol. II., *ibid.*, 1-166, 1928.
93. ——. Vol. III. *Climatic Cycles and Tree Growth; A study of cycles*, 1-171, 1936.
94. DRUDE, O. *Handbuch der Pflanzengeographie.* Stuttgart: J Engelhorn, 1890. 582 pp.
95. EGGLER, W. A. The maple-basswood forest type in Washburn County, Wisconsin. *Ecology*, **19**: 243-263, 1938.
96. ELLISON, L. A comparison of methods of quadratizing short-grass vegetation. *Jour. Agr. Res.*, **64**: 595-614, 1942.
97. ERDTMAN, G. *An Introduction to Pollen Analysis.* Waltham, Mass.: Chronica Botanica Co., 1943. 239 pp.
98. FLOWERS, S. Vegetation of the Great Salt Lake Region. *Bot. Gaz.*, **95**: 353-418, 1934.
99. FREELAND, R. O. Apparent photosynthesis in some conifers during winter. *Plant Physiol.*, **19**: 179-185, 1944.
100. GABRIELSON, I. N. *Wildlife Conservation.* New York: The Macmillan Company, 1941; 249 pp.
101. ——. *Wildlife Refuges.* New York: The Macmillan Company, 1943. 257 pp.
102. GARNER, W. W. Photoperiodism. In Duggar, *Biological Effects of Radiation.* Vol. II, 677-713, New York: McGraw-Hill Book Co., 1936.

103. GARNER, W. W. Recent work on photoperiodism. *Bot. Rev.*, **3**: 259-275, 1937.

104. ——, and ALLARD, H. A. Effect of the relative length of day and night and other factors of the environment on growth and reproduction in plants. *Jour. Agr. Res.*, **18**: 553-606, 1920.

105. GARREN, K. H. Effects of fire on vegetation of the southeastern United States. *Bot. Rev.*, **9**: 617-654, 1943.

106. GLINKA, K. D. *The Great Soil Groups of the World and Their Development* (Engl. transl. by C. F. Marbut). Ann Arbor, Mich.: Edwards Brothers, 1927. 150 pp.

107. GLOCK, W. S. *Principles and Methods of Tree-Ring Analysis.* Carnegie Inst. Wash. Publ. 486: 1-100, 1937.

108. GORDON, W. E. Nomograms for conversion of psychrometric data. *Ecology*, **21**: 505-508, 1940.

109. GRAHAM, E. H. *Natural Principles of Land Use.* New York: Oxford University Press, 1944. 274 pp.

110. GRIGGS, R. F. The edge of the forest in Alaska and the reasons for its position. *Ecology*, **15**: 80-96, 1934.

111. GRISEBACH, A. H. R. *Die Vegetation der Erde nach ihrer klimatischen Anordnung.* Leipzig: W. Engelmann, 1872. 2 vol., 603 and 635 pp.

112. HAECKEL, E. Ueber Entwicklungsgang und Aufgabe der Zoologie. *Jenaischer Zeitschr. für Naturwiss.* **5**: 353-370, 1869.

113. HALDANE, J. S., and GRAHAM, J. I. *Methods of Air Analysis.* London: Charles Griffin, 1935. 177 pp.

114. HALL, T. F., and PENFOUND, W. T. Cypress-gum communities in the Blue Girth Swamp near Selma, Alabama. *Ecology*, **24**: 208-217, 1943.

115. HANSON, H. P. Postglacial forest succession, climate and chronology in the Pacific northwest. *Trans. Am. Phil. Soc.* **37**: 1-130, 1947.

116. HANSON, H. C. Ecology in agriculture. *Ecology*, **20**: 111-117, 1939.

117. ——. Fire in land use and management. *Am. Midl. Nat.*, **21**: 415-434, 1939.

118. HARSHBERGER, J. W. *Phytogeographic Survey of North America.* New York: G. E. Stechert & Company, Inc., 1911.

119. HAWLEY, FLORENCE. *Tree-Ring Analysis and Dating in the Mississippi Drainage.* Chicago: University of Chicago Press, 1941. 110 pp.

120. HEIBERG, S. O., and CHANDLER, R. F. A revised nomenclature of forest humus layers for the northeastern United States. *Soil Sci.*, **52**: 87-99, 1941.

121. HEIMBURGER, C. *Forest Type Studies in the Adirondack Region.* Cornell Univ. Agr. Exp. Sta. Mem. 165:1-122, 1934.

122. HENDERSON, L. J. *The Fitness of the Environment.* New York: The Macmillan Company, 1913. 317 pp.

123. HENDRICKS, B. A. Effect of forest litter on soil temperature. *Chronica Botanica*, **6**: 440-441, 1941.

124. HOFMAN, J. V. The establishment of a Douglas fir forest. *Ecology*, **1**: 49-53, 1920.

125. HUFFAKER, C. B. Vegetational correlations with vapor pressure deficit and relative humidity. *Am. Midl. Nat.*, **28**: 486-500, 1942.

126. HUMBOLDT, A. VON. *Ideen zu einer Geographie der Pflanzen nebst einem Naturgemälde der Tropenländer.* Tübingen: 1807. 182 pp.

127. HUMM, H. J. Bacterial leaf nodules. *Jour. N. Y. Botanical Garden*, **45**: 193-199, 1944.

128. HUMPHREYS, W. J. *Fogs and Clouds.* Baltimore: Williams and Wilkins Co., 1926.

129. ——. *Ways of the Weather.* Lancaster Pa.: Jaques Cattell Press, 1942. 400 pp.

130. JACCARD, P. Die statistische-floristische Methode als Grundlage der Pflanzensoziologie. *Handb. Biol. Arbeitsmeth. Abderhalden* XI. **5**: 165-202, 1928.

131. JENNY, H. *Factors of Soil Formation.* New York: McGraw-Hill Book Co., 1941. 281 pp.

132. ——, and COWAN, E. W. The utilization of adsorbed ions by plants. *Science*, **77**: 394-396, 1933.

133. JONES, G. N. *A Botanical Survey of the Olympic Peninsula, Washington.* U. of Wash. Publ. in Biol. **5**: 1-286, 1936.

134. KEARNEY, T. H., BRIGGS, L. J., SHANTZ, H. L., McLANE, J. W. and PIEMEISEL, R. L. Indicator significance of vegetation in Tooele Valley, Utah. *Jour. Agr. Res.*, **1**: 365-417, 1914.

134a. KELLEY, A. P. Plant indicators of soil types. *Soil Sci.*, **13**: 411-423, 1922.

135. KELLOGG, C. E. Development and Significance of the Great Soil Groups of the United States. *U. S. Dept. Agr. Misc. Pub.* 229, 1936.

136. ——. *The Soils That Support Us.* New York: The Macmillan Company, 1941. 370 pp.

137. KENOYER, L. A. A study of Raunkiaer's law of frequency. *Ecology*, **8**: 341-349, 1927.

138. ——. Ecological notes on Kalamazoo County, Michigan based on the original land survey. *Paps. Mich. Acad. Sci., Arts and Letters*, **11**: 211-217, 1930.

139. ——. Forest distribution in southwestern Michigan as interpreted from the original land survey (1826-32). *Paps. Mich. Acad. Sci., Arts and Letters*, **19**: 107-111, 1934.

140. KIMBALL, H. H. Intensity of solar radiation at the suface of the earth and its variations with latitude, altitude, season and time of the day. *Mo. Weath. Rev.*, **63**: 1-4, 1935.

141. KINCER, J. B. Climate and weather data for the United States. In *Climate and Man*. 685-699. (*See* No. 260.)

142. KITTREDGE, J. Forests and water aspects which have received little attention. *Jour. For.*, **34**: 417-419, 1936.

143. KLAGES, K. H. W. *Ecological Crop Geography*. New York: The Macmillan Company, 1942. 615 pp.

144. KLYVER, F. D. Major plant communities in a transect of the Sierra Nevada mountains of California. *Ecology*, **12**: 1-17, 1931.

145. KORSTIAN, C. F., and BRUSH, W. D. Southern white cedar. *U. S. Dept. Agr. Tech. Bull*, 251, 1931.

146. ——, and COILE, T. S. Plant competition in forest stands. *Duke Univ. School of Forestry Bull.* 3, 1938. 125 pp.

147. KRAMER, P. J. Photoperiodic stimulation of growth by artificial light as a cause of winter killing. *Plant Physiol.*, **12**: 881-883, 1936.

148. ——. Species differences with respect to water absorption at low temperatures. *Am. Jour. Bot.*, **29**: 828-832, 1942.

149. ——. Soil moisture in relation to plant growth. *Bot. Rev.*, **10**: 525-559, 1944.

150. KURZ, H. and DEMAREE, D. Cypress buttresses and knees in relation to water and air. *Ecology*, **15**: 36-41, 1934.

151. LARSON, L. T., and WOODBURY, T. D. Sugar pine. *U. S. Dept. Agr. Bull.* 426, 1916. 40 pp.

152. LAWRENCE, D. B. Some features of the vegetation of the Columbia River Gorge with special reference to asymmetry in trees. *Ecol. Monog.*, **9**: 217-257, 1939.

153. LEOPOLD, A. Conservation economics. *Jour. Forest.* **32**: 537-544, 1934.

154. LEWIS, F. J. The vegetation of Alberta. II. The swamp moor and bog forest. *Jour. Ecol.*, **16**: 18-70, 1928.

155. LEWIS, I. F. *The Vegetation of Shackleford Bank, Carteret County, North Carolina.* N. C. Geol. Surv. Econ. Pap. 46, 1918.

156. LIVINGSTON, B. E. A single index to represent both moisture and temperature conditions as related to plant growth. *Physiol. Research* no. 9: 421-440, 1916.

157. ——. Atmometers of porous porcelain and paper, their use in physiological ecology. *Ecology*, **16**: 438-472, 1935.

158. ——, and KOKETSU, R. The water-supplying power of the soil as related to the wilting of plants. *Soil Sci.*, **9**: 469-485, 1920.

159. ——, and SHREVE, F. *The Distribution of Vegetation in the United States, as related to Climatic Conditions.* Carnegie Inst. Wash. Publ. 284, 1921. 590 pp.

160. LUTZ, H. J. Effect of cattle grazing on vegetation of a virgin forest in northwestern Pennsylvania. *Jour. Agr. Res.*, **41**: 561-570, 1930.

161. ——. Origin of white pine in virgin forest stands of northwestern Pennsylvania. *Ecology*, **16**: 252-256, 1935.

162. ——. Determinations of certain physical properties of forest soils: I. Methods utilizing samples collected in metal cylinders. *Soil Sci.*, **57**: 475-487, 1944.

163. ——. Determination of certain physical properties of forest soils: II. Methods utilizing loose samples collected from pits. *Soil Sci.*, **58**: 325-333, 1944.

164. LYON, C. Tree ring width as an index of physiological dryness in New England. *Ecology*, **17**: 457-478, 1936.

165. MACKINNEY, A. L. Effects of forest litter on soil temperature and soil freezing in autumn and winter. *Ecology*, **10**: 312-322, 1929.

166. MCCUBBIN, W. A. Preventing plant disease introduction. *Bot. Rev.*, **12**: 101-139, 1946.

167. MCDOUGALL, W. B. *Plant Ecology.* Philadelphia: Lea & Febiger, 1941, 3rd ed. 285 pp.

168. ——, and JACOBS, M. C. Tree mycorhizas from the central Rocky Mountain region. *Am. Jour. Bot.*, **14**: 258-266, 1927.

169. MARBUT, C. F. A scheme for soil classification. *First Internatl. Congr. Soil Sci.* (1927) *Proc. and Paps.* 4, 1-31. 1928.

170. ——. Soils of the United States. In *Atlas of American Agriculture.* Pt. III. 98 pp. Washington, D. C.: U. S. Dept. Agr. Bur. Chem. and Soils, 1935.

171. MATZKE, E. B. Effect of street lights in delaying leaf-fall in certain trees. *Am. Jour. Bot.*, **23**: 446-452, 1936.

172. MENDELL, F. H., and AIKMAN, J. M. Soil and water conservation. In *Present Status and Outlook of Conservation in Iowa.* Rep. of the Conservation Comm. Ia. Acad. Sci. **51**: 87-96, 1944.

173. MERRIAM, C. H. *The Geographic Distribution of Animals and Plants in North America.* (U.S. Dept. Agr. Yearbook.) Washington, D.C.: Govt. Printing Office, 1894, 203-214.

174. MICKEY, K. B. *Man and the Soil.* Chicago: International Harvester Co., 1945. 110 pp.

175. MOSS, E. H. The vegetation of Alberta. IV. The poplar association and related vegetation of central Alberta. *Jour. Ecol.*, **20**: 380-415, 1932.

176. MUENSCHER, W. C. *Weeds.* New York: The Macmillan Company, 1935. 577 pp.

177. MUKERJEE, R. *Man and His Habitation. A Study in Social Ecology.* New York: Longmans, Green & Co., 1940. 313 pp.

178. ——. *Social Ecology.* New York: Longmans, Green & Co., 1945 (?). 364 pp.

179. NICHOLS, G. E. The vegetation of northern Cape Breton Island, Nova Scotia. *Trans. Conn. Acad. Arts and Sci.*, **22**: 249-467, 1918.

180. ——. The hemlock-white pine-northern hardwood region of eastern North America. *Ecology*, **16**: 403-422, 1935.

181. OLIVER, W. R. B. New Zealand epiphytes, *Jour. Ecol.*, **18**: 1-51, 1930.

182. OLMSTED, L. B., ALEXANDER, L. T., and MIDDLETON, H. E. A pipette method of mechanical analysis of soils based on improved dispersion procedure. *U. S. Dept. Agr. Tech. Bull.* 170, 1930. 22 pp.

183. OOSTING, H. J. An ecological analysis of the plant communities of Piedmont, North Carolina. *Am. Midl. Nat.*, **28**: 1-126, 1942.

184. ——. The comparative effect of surface and crown fire on the composition of a loblolly pine community, *Ecology*, **25**: 61-69, 1944.

185. ——. Botanical notes on the flora of East Greenland. In *The Coast of Northeast Greenland, The Louise A. Boyd Expeditions of 1937 and 1938*, pp. 225-269. Am. Geogr. Soc. Spec. Publ. 30, 1948.

186. ——, and ANDERSON, L. E. Plant succession on granite rock in eastern North Carolina. *Bot. Gaz.*, **100**: 750-768, 1939.

187. ——, and BILLINGS, W. D. Edaphovegetational relations in Ravenel's Woods. *Am. Midl. Nat.*, **22**: 333-350, 1939.

188. ——, and BILLINGS, W. D. Factors effecting vegetational zonation on coastal dunes. *Ecology*, **23**: 131-142, 1942.

189. ——, and BILLINGS, W. D. The red fir forest of the Sierra Nevada: Abietum magnificae. *Ecol. Monog.*, **13**: 261-274, 1943.

190. ——, and KRAMER, P. J. Water and light in relation to pine reproduction. *Ecology*, **27**: 47-53, 1946.

191. ——, and REED, J. F. Ecological composition of pulpwood forests in northwestern Maine. *Am. Midl. Nat.*, **31**: 182-210, 1944.

192. PARISH, S. B. Vegetation of the Mohave and Colorado deserts of southern California. *Ecology*, **11**: 481-499, 1930.

193. PEARSE, K., PECHANEC, J. F, and PICKFORD, G. D. An improved pantograph for mapping vegetation. *Ecology*, **16**: 529-530, 1935.

194. PECHANEC, J. F., and STEWART, G. Sagebrush-grass range sampling studies: size and structure of sampling unit. *Jour. Amer. Soc. Agron.*, **32**: 669-682, 1940.

195. PECK, M. E. A preliminary sketch of the plant regions of Oregon. I. Western Oregon. *Am Jour. Bot.*, **12**: 69-91, 1925.

196. PENFOUND, W. T. A study of phytosociological relationships by means of aggregations of colored cards. *Ecology*, **26**: 38-57, 1945.

197. ——, and O'NEILL, M. E. The vegetation of Cat Island, Mississippi. *Ecology*, **15**: 1-16, 1934.

198. ——, and HATHAWAY, E. S. Plant communities of the marshlands of southeastern Louisiana. *Ecol. Monog.*, **8**: 1-56, 1938.

199. PENFOUND, W. T., and HOWARD, J. R. A phytosociological study of an evergreen oak forest in the vicinity of New Orleans, Louisiana. *Am. Midl. Nat.*, **23**: 165-174, 1940.

200. ——, and MACKANESS, F. P. A note concerning the relation between drainage pattern, bark conditions and the distribution of corticolous bryophytes. *Bryol.*, **43**: 168-170, 1940.

201. PHILLIPS, J. Succession, development, the climax, and the complex organism: An analysis of concepts. *Jour. Ecol.*, **22**: 554-571; **23**: 210-246, 488-508, 1931.

202. RAUNKIAER, C. *The Life Forms of Plants and Statistical Plant Geography; Being the Collected Papers of C. Raunkiaer.* Oxford: Clarendon Press, 1934. 632 pp.

203. RAUP, H. M. Recent changes of climate and vegetation in southern New England and adjacent New York. *Jour. Arnold Arboretum*, **18**: 79-117, 1937.

204. ——. Botanical problems in boreal America. *Bot. Rev.*, **7**: 147-248, 1941.

205. REED, JOHN FREDERICK. *Root and Shoot Growth of Shortleaf and Loblolly Pines in Relation to Certain Environmental Conditions.* Duke Univ. School of Forestry Bull. 4, 1939. 52 pp.

206. REED, J. F., and CUMMINGS, R. W. Soil reaction-glass electrode and colorimetric methods for determining pH values of soils. *Soil Sci.*, **59**: 97-104, 1945.

207. RICHARDS, L. A. Soil moisture tensiometer materials and construction. *Soil Sci.*, **53**: 241-248, 1942.

208. ROBBINS, W. W., CRAFTS, A. S., and RAYNOR, R. N. *Weed Control.* New York: McGraw-Hill Book Co., 1942. 543 pp.

209. ROGERS, H. T., PEARSON, R. W., and PIERRE, W. H. The source and phosphatase activity of exoenzyme systems of corn and tomato roots. *Soil Sci.*, **54**: 353-366, 1942.

210. RÜBEL, E. Plant communities of the world. In *Essays in Geobotany*, pp. 263-290. Berkeley, Calif.: Univ. of Calif. Press, 1936.

211. RUSSELL, E. J., and APPLEYARD, A. The atmosphere of the soil; its composition and causes of variation. *Jour. Agr. Sci.*, **7**: 1-48, 1915.

212. SAMPSON, A. W. Plant indicators—concept and status. *Bot. Rev.*, **5**: 155-206, 1939.

213. SCHIMPER, A. F. W. *Plant Geography upon a Physiological Basis.* (Transl. by W. R. Fisher.) Oxford: Clarendon Press, 1903, 839 pp.

214. SCHOUW, J. F. *Grundzüge einer allgemeinen Pflanzengeographie.* Berlin, 1823. 524 pp.

215. SCHREINER, O., and REED, H. S. The production of deleterious excretions by roots. *Bull. Torr. Bot. Cl.* **34**: 279-301, 1907.

216. SCHUMACHER, F. X., and CHAPMAN, R. A. *Sampling Methods in Forestry and Range Management.* Duke Univ. School of Forestry Bull. 7, 1942. 213 pp.

217. SCOFIELD, C. S. The measurement of soil water. *Jour. Agr. Res.*, **71**: 375-402, 1945.

218. SEARS, P. B. The natural vegetation of Ohio. *Ohio Jour. Sci.*, **25**: 139-149; **26**: 128-146, 139-231, 1925-26.

219. ——. Climatic interpretation of postglacial pollen deposits in North America. *Bull. Amer. Meteorol. Soc.*, **19**: 177-185, 1938.

220. ——. *Life and Environment.* New York: Teachers College, Columbia University, 1939. 175 pp.

221. ——. Postglacial vegetation in the Erie-Ohio area. *Ohio Jour. Sci.*, **41**: 225-234, 1941.

222. ——. Xerothermic theory. *Bot. Rev.*, **8**: 708-736, 1942.

223. ——. The ecological basis of land use and management. *Proc. 8th Am. Sci. Congr.*, **5**: 223-233. 1942.

224. ——. History of conservation in Ohio. In *The History of the State of Ohio. VI: Ohio in the Twentieth Century*—pp. 219-240, Columbus, Ohio. Ohio State Archaeological Society, 1942.

225. ——. Grazing versus maple syrup. *Science*, **98**: 83-84, 1943.

226. ——. Man and nature in the modern world. In *Education for Use of Regional Resources* (Rept. of Gatlinburg Conference II, sponsored by Committee on Southern Regional Studies and Education of the American Council in Education), 1944. Chp. 3: 25-44.

227. ——. Importance of ecology in the training of engineers. *Science.* **106**: 1-3, 1947.

228. SHANTZ, H. L. Natural vegetation as an indicator of the capabilities of land for crop production in the Great Plains area. *U. S. Dept. Agr. Bur. Pl. Ind. Bull.* 201, 1-100, 1911.

229. ——. Plants as soil indicators. In *Soils and Men*, pp. 835-860. (*See* No. 259.)

230. SHANTZ, H. L., and ZON, R. The physical basis of agriculture: Natural vegetation. In *Atlas of American Agriculture*. (Pt. I, Sect. E. 29 pp.) Washington, D. C.: U. S. Dept. Agr., 1924.

231. SHELFORD, V. E. (editor). *Naturalist's Guide to the Americas*. Baltimore: Williams & Wilkins Company, 1926. 761 pp.

232. SHERMAN, L. K., and MUSGRAVE, G. W. Infiltration. In *Hydrology*, (O. E. Meinzer, ed.) pp. 244-258. New York: McGraw-Hill Book Co., 1942.

233. SHIRLEY, H. L. Light as an ecological factor and its measurement. *Bot. Rev.*, 1: 355-381, 1935.

234. ——. Reproduction of upland conifers in the Lake States as affected by root competition and light. *Am. Midl. Nat.*, 33: 537-612, 1945.

235. ——. Light as an ecological factor and its measurement, II. *Bot. Rev.*, 11: 497-532, 1945.

236. SHREVE, F. A map of the vegetation of the United States. *Geog. Rev.*, 3: 119-125, 1917.

237. ——. The plant life of the Sonoran Desert. *Sci. Mo.*, 42: 195-213, 1936.

238. ——. The desert vegetation of North America. *Bot. Rev.*, 8: 195-246, 1942.

239. SINCLAIR, J. G. Temperatures of the soil and air in a desert. *Mo. Weath. Rev.*, 50: 142-144, 1922.

240. SMALL, J. *pH and Plants*. New York: D. Van Nostrand Company, Inc., 1946. 216 pp.

241. SMILEY, F. J. *A Report upon the Boreal Flora of the Sierra Nevada of California*. Univ. of Calif. Publ. in Botany 9, 1921. 423 pp.

242. SMITH, A. Seasonal subsoil temperature variations. *Jour. Agr. Res.*, 44: 421-428, 1932.

243. SMITH, A. D. A discussion of the application of a climatological diagram, the hythergraph, to the distribution of natural vegetation types. *Ecology*, 21: 184-191, 1940.

244. SPURR, S. H. A new definition of silviculture. *Jour. Forest.*, 43: 44, 1945.

245. ——, and CLINE, A. C. Ecological forestry in central New England. *Jour. Forest.*, 40: 418-420, 1942.

246. STAKMAN, E. C., and CHRISTENSEN, C. M. Aerobiology in relation to plant disease. *Bot. Rev.*, 12: 205-253, 1946.

247. STEWART, G. and HUTCHINGS, S. S. The point-observation-plot (square-foot density) method of vegetation survey. *Jour. Amer. Soc. Agron.*, 28: 714-722, 1936.

248. STODDART, L. A., and SMITH, A. D. *Range Management*. New York: McGraw-Hill Book Co., 1943. 547 pp.

249. TALBOT, M. W. Indicators of southwestern range conditions. *U. S. Dept. Agr. Farmers' Bull.* 1782, 1937. 35 pp.

250. TAYLOR, W. P. What is ecology and what good is it? *Ecology*, 17: 333-346, 1936.

251. THORNTHWAITE, C. W. The climates of North America. *Geog. Rev.*, 21: 633-654, 1931.

252. ——. Atmospheric moisture in relation to ecological problems. *Ecology*, 21: 17-28, 1940.

252a. TIPPETT, L. H. C. *Random Sampling Numbers. Tracts for Computers XV*. Cambridge University Press, 1927.

253. TOUMEY, J. W., and KIENHOLZ, R. *Trenched Plots under Forest Canopies*. Yale Univ. School of Forestry Bull. 30, 1931. 31 pp.

254. ——, and KORSTIAN, C. F. *Foundations of Silviculture upon an Ecological Basis*. New York: John Wiley & Sons, Inc., 1947, 2nd ed. 468 pp.

255. TRANSEAU, E. N. Forest centers of eastern North America. *Am. Nat.* 39: 875-889, 1905.

256. ——. The prairie peninsula. *Ecology*, 16: 423-437, 1935.

257. ——, SAMPSON, H. C., and TIFFANY, L. H. *Textbook of Botany*. New York: Harper and Brothers, 1940. 812 pp.

258. TREWARTHA, G. T. *An introduction to Weather and Climate*. New York: McGraw-Hill Book Co., 1943. 545 pp.

259. U. S. Department of Agriculture. *Soils and Men*. (U. S. Dept. Agr. Yearbook). Washington, D. C.: Gov. Printing Office, 1938. 1232 pp.

260. U. S. Department of Agriculture. *Climate and Man*. (U. S. Dept. Agr. Yearbook). Washington, D. C.: Gov. Printing Office, 1941. 1248 pp.

261. U. S. Weather Bureau. *Cloud Forms According to the International System of Classification*. Washington, D. C.: Gov. Printing Office, 1928.

262. VEIHMEYER, F. J. Evaporation from soils and transpiration. *Trans Am. Geophysical Union* (19th Ann. Meeting), 612-619, 1938.

263. WAKSMAN, S. A. *Principles of Soil Microbiology*. Baltimore: Williams & Wilkins Company, 1932, 2nd ed. 894 pp.

264. WAKSMAN, S. A. *Humus: Origin, Chemical Composition, and Importance in Nature.* Baltimore: Williams & Wilkins Company, 1936. 494 pp.

265. WARD, H. B., and POWERS, W. E. *Weather and Climate.* Evanston, Ill., 1942. 112 pp.

266. WARMING, E. *Oecology of Plants.* (Transl. by P. Groom and I. B. Balfour.) Oxford: Clarendon Press, 1909. 422 pp.

267. WEAVER, J. E. Replacement of true prairie by mixed prairie in eastern Nebraska and Kansas. *Ecology*, 24: 421-434, 1943.

268. ——, and CLEMENTS, F. E. *Plant Ecology.* New York: McGraw-Hill Book Co., 1938 (2nd ed.). 601 pp.

269. WELLS, B. W. Plant communities of the coastal plain of North Carolina and their successional relations. *Ecology*, 9: 230-242, 1928.

270. ——. Salt spray: an important factor in coastal ecology. *Bull. Torr. Bot. Cl.*, 65: 485-492, 1938.

271. ——. A new forest climax: the salt spray climax of Smith Island, North Carolina. *Bull. Torr. Bot. Cl.*, 66: 629-634, 1939.

272. ——, and SHUNK, I. V. The vegetation and habitat factors of the coarser sands of the North Carolina coastal plain. *Ecol. Monog.*, 1: 465-521, 1931.

273. WENT, F. W. The dependence of certain annual plants on shrubs in California deserts. *Bull. Torr. Bot. Cl.*, 69: 100-114, 1942.

274. WODEHOUSE, R. P. *Pollen Grains, Their Structure, Identification and Significance in Science and Medicine.* New York: McGraw-Hill Book Co., 1935. 574 pp.

275. WOLFENBARGER, D. O. Dispersion of small organisms. Distance dispersion rates of bacteria, spores, seeds, pollen, and insects; incidence rates of diseases and injuries. *Am. Midl. Nat.*, 35: 1-152, 1946.

276. WOODBURY, A. M. Distribution of pigmy conifers in Utah and Northeastern Arizona. *Ecology*, 28: 113-126, 1947.

Index

Page numbers in bold face type indicate illustrative material.

(2)